Water Distribution Operator
Training Handbook

Water Distribution Operator Training Handbook

Second Edition

Harry Von Huben
Technical Editor

American Water Works Association

Water Distribution Operator Training Handbook, Second Edition

Library of Congress Cataloging-in-Publication Data

Water distribution operator training handbook.-- 2nd ed.
    p. cm.
    Includes bibliographical references and index.
    ISBN 1-58321-014-8
    1. Water--Distribution--Handbooks, manuals, etc. 2. Water-supply engineering--Field work--Handbooks, manuals, etc. 3. Water-supply engineers--Training of--Handbooks, manuals, etc. I. Von Huben, Harry.

    TD481 W373 1999
    628.1'42
                                                                        99-049507

Disclaimer
Many of the photographs and illustrative drawings that appear in this book have been furnished through the couresty of various product distributors and manufacturers. Any mention of trade names, commercial products, or services does not constitute endorsement or recommendation for use by the American Water Works Association.

ISBN 1-58321-014-8

Project Manager: David Talley
Cover Design: Carol Magin/Karen Staab
Production Editor: Michael Malgrande

Printed in the United States of America

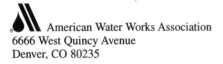 American Water Works Association
6666 West Quincy Avenue
Denver, CO 80235

Printed on
recycled paper.

Contents

Foreword

A reliable water supply is one of the most important resources for a community. Sufficient quantities of water must always be available at adequate pressure, and the water must be safe for human consumption at all times. A water distribution operator is legally and morally responsible to see that this goal is accomplished.

The distribution operator is typically the first line of contact between the general public and the water utility. Therefore, he or she must conduct public contacts in a manner that will maintain a good image of the utility and maintain customer confidence in the service being provided.

The chapters in this handbook discuss various types of available water system equipment and facilities. The specific types of equipment and facilities used by each water system are generally governed by a combination of local conditions, past practices, and economics. Well-informed operators should know about all available types of equipment and operating methods so that the water system may be operated with maximum efficiency and safety.

This handbook is intended to be an introduction to water distribution system operation. In order to maintain the publication at a reasonable size, many subjects receive only superficial coverage. Many sources of additional, specific information are available in other publications. The publications referenced at the end of each chapter are available from the American Water Works Association (AWWA) and other sources, at nominal cost.

Water system operators are urged to obtain a copy of the latest AWWA Bookstore Catalog, which lists available publications, by calling 800-926-7337. New publications are added every year, as are an increasing number of new videos and computer programs.

Operators are also urged to keep an up-to-date copy of their state's public water supply regulations available for reference. Although basic requirements for water system operation are dictated by regulations under the Safe Drinking Water Act, in many cases each state has latitude in applying the regulations and, on occasion, may actually be more restrictive than the federal regulations. Each state also has many additional requirements that can only be found by reviewing the state regulations.

The first edition of this handbook was prepared by AWWA in 1976, using in part, material prepared by members of the Pacific Northwest Section of AWWA, and contributions from many additional AWWA members.

Because of the great advances in materials, technology, and regulations in the intervening years, the second edition has been completely revised under the auspices of the AWWA Operations and Maintenance Committee, with Mr. Kan Oberoi, Chairman. The technical editor was Harry Von Huben.

Special thanks are extended to Bill Lauer of AWWA, who provided a technical review of the second-edition manuscript.

Chapter 1

Distribution Mathematics

In order to devote more space in this handbook to work-related information, this chapter does not cover basic arithmetic. It is expected that the reader already has a foundation in working with fractions, decimals, percentages, and averages, and in computing areas and volumes. If review of these subjects is necessary, one of the references listed at the end of this chapter is suggested.

This chapter covers some of the more advanced mathematics that water distribution system operators may be required to use in conjunction with their work, including working with exponential numbers, proportions and solving for the unknown, conversion factors, and working with the metric system.

Working With Numbers

Two of the more advanced math concepts that a distribution system operator will probably have to use on occasion are exponential numbers and proportions.

Exponential Numbers

Working with numbers having a large number of zeros is very cumbersome and mistakes can be easily made. For example, to multiply 10 million by 9 billion, the older notation would be

$$10,000,000 \times 9,000,000,000 = 90,000,000,000,000,000$$

Working this problem by hand is very cumbersome. The number of digits is also beyond the range of most electronic calculators.

Scientific notation is a method by which any number can be expressed as a term multiplied by a power of 10. The term itself is greater than or equal to 1, but less than 10. The modern way of performing the above calculation is as follows:

$$10,000,000 = 10 \times 10^6 \text{ (10 times 10 to the 6th power)}$$
$$9,000,000,000 = 9 \times 10^9 \text{ (9 times 10 to the 9th power)}$$
$$\text{so } 10 \times 10^6 \times 9 \times 10^9 = 90 \times 10^{15} \text{ or } \mathbf{9 \times 10^{16}} \text{ (9 followed by 16 zeros)}$$

The calculation is made by multiplying the integers: $10 \times 9 = 90$, and adding the exponents: $6 + 9 = 15$.

Examples of scientific notation are

$$10^2 = 10 \times 10 = 100$$
$$10^3 = 10 \times 10 \times 10 = 1{,}000$$
$$10^6 = 10 \times 10 \times 10 \times 10 \times 10 \times 10 = 1{,}000{,}000$$
$$10^{-1} = 0.1 \text{ or } 1/10$$
$$10^{-2} = 0.01 \text{ or } 1/100$$
$$10^{-3} = 0.001 \text{ or } 1/1{,}000$$

As can be seen from the above examples, if the exponent is positive, you add the specified number of zeros to the number. If the number is negative, the number of zeros placed to the right of the decimal point is one less than the exponent.

Numbers in scientific notation can also be divided in a process similar to the example above, except the exponents are subtracted as illustrated in the following example:

$$\frac{6 \times 10^4}{3 \times 10^2} = \left(\frac{6}{3}\right) \times 10^{(4-2)} = 2 \times 10^2 \text{ or } 200$$

Numbers in the scientific notation may be added or subtracted only when the powers of 10 are equal for both, as in the following examples:

$$3.72 \times 10^3 + 8.56 \times 10^3 = (3.72 + 8.56) \times 10^3$$
$$= 12.28 \times 10^3$$
$$= \mathbf{1.228 \times 10^4}$$
$$= 12{,}280$$
$$4.53 \times 10^3 + 1.271 \times 10^4 =$$
$$4.53 \times 10^3 + 12.71 \times 10^3 = (4.53 + 12.71) \times 10^3$$
$$= 17.24 \times 10^3$$
$$= \mathbf{1.724 \times 10^4}$$
$$= 17{,}240$$

Proportions

The division of two numbers is actually a ratio. For instance, the ratio of 3 to 4 may be expressed as 3/4 or 3:4.

A proportion is an equality of two ratios. It may written in the following forms:

$$a{:}b \;=\; c{:}d \quad \text{or}$$

$$\frac{a}{b} \;=\; \frac{c}{d}$$

Verbally, this may be expressed "a is to b as c is to d."

If three of the four values of a proportion are known, the other can always be found. By cross-multiplying the terms, the following proportional expressions can be obtained:

$$a \ = \ \frac{b \times c}{d}$$

$$b \ = \ \frac{a \times d}{c}$$

$$c \ = \ \frac{a \times d}{b}$$

$$d \ = \ \frac{c \times b}{a}$$

A simple example would be:

If 6 lb of a chemical are dissolved in 20 gal of water, how many pounds should be dissolved in 60 gal to obtain the same concentration? If we call x the unknown quantity, the proportions are

$$\frac{6 \ lb}{20 \ gal} \ = \ \frac{x \ lb}{60 \ gal}$$

$$or \quad x \ = \ \frac{6 \times 60}{20}$$

$$= \ 18 \ lb$$

The important point to remember in proportions is that both sides of the equation must always be in the same units. In the above example, lb:gal = lb:gal. Other typical examples of problems that may be encountered in a water distribution system and may be computed using proportions are:

If the water discharged by a pump is measured at 55 gal in 3 min, what is the pump output in gallons per hour (gph)?

$$\frac{55 \ gal}{3 \ min} \ = \ \frac{x \ gal}{60 \ min}$$

$$x \ = \ \frac{55 \times 60}{3} \ = \ 1{,}100 \ gph$$

A pump operating at 86 percent efficiency can fill a tank in 49 min. How many minutes will it take the pump to fill the tank if the pump efficiency is 59 percent?

$$\left(\frac{86\%}{59\%} \right) \ \times \ \left(49 \ min \right) \ = \ x$$

$$x \ = \ 71 \ min$$

Conversion of US Customary Units

The fastest method of converting units of measure is to use a conversion table. A table of direct conversions of most of the units encountered in public water system work is provided in appendix A. For instance, using the first page of the table, if you wish to convert acres to square feet, the procedure is to multiply the number of acres by 43,560.

Another common way of converting units is the box method. By knowing only a few basic conversion factors, it is possible to quickly convert commonly used units. Probably the most common conversion required in the water industry is from cubic feet to gallons to pounds of water. The relationship between them can be shown by the following box diagram (*Basic Science* 1996):

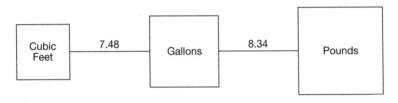

Source: Basic Science.

The diagram indicates that there are 7.48 gal in 1 cubic foot (ft³), and 1 gal of water weighs 8.34 pounds. The lines connecting the boxes can be thought of as bridges that tie any two boxes together.

Depending on the size of the boxes, it is easy to determine whether multiplication or division is required to obtain the answer. The rules are

• If you are moving from a smaller box to a larger box, you **multiply**.
• If you are moving from a larger box to a smaller box, you **divide**.

As an example, a tank has a capacity of 60,000 ft³, and you wish to know the capacity in gallons. When converting from cubic feet to gallons, move from a smaller box to a larger one, so the conversion factor of 7.48 is multiplied.

60,000 × 7.48 = 448,800 gal

Another box diagram widely used in the water industry shows the relationships between the various units of flow. Using the same technique described above, one could, for example, convert cubic feet per second (ft³/s) to pounds per day (lb/d) by successively multiplying the initial number by 7.48, then 8.34, then 60, then 1,440.

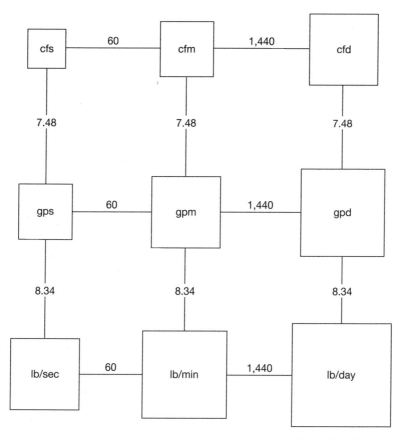

Source: Basic Science.

The Metric System

There is increasing interest in the United States to convert to the metric system. Not only is the metric system of measure easier to work with, but most of the countries of the world use it, and as we become an increasingly global market, it would be useful in dealing with other countries if all products were made to the same dimensional standards.

Understanding the Metric System

The metric system is based on the powers of 10. The progression of prefixes is shown in the following table:

Prefix	Symbol	Mathematical Values
exe-	E	1,000,000,000,000,000,000
peta-	P	1,000,000,000,000,000
tera-	T	1,000,000,000,000
giga-	G	1,000,000,000
mega-	M	1,000,000
kilo-	k	1,000
hecto-	h	100
deka-	da	10
(metre, litre, gram)	1	
deci-	d	0.1
centi-	c	0.01
milli-	m	0.001
micro-	µ	0.000001
nano-	n	0.000000001
pico-	p	0.000000000001
femto-	f	0.000000000000001
atto-	a	0.000000000000000001

The unit of measure for distance is the metre (m), and some of the more commonly used units are

kilometre (km)	= 1,000 m
metre	= 1 m
centimetre (cm)	= 0.01 m
millimetre (mm)	= 0.001 m
nanometre (nm)	= 0.000000001 m

The unit of measure for capacity is the litre (L), and some of the more commonly used larger and smaller units are kilolitre (kL), centilitre (cL), and millilitre (mL).

The metric unit of measure for weight is the gram (g), and some of the more commonly used units are kilogram (kg) and milligram (mg).

Conversions Within the Metric System

When making conversions of linear, capacity, or weight measurements in the metric system, each change in prefix represents a one decimal point move. If you move downward on the chart, the decimal places will be added to the right. If you move upward, the decimal places are moved to the left. For example, to change metres to nanometres you must move five positions down on the chart, so you would add five zeros. One metre (1 m) would therefore be equal to 1 billion nanometres (1 billion nm).

When the number to be converted is a *square*, each prefix value move requires *two* decimal point moves. For instance, to convert 1 square metre to square centimetres there is a two-position move on the chart, which indicates that there should be a *four* decimal point move. One square metre (1 m^2) would then be equal to 10,000 square centimetres (10,000 cm^2).

When the number to be converted is a *cube*, each prefix value move requires *three* decimal point moves. For example, to convert 3 cubic metres (3 m^3) to cubic centimetres (cm^3), there is a two position move on the chart, which indicates a six decimal point move. Accordingly, 3 m^3 would be equal to 3,000,000 cm^3.

Metric–US Customary Unit Conversions

Because US customary units are not divisible by 10, there is no easy conversion factor that can be applied to all units, such as the inch, foot, yard, and mile. The easiest method for most purposes is to use a conversion chart such as the one in appendix B.

Temperature Conversions

While the United States reads temperature on the Fahrenheit scale, most of the other countries of the world use the Celsius scale. The Fahrenheit–Celsius relationship is as follows:

boiling point = 212°, 100°C
freezing point = 32°F, 0°C

The formulas for converting between the two temperature scales are

°C = 5/9 (°F – 32°)
°F = 9/5 (°C) + 32°

A graph of the comparison between the two scales that is sufficiently accurate for many general purposes is provided in appendix C.

Bibliography

Basic Science Concepts and Applications. 1996. Denver, Colo.: American Water Works Association.

Price, J.K. 1991. *Basic Math Concepts for Water or Wastewater Plant Operators.* Lancaster, Pa.: Technomick Publishing Company, Inc.

Price, J.K. 1991. *Applied Math for Water Plant Operators.* Lancaster, Pa.: Technomic Publishing Company, Inc.

Chapter 2

Distribution System Hydraulics

An understanding of hydraulics is necessary for the proper operation of a water distribution system. Some of the basic concepts used in the operation of water distribution systems are covered in this chapter. More complete coverage of the subject can be found in the referenced publications listed at the end of the chapter.

Fluids at Rest and in Motion

Hydraulics is the study of fluids in motion or under pressure. In this handbook, the subject will be confined to the behavior of water in water distribution systems.

Static Pressure

Water flows in a water system when it is under a force that makes it move. The force on a unit area of water is termed *pressure*. The pressure in a water system is a measure of the height to which water theoretically will rise in an imaginary stand-pipe open to atmospheric pressure. The pressure can be *static*; i.e., it exists although the water does not flow. Pressure can also be *dynamic*, existing as "moving energy."

All objects have weight because they are acted on by gravity. When a 1-lb brick is placed on a table with an area of 1 square inch (1 in.²), it exerts a force of 1 pound per square inch (psi) on the table. Two stacked bricks on the 1-in.² table would exert a force of 2 psi. But if the size of the table is doubled, the pressure is halved. And if the table size is tripled, the pressure in psi is reduced by one third.

Likewise, a column of water 10 ft high exerts a total force of 4.33 psi. If you connect a pressure gauge at the bottom of a water tube with 10 ft of water in it, this is what it will read. If you also connect the gauge to the bottom of a larger-diameter column with 10 ft of water, the pressure at the bottom will still read the same (Figure 2-1). Water pressure is dependent only on the height of the column. On the other hand, the total weight exerted on the floor by the water in the large column will obviously be much more.

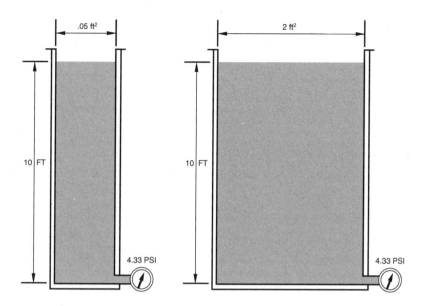

Figure 2-1 Hydraulic head depends only on column height

Dynamic Pressure

If the water in the column is permitted to empty horizontally from the bottom of a column, the water will begin to flow under the hydrostatic pressure applied by the height of the column. The flowing water will have little hydrostatic pressure, but will have gained moving, dynamic pressure, or kinetic energy. The hydrostatic pressure is static potential energy converted into moving energy.

One can add energy to a water system and thereby increase hydrostatic and dynamic pressure. A pump does this when it pumps water into elevated storage. The hydrostatic pressure (height) to which the water can be pumped is equivalent to pressure (less losses) at the pump discharge.

Pressure is usually measured in either pressure in pounds per square inch (psi) or feet of head in US units, or as kilopascals (kPa) pressure or metres (m) head in metric units. A pressure of 1 lb/in.^{2} is equal to approximately 6.895 kPa.

Velocity

The speed at which water moves is called *velocity*, usually abbreviated V. The velocity of water is usually measured in feet per second (ft/s) in US units and metres per second (m/s) in metric terms. For comparison, a rapidly moving river might move at about 7 ft/s (2.13 m/s).

The quantity of water (Q) that flows through a pipe depends on the velocity (V) and the cross-sectional area (A) of the pipe. This is stated mathematically as the formula $Q = A \times V$. Or, in terms of velocity,

$$V = \frac{Q}{A}$$

For example, a flume is 2 ft wide and 2 ft deep, so the cross-sectional area of the flume is 4 ft². The flume is flowing full of water and the quantity is measured at 12 ft³ in 1 second (12 ft³/s). The velocity of the water would therefore be

$$V \ = \ \frac{Q}{A}$$

$$= \ \frac{12 \ ft^3/s}{4 \ ft^2} \ = \ 3 \ ft/s$$

Friction Loss

As water flows through a pipeline, there is friction between the water and the walls of the pipe. The friction loss causes a loss of head (pressure) as the water flows through the pipe. The amount of friction depends partly on the smoothness of the pipe walls. All new pipe is quite smooth, whereas old, badly corroded cast-iron pipe will have a very high friction factor. The degree of pipe roughness is commonly denoted by a C factor, which is a coefficient in the Hazen–Williams formula that has long been used for determining flow in pipe. High C values imply less friction.

The head loss due to friction also depends on the velocity of the water flowing through the pipe, the diameter of the pipe, and the distance the water travels through the pipe.

Figure 2-2 is a commonly used nomograph for approximating the flow in ductile-iron pipe. In the example shown by a dashed line, a 12-in. pipe is flowing at approximately 600 gpm and the pipe has a C factor of 140. A line is drawn from the 600-gpm point on the discharge line, through the point for 12-in. pipe, and to the pivot line. A line is then drawn from that point to 140 on the flow coefficient line. This line crosses the loss of head line at about 0.7, indicating this is the head loss per 1,000 ft of pipeline. If, for example, you are determining the loss of head in a pipeline 3,000 ft long with no valves or bends, the theoretical loss of head would be three times the indicated value ($3 \times 0.7 = 2.1$ ft of head).

Pipe fittings also add a significant pressure loss in flow, and this is usually expressed as the equivalent length of straight pipe. To use the nomograph in Figure 2-3, a line is drawn from the pipe size to the point for each type of fitting, and the equivalent pipe length is read from the center scale. The total of all readings is then added to the actual length of the pipeline in determining the expected loss of head.

Referring to the dashed line in the figure, each medium sweep elbow in the 12-in. pipeline example above would add friction loss equal to about 26 ft of pipe. So if the example pipeline has 20 elbows along the 3,000-ft length, it would add friction loss equal to an additional $20 \times 26 = 520$ ft of pipe. This would cause additional loss of head as follows:

loss of head per 1,000 ft $= 0.7$ ft

loss of head for 520 ft $= \dfrac{520}{1,000} \times 0.7 = 0.36$ ft loss of head due to elbows

This would be added to the loss of head determined for 3,000 ft of pipe, so the total loss would be $2.1 + 0.36 = 2.46$ ft of head. If there are also tees, valves, and other fittings in the pipeline, the head loss that they cause can be computed and added to the total.

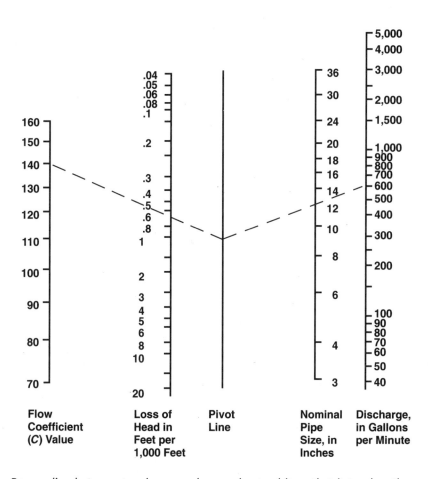

Flow
Coefficient
(*C*) Value

Loss of
Head in
Feet per
1,000 Feet

Pivot
Line

Nominal
Pipe
Size, in
Inches

Discharge,
in Gallons
per Minute

*Draw a line between two known values and extend it so that it touches the
pivot line. Draw a line between that point on the pivot line and the other known
value. Read the unknown value where the second line intersects the graph.*

Figure 2-2 Flow of water in ductile-iron pipe

This example also illustrates that the loss in head can become quite significant
over a long pipeline. If, for example, after adding up the losses caused by all the
other fittings, the total loss of head in the pipeline is 50 ft, this loss in terms of
pressure would be 50 ft $\times$ 0.433 lb/in.^{2}/ft = 21.65 psi. In other words, if the pressure
entering the pipe is 50 psi, the theoretical pressure at the far end would be reduced
to 50 − 21.65 = 28.35 psi.

To convert the information on the nomographs for metric use, refer to Table 2-1
for the metric equivalents of US unit pipe sizes. Flow in gpm can be converted to
L/s by multiplying by 0.06308. Head of water expressed in feet can be converted to
metres of water by multiplying by 0.3048.

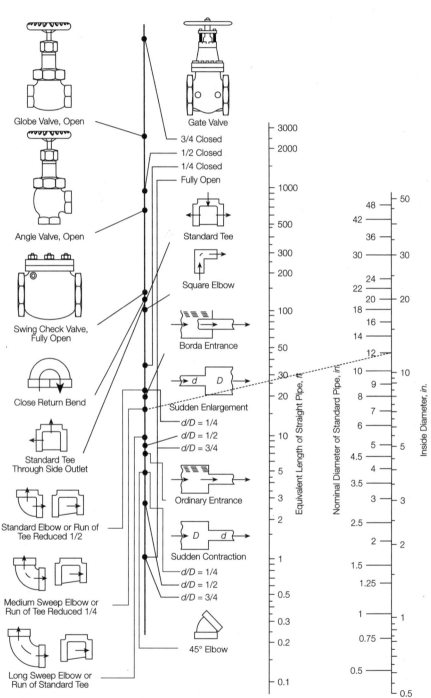

Figure 2-3 Resistance of valves and fittings to flow of fluids

Customary Inches	Proposed Millimetres	Customary Inches	Proposed Millimetres
$\frac{1}{4}$	8	16	400
$\frac{3}{8}$	10	18	450
$\frac{1}{2}$	15	20	500
$\frac{3}{4}$	20	21	525
1	25	24	600
$1\frac{1}{4}$	32	27	675
$1\frac{1}{2}$	40	30	750
2	50	33	825
$2\frac{1}{2}$	65	36	900
3	80	42	1,050
$3\frac{1}{2}$	90	48	1,200
4	100	54	1,350
6	150	60	1,500
8	200	66	1,650
10	250	72	1,800
12	300	78	1,950
14	350	84	2,100
15	375		

Table 2-1 Designation of US pipe sizes to the metric system

Hydraulic Gradient

The head of water at any point in a water system refers to the height to which water would rise in a freely vented standpipe. The head at each point would be the height of the water column. The imaginary line joining the elevations of these heads is called the *hydraulic grade line*. The slope or steepness of this line is called the *hydraulic gradient*.

A simple hydraulic gradient is illustrated in Figure 2-4. Assuming there is equal flow in all sections of the line, the gradient becomes steeper as the pipe becomes smaller because of the friction headloss. If there were no flow in the line, the water head at the end of the line would be at the same level as the water

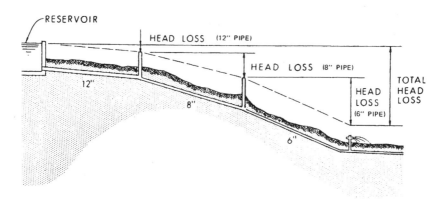

Figure 2-4 Pipe size affects hydraulic gradient

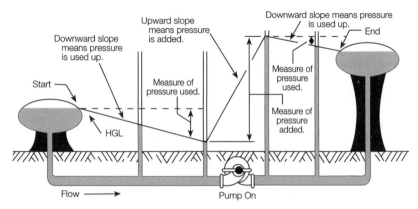

Figure 2-5 Five basic principles of hydraulic grade lines (HGLs) in dynamic systems

in the reservoir.

In the example in Figure 2-5, water flows from a reservoir toward a booster pump. The pump adds pressure and causes an upward slope of the hydraulic grade line, then the head falls as the water travels to the end of the system.

Bibliography

Basic Science Concepts and Applications. 1996. Denver, Colo.: American Water Works Association.

Hauser, B.A. 1991. *Practical Hydraulics Handbook.* Boca Raton, Fla.: CRC/Lewis Publishers.

Chapter 3

State and Federal Regulations

Drinking water regulations have undergone major and dramatic changes during the past two decades, and trends indicate that they will continue to become more stringent and complicated. It is important that all water system operators understand the basic reasons for having regulations, how they are administered, and why compliance with them is essential.

Federal Regulations

Although the regulations required by the Safe Drinking Water Act (SDWA) are of prime interest in the operation and administration of water distribution systems, operators must also adhere to regulations required by several federal environmental and safety acts.

Safe Drinking Water Act Requirements

Requirements under the SDWA are quite extensive, and complete details can be found in publications listed at the end of this chapter. The following discussion will primarily center on requirements that affect the operation of water distribution systems.

Prior to 1975, review of public water supplies was done by each state, usually by the state health department. The SDWA was passed by Congress in 1975 for a combination of reasons. One of the primary purposes was to create uniform national standards for drinking water quality to ensure that every public water supply in the country would meet minimum health standards. Another was that scientists and public health officials had recently discovered many previously unrecognized disease organisms and chemicals that could contaminate drinking water and might pose a health threat to the public. It was considered beyond the capability of the individual states to deal with these problems.

The SDWA delegates responsibility for administering the provisions of the act to the US Environmental Protection Agency (USEPA). The agency is headquartered in Washington, D.C., and has 10 regional offices in major cities of the United States. Some principal duties of the agency are to:

• set maximum allowable concentrations for contaminants that might present a health

15

threat in drinking water; these are called maximum contaminants levels (MCLs)
- delegate primary enforcement responsibility for local administration of the requirements to state agencies
- provide grant funds to the states to assist them in operating the greatly expanded program mandated by the federal requirements
- monitor state activities to ensure that all water systems are being required to meet the federal requirements
- provide continued research on drinking water contaminants and improvement of treatment methods

State Primacy

The intent of the SDWA is for each state to accept primary enforcement responsibility (primacy) for the operation of the state's drinking water program. Under the provisions of the delegation, the state must establish requirements for public water systems that are at least as stringent as those set by USEPA. The primacy agency in each state has been designated by the state governor. In some states the primacy agency is the state health department, and in others it is the state environmental protection agency, department of natural resources, or pollution control agency.

Classes of Public Water Systems

The basic definition of a public water system in the SDWA is, in essence, a system that supplies piped water for human consumption and that has at least 15 service connections or serves 25 or more persons for 60 or more days of the year. Examples of water systems that would *not* fall under the federal definition are private homes, groups of fewer than 15 homes using the same well, and summer camps that operate for fewer than 60 days per year. These systems are, however, generally under some degree of supervision by a local, area, or state health department.

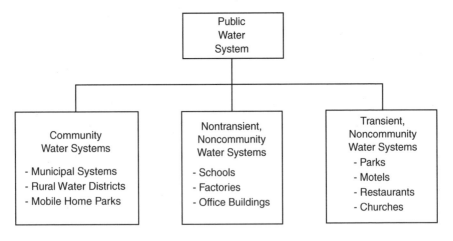

Source: Drinking Water Handbook for Public Officials (1993).

Figure 3-1 Classification of public water systems

USEPA has further divided public water systems into three classifications (Figure 3-1):
• community public water systems serve 15 or more homes. Besides municipal water utilities, this classification also covers mobile home parks and small homeowner associations that have their own water supply and serve more than 15 homes.
• nontransient, noncommunity public water systems are establishments that have their own private water systems, serving an average of at least 25 persons who do not live at the location, but the same people use the water for more than 6 months per year. Examples are schools and factories.
• transient, noncommunity public water systems are establishments such as parks and motels that have their own water systems and serve an average of at least 25 persons per day, but these persons use the water only occasionally and for short periods of time.
The monitoring requirements for community and nontransient, noncommunity systems include all contaminants that are considered a public health threat. Transient, noncommunity systems are only required to monitor for nitrate, nitrite, and microbiological contamination.

Regulation of Contaminants

The National Primary Drinking Water Regulations (NPDWRs) specify MCLs or a treatment technique requirement for contaminants that may be found in drinking water and could have an adverse health effect on humans. Specific concentration limits for the chemicals are listed and all community and nontransient, noncommunity systems must test for their presence. If a water system is found to have concentrations of chemicals present above the MCL, the system must either change its water source or treat the water to reduce the chemical concentration. Primary regulations are mandatory and must be complied with by all water systems to which they apply.

The National Secondary Drinking Water Regulations basically apply to drinking water contaminants that may adversely affect the aesthetic qualities of the water, such as taste, odor, or color. These qualities have no known adverse health effect, but they seriously affect public acceptance of the water. Secondary regulations are not mandatory, but are strongly urged by USEPA. Some state regulatory agencies have made some of the secondary limits mandatory in their states.

Public Notification

The SDWA mandates that the public be kept informed of noncompliance with federal requirements by requiring that noncomplying systems provide public notification (PN). If public water systems violate any of the operating, monitoring, or reporting requirements, or if the water quality exceeds an MCL, the system must inform the public of the problems. Even though the problem may have already been corrected, an explanation must be provided in the news media describing the public health significance of the violation.

The language and methods of providing PN are mandated by USEPA to make sure the public is fully informed. If a system is required to provide PN, the state primacy agency will provide full instructions.

Water distribution operators should understand that, although PN is intended to keep the public informed, if it is caused by a simple mistake such as forgetting to send in the monthly samples, it can cause some embarrassment for the system staff. There are two pieces of advice that can be provided. First, pay careful attention to state requirements. If there is any problem in meeting any of the requirements, discuss it with the state agency representative. For instance, if the person who normally sends in the water samples is sick or on vacation, do not forget to have someone else assigned to do the work.

The second piece of advice is, if you are required to provide PN, make it as positive as possible. Although the basic wording is mandatory, other wording can be added to keep it from sounding completely negative to the public.

Requirements Affecting Distribution System Operations

Some of the federal requirements that particularly apply to water distribution operations are detailed below.

Monitoring and Reporting

To ensure that the drinking water supplied by all public water systems meets federal and state requirements, system operators are required to regularly collect samples and have the water tested. The regulations specify minimum sampling frequencies, sampling locations, testing procedures, methods of keeping records, and frequency of reporting to the state. The regulations also mandate special reporting procedures to be followed if a contaminant exceeds an MCL.

All systems must provide periodic monitoring for microbiological contaminants and some chemical contaminants. The frequency of sampling and the chemicals that must be tested for depend on the size of the water system, the source of water, and the history of analyses. General sampling procedures are covered in more detail in chapter 4.

State policies vary on providing laboratory services. Some states have the laboratory facilities available to perform all required analyses, or, in some cases, a certain number of the required analyses for a system. In most states there is a charge for all or some of the laboratory services. Sample analyses that are required and cannot be performed by a state laboratory must be taken or sent to a state-certified private laboratory.

If the analysis of a sample exceeds an MCL, resampling is required, and the state should be contacted immediately for special instructions. There is always the possi-

Type of Information	Summary Requirement
Sampling information	Date, place, and time of sampling
	Name of sample collector
	Identification of sample
	• Routine or check sample
	• Raw or treated water
Analysis information	Date of analysis
	Laboratory conducting analysis
	Name of person responsible for analysis
	Analytical method used
	Analysis results

Table 3-1 Lab report summary requirements

Type of Records	Time Period
Bacteriological and turbidity analyses	5 years
Chemical analyses	10 years
Actions taken to correct violations	3 years
Sanitary survey reports	10 years
Exemptions	5 years following expiration

Table 3-2 Record-keeping requirements

bility that such a sample was caused by a sampling or laboratory error, but it must be handled as though it was actually caused by contamination of the water supply.

The results of all water analyses must be periodically sent to the state. Failure to have the required analyses performed or to report the results to the state will usually result in the system having to provide PN. States typically have special forms for submitting the data, and specify a number of days following the end of the monitoring period by which the form must be submitted. The minimum information that must be provided in the form is listed in Table 3-1. State regulators may also require other information for their own records and documentation.

There are also specific requirements for the length of time a water system must retain records. Table 3-2 lists the record-keeping requirements mandated by USEPA.

The Lead and Copper Rule

The Lead and Copper Rule (LCR) is a requirement that specifically applies to water distribution systems. The rule was created because it was found that, even though water entering a distribution system may be of acceptable quality, the quality may change by the time it gets to the consumer's tap. If the water is "aggressive," lead and copper may dissolve from water piping systems. The requirements were prompted by findings that showed consumption of even minute quantities of lead may have an adverse health effect on all humans, and particularly children.

The rules require that samples be collected at customers' taps after the water has remained undisturbed in the water piping for at least 6 hours. If the samples are found to contain excessive levels of lead or copper, the water system must implement corrosion control techniques. Specific monitoring procedures to be used and monitoring frequency are provided to each system by the state primacy agency.

General Disinfection Requirements

Disinfection is absolutely required for all water systems using surface water sources. Various chemicals other than chlorine can be used for the treatment of surface water, but as the water enters the distribution system, it must carry a continuous chlorine residual that will be retained throughout the distribution system. Water samples from points on the distribution system must be periodically analyzed to make sure an adequate chlorine residual is being maintained.

In spite of the fact that use of chlorine has almost completely eliminated occurrences of waterborne diseases in the United States, there is now concern for by-products formed when chlorine reacts with naturally occurring substances in raw water (such as decaying vegetation containing humic and fulvic acids). The first group of by-product chemicals identified were trihalomethanes

(THMs), a group of organic chemicals that are known carcinogens (cancer-forming) to some animals, so they are assumed to also be carcinogenic to humans. Other by-products of disinfection have been identified that may be harmful, and there is now also concern that disinfectants themselves may cause some adverse health reactions.

Water treatment systems have been trying for several years to limit the formation of THMs without impairing the bacteriological safety of the water. Proposed new regulation of disinfectants is called the Disinfectants-Disinfection By-Product Rule (D-DBP Rule). Methods of how best to disinfect water to protect the public are still under study, and will result in additional new chemical addition and monitoring requirements in the future.

Disinfection of Groundwater

Federal regulations do not currently require disinfection of groundwater unless the well has been designated by the state as vulnerable to contamination by surface water (termed "groundwater under the direct influence of surface water"). These are generally relatively shallow wells. Many states, though, have been phasing in their own requirements for required disinfection of various sizes, types, or classes of well systems.

The Safe Drinking Water Act (SDWA) amendments of 1996 specifically state that USEPA must promulgate regulations requiring disinfection as a treatment technique "as necessary" for groundwater systems. The final rules will probably give the states authority to allow well water systems that are considered properly constructed and operated, and meet other criteria, to forgo applying disinfection treatment.

Consumer Confidence Reports

One of the very significant provisions of the 1996 SDWA amendments is the consumer confidence report (CCR) requirement. The purpose of the CCR is to provide all water customers with basic facts regarding their drinking water so that individuals can make decisions about water consumption based on their personal health. This directive has been likened to the requirement that packaged food companies disclose what is in their food product.

The reports must be prepared yearly by every community water system. Water systems serving more than 10,000 people must mail the report to customers. Smaller systems must notify customers as directed by the state primacy agency. The first-year reports are to be delivered to consumers by October 19, 1999. Beginning in the year 2000, reports are to be delivered by July 1.

A water system that only distributes purchased water (satellite system) must prepare the report for their consumers. Information on the source water and chemical analyses must be furnished to the satellite system by the system selling the water (parent system).

Some states are preparing much of the information for their water systems, but the system operator must still add local information. Templates for preparing a report are also available from the American Water Works Association and the National Rural Water Association. Water system operators should keep in mind that CCRs provide an opportunity to educate consumers about the sources and quality of their drinking water. Educated consumers are more likely to help protect drinking water sources and be more understanding of the need to upgrade the water system to make their drinking water safe.

USEPA Regulation Information

Current information on USEPA regulations can be obtained by contacting the Safe Drinking Water Hotline at 800-426-4791. Also see the Office of Ground Water and Drinking Water web page at: http://www.epa.gov/safewater/standards.html.

State Regulations

Under the provisions of primacy delegation, each state must have requirements applying to public water systems that are at least as stringent as those set by the USEPA. States occasionally establish requirements that are more stringent. Federal requirements are only for factors that the USEPA considers directly related to public health. So, in addition to the federal requirements, each state also establishes other requirements to ensure proper water system operation.

Operator Certification

One requirement of the 1996 SDWA amendments is that the USEPA must establish minimum standards for state operator certification programs. Most states have had some form of certification for water system operators but, unfortunately, each state has its own idea of how operators should be classified so there has been little national consistency.

The new requirements will not correct the inconsistency, but will require most states to make some changes in their certification programs. Among the more important requirements are that each water system must at all times be under the direct supervision of a certified operator, operators must have a high school or equivalent education and pass an examination to receive certification, and the state must establish training requirements for certification renewal. Most states have a separate certification class for distribution system operators.

Cross-Connection Control

The states also generally promote cross-connection control programs for all water systems. Many states have their own cross-connection control manuals and assist water systems in setting up local programs. Cross-connection control is covered in detail in chapter 14.

Construction Approval

The SDWA requires states to review plans for water system construction and improvements. In general, plans and specifications for the proposed work must be prepared by a professional engineer and submitted for approval before work begins. State engineers review the plans for suitability of materials, conformance with state regulations, and other factors.

Some states allow small distribution system additions without approval or allow approval after construction. State regulations should be reviewed to ensure compliance with requirements.

Sanitary Surveys

A sanitary survey is an on-site inspection of a water system's facilities and operation. The survey is usually performed by a state employee, but the state may also contract with another person to do the work. Survey visits range in frequency from yearly to once every several years, depending on the water source and treatment process being used, size of the distribution system, history of compliance with monitoring and reporting requirements, and various other factors.

A sanitary survey usually involves a review of operating methods and records and a physical review of various facilities and equipment. The survey is designed to note problems or deficiencies that could cause contamination of the water supply or interrupt continuity of service. Surveys also produce recommendations on needed programs and changes to improve water quantity, quality, and reliability. A summary of the observations and suggestions or directives resulting from the survey are usually furnished in writing to the water system owner or person in charge.

Technical Assistance

One of the staff functions of the state drinking water program is to provide technical assistance to water system operators. Field staff with training and experience are usually available to provide advice and assistance. If possible, they will provide advice over the phone, but if the problem is of sufficient magnitude, they will arrange personal visits. They may also, on some occasions, suggest other sources of information or assistance.

Enforcement

Because of the direct relationship between drinking water quality and public health, it is rare for anyone to purposely disregard state and federal regulations. Most violations of regulations are due to not understanding requirements or forgetting something that must be done.

The SDWA requires states to use enforcement actions when federal requirements are violated. And if the state does not take appropriate action, the USEPA is prepared to step in and do it. Minor infractions are handled by public notification, but intentional disregard for requirements can result in substantial monetary fines.

Bibliography

Lead and Copper: How to Comply for Small and Medium Systems. 1993. Denver, Colo.: American Water Works Association.

Lead Control Strategies. 1989. Denver, Colo.: American Water Works Association Research Foundation and American Water Works Association.

SDWA Advisor Regulatory Update Service. (Hard copy or CD-ROM). Denver, Colo.: American Water Works Association.

Water Quality. 1996. Denver, Colo.: American Water Works Association.

Chapter 4

Public Health Considerations

Sources of Contamination

Water may be contaminated by biological, chemical, or radiological agents. Although water is supposed to be free of harmful and objectionable contamination when it enters the distribution system, there are a number of opportunities for water quality to change before it reaches the customers' taps. It is the distribution system operator's responsibility to ensure safe and pleasing water is delivered to each tap.

Biological Contamination

Pathogenic organisms is the term often used to cover all organisms that may cause human sickness or death. All pathogenic organisms have their origin in fecal waste from humans or other warm-blooded animals. Although most disease-causing organisms die quickly after being released to the environment, there are a few that can remain viable for days or even weeks.

Some of the historic waterborne diseases were typhoid, cholera, and dysentery. These are now rarely found in the United States, but the organisms now more likely to cause contamination in water are *Legionella, Cryptosporidium* oocysts, and *Giardia lamblia* cysts.

Bacterial Contamination

Although bacteria are the most plentiful of all living organisms, only a few are pathogenic. Many bacteria are helpful and even necessary for everyday living. Disease-causing bacteria reside in the intestinal tracts of humans and warm-blooded animals. It is almost impossible to specifically identify the disease bacteria, so water samples are tested for the presence of any bacteria of the coliform group, which is used as an indicator of fecal contamination. The theory is, if any coliform bacteria are present, there could be disease-causing bacteria among them.

Viral Contamination

Viruses that are of particular concern as causes of waterborne disease include infectious hepatitis, polio, and several types that cause gastrointestinal disease. Tests for specific viruses are very difficult, but because viruses originate from the fecal matter of warm-blooded animals, the lack of coliform bacteria in a sample is also taken as an indication that there are no harmful viruses present.

Radiological Contamination

There is some slight danger of water being contaminated by radioactive industrial wastes that have been improperly disposed of, but government regulations on handling and disposal of radioactive materials are very strict so this danger is generally minimal.

There are, though, many groundwater aquifers in the United States that have naturally occurring radium. The US Environmental Protection Agency (USEPA) has set limits on the concentration of radium that is considered a danger to public health. Water systems with wells drawing water from these aquifers must either change their water sources or install treatment to reduce the radium level of water furnished to customers.

Many wells also produce water containing quantities of radon gas. This is considered a danger to health because the radon is released into homes as the water is used in showers and other appliances, and continued inhalation of radon gas is considered to contribute to lung cancer risk. The USEPA plans to establish maximum limits for radon in drinking water, so water systems with well water exceeding the limits will have to install treatment for radon removal.

Chemical Contamination

Chemical contamination of drinking water can be due either to naturally occurring chemicals or to wastes from human activities. Limits on chemicals such as arsenic, barium, and cadmium have been established in the Primary Drinking Water Regulations. It has also been found in recent years that some manufactured organic chemicals disposed of on the ground over the years do not disintegrate as previously supposed. Instead, some of these chemicals have been found to travel considerable distances in aquifers and are now found in wells at concentrations considered a danger to public health.

The USEPA has established limits for the concentration of several organic chemicals in drinking water, and limits for additional chemicals will probably be added in the future as research reveals that they pose a threat to public health.

Water Quality Monitoring

Although most water quality monitoring is related to ensuring proper quality of the source water or treatment processes, many of the samples are collected from the distribution system. Thus, sample collection often becomes a duty of distribution system personnel. The reason for collecting samples from the distribution system is that there are some opportunities for water quality to change after if enters the distribution system, and under the requirements of the Safe Drinking Water Act (SDWA), it is the duty of the water purveyor to deliver water of proper quality to the consumer's tap.

Methods of Collecting Samples

There are two basic methods of collecting samples—grab sampling and composite sampling. A *grab sample* is a single volume of water collected at one time from a single place. To sample water in the distribution system, a faucet is used to fill a bottle. This sample represents the quality of the water only at the time the sample was collected. If the quality of the water is relatively uniform, the sample will be quite representative. If the quality varies, the sample may not be representative.

A *composite sample* consists of a series of grab samples collected from the same point at different times and mixed together. The composite is then analyzed to obtain the average value. If the composite sample is made up of equal-volume samples collected at regular intervals, it is called a *time composite* sample. Another method is to collect samples at regular time intervals, but the size of each grab sample is proportional to the flow at the time of sampling. This is called a *flow-proportional* composite sample.

Although composite sampling appears to be a good idea because it provides an average of water quality, it cannot be used for most analyses of drinking water quality because most parameters are not stable over a period of time.

Sample Storage and Shipment

Care must always be taken to use the exact sample containers specified or provided by the laboratory that will be doing the analyses. Most sample containers are now plastic to avoid the possibility of glass breaking during shipment. There are some samples for organic chemical analysis that must be collected in special glass containers because some of the chemical might be lost by permeating through the walls of a plastic container.

Sample holding time before analysis is quite critical for some parameters. If a laboratory receives a sample that has passed the specified holding time, it is supposed to declare the sample invalid and request resampling. There are some samples that can be refrigerated or treated once they arrive at the laboratory to extend the holding time, allowing the laboratory a few more days before the analyses must be completed.

Many laboratories do not work on weekends, so this should be taken into consideration when sending samples. Bacteriological analyses must, for example, be performed immediately by the laboratory. The best time to collect and send these samples is on a Monday or Tuesday so they will reach the laboratory by mid-week. Samples should be sent to the laboratory by the fastest means available, such as first class mail or special carrier.

Sample Point Selection

Samples are collected from various points in the distribution system to determine the quality of water delivered to consumers. In some cases, distribution system samples may be significantly different from samples collected as the water enters the system. For example, corrosion in pipelines, bacterial growth, or algae growth in the pipes can cause increases in color, odor, turbidity, and chemical content (e.g., lead and copper). More seriously, a cross-connection between the distribution system and a source of contamination can result in chemical or biological contamination of the water.

Most of the samples collected from the distribution system will be used to test for coliform bacteria and chlorine residual. The two primary considerations in determining the number and location of sampling points are that they should be

- representative of each different source of water entering the system (i.e., if there are several wells that pump directly into the system, samples should be obtained that are representative of the water from each one)
- representative of the various conditions within the system (such as dead ends, loops, storage facilities, and each pressure zone)

The required number of samples that must be collected and the frequency of sampling depend on the number of customers served, the water source, and other factors. Specific sampling instructions must be obtained from the state primacy agency.

Sample Faucets

Once representative sample points have been located on the distribution system, specific locations having suitable faucets for sampling must be identified. If suitably located, public buildings and the homes of utility employees are convenient places to collect samples. Otherwise, arrangements must be made to collect samples from businesses or private homes.

Following is a list of types of sampling faucets that *should not* be used:

- any faucet located close to the bottom of a sink, because containers may touch the faucet
- any leaking faucet with water running out from around the handle and down the outside
- any faucet with threads, such as a sill cock, because water generally does not flow smoothly from them and may drip contamination from the threads
- any faucet connected to a home water-treatment unit, such as a water softener or carbon filter
- drinking fountain

It is also best to try to find a faucet without an aerator. If faucets with aerators must be used, follow the state recommendations on whether or not the aerator should be removed for sampling.

Some years ago it was recommended that faucets be "flamed" before samples were taken. This generally consisted of running the flame from a propane torch over the outside of the faucet to kill any germs that may be present. Problems with the process included customers objecting because of possible damage to the finish on their faucets, and that many new faucets that look like metal are actually plastic. It has now been determined that, if a proper faucet and technique for sampling are used, flaming is not necessary or desirable.

Each sample point must be described in detail on the sample report form—not just the house address, but which faucet, in which room. If resampling is necessary, the same faucet used for the first sample must be used.

When it is necessary to establish a sampling point at a location on the water system where no public building or home gives access for regular sampling, a permanent sampling station can be installed (Figure 4-1).

Sample Collection

For collection of bacteriological and most other samples, the procedure is to open the faucet so that it will produce a steady, moderate flow (Figure 4-2). Opening the faucet to full flow for flushing is not usually desirable because the flow may not be smooth and water will splash up onto the outside of the spout. If a steady flow cannot be obtained, the faucet should not be used.

The water should be allowed to run long enough to flush any stagnant water from the house plumbing, which usually takes 2 to 5 minutes. The line is usually clear when the water temperature drops and stabilizes. The sample is then collected with-

Figure 4-1 Example of a permanent sampling station   *Courtesy of Gil Industries, Inc.*

out changing the flow setting. The sample container lid should be held (not set down on the counter) with the threads down during sample collection and replaced immediately. The sample container should then be labeled.

The exception to the above procedure is sampling for lead and copper analysis. These are to be first-draw samples, and require special procedures.

Bottles to be used for collection of bacteriological samples should not be rinsed before they are filled. These bottles usually are prepared with a small quantity of thiosulfate at the bottom to immediately stop the action of the residual chlorine in the water.

Special-Purpose Samples

It is occasionally necessary to collect special samples, particularly in response to customer complaints, such as taste and odor issues. To check on this type of complaint, one sample should be collected immediately as the tap is opened to be representative of water that has been in the plumbing system, then a second sample should

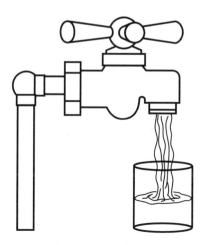

Figure 4-2 Sample faucet should be set to produce a steady, moderate flow

be collected after the line has been flushed. It is sometimes helpful to collect both hot- and cold-water samples in this manner. These samples can be used to identify whether the problem is in the customer's plumbing system or coming from the water distribution system. Many customer complaints of taste, odor, or color are found to be from their own water heaters, water softeners, or home water-treatment devices.

Laboratory Certification

It is imperative that the monitoring of all water systems be consistent, so all laboratory analyses must be performed by experienced technicians under carefully controlled conditions. For this reason, compliance sample analyses are acceptable to the state only if they have been performed by a certified laboratory. The only exceptions are measurements for turbidity, chlorine residual, temperature, and pH, which may be performed by a person acceptable to the state, using approved equipment and methods.

Most states operate certified laboratories that can accept some or all of the samples from water systems. The states also certify private laboratories that may be used for performing water analyses. Most large water utilities have their own certified laboratories because of the large number of samples that must be processed.

Distribution System Water Quality Problems

Turbidity

Turbidity is caused by particles suspended in water. These particles scatter or reflect light rays, making the water appear cloudy. Turbidity is expressed in nephelometric turbidity units (ntu) and a reading in excess of 5 ntu is generally noticeable to customers.

Besides the appearance being unpleasant to customers, turbidity in water is significant from a public health standpoint because the suspended particles could shelter microorganisms from the disinfectant and allow them to still be viable when they reach the customer. USEPA regulations direct that for most water systems, the turbidity of water entering the distribution system must be equal or less than 0.5 ntu in at least 95 percent of the measurements taken each month. At no time may the turbidity exceed 5 ntu.

Turbidity changes in the distribution system can indicate developing problems. Increases in turbidity may be caused by changes in velocity or inadequate flushing following main replacement.

Hardness

Hardness is a measure of the concentration of calcium and magnesium in water. Water hardness is usually derived from water contacting rock formations, such as water from wells in limestone formations. Soft groundwater may occur where topsoil is thin and limestone formations are sparse or absent. Most surface water is of medium hardness.

Hard and soft waters are both satisfactory for human consumption, but customers may object to very hard water because of the scale it forms in plumbing fixtures and on cooking utensils. Hardness is also a problem for some industrial and commercial users because of scale buildup in boilers and other equipment.

Water is generally considered most satisfactory for household use when the hardness is between 75 and 100 mg/L as calcium carbonate ($CaCO_3$). Water with 300 mg/L of hardness is usually considered too hard. Very soft waters having a hardness of 30 mg/L or less are found in some sections of the United States. Soft water is usually quite corrosive and may have to be treated to reduce the corrosivity.

Iron

Iron occurs naturally in rocks and soils and is one of the most abundant elements. It exists in two forms. Ferrous iron (Fe^{+2}) is in a dissolved state, and water containing ferrous iron is colorless. Ferric iron (Fe^{+3}) has been oxidized, and water containing it is rust-colored. Water from some well sources contains significant levels of dissolved iron, which is at first colorless, but rapidly turns brown as air reaches the water and oxidizes the iron.

There are no known harmful health effects to humans from drinking water containing iron, but the Secondary Drinking Water Standards suggest a limit of 0.5 mg/L. At higher levels, the staining of plumbing fixtures and clothing becomes objectionable. Iron also provides a nutrient source for some bacteria that grow in distribution systems and wells. Iron bacteria, such as *Gallionella*, cause red water, tastes and odors, clogged pipes, and pump failure.

Whenever tests on water samples show increased iron concentrations between the point where water enters the distribution system and the consumer's tap, either corrosion, iron bacteria, or both are probably taking place. If the water is corrosive, pH adjustment is usually the first corrective action to consider. If the problem is caused by bacteria, flushing mains, shock chlorination, and carrying increased residual chlorine are alternatives to consider.

Manganese

Manganese in groundwater creates problems similar to iron. It does not usually discolor the water, but will stain washed clothes and plumbing fixtures black—which is very unpopular with customers. Consumption of manganese has no known harmful effects on humans, but the secondary standards recommend a concentration not to exceed 0.05 mg/L to avoid customer complaints.

Water Quality Safeguards

The critical safeguards for water distribution system operation are
• continuous positive pressure in the mains
• maintenance of a chlorine residual
• cross-connection control
• frequent testing

Continuous positive pressure is necessary to prevent backsiphonage and the entry of contaminants. This can primarily be achieved by maintaining an adequate water supply and storage capable of meeting peak water demands. If water demands are so great during peak demand periods that pressure declines in parts of the system, either water use must be restricted or the system must be upgraded to be capable of supplying more water.

System pressure may also be reduced during a main break because of the large amount of escaping water. The best safeguards against having serious pressure loss during a main break are to have adequate system storage and to be well organized to swiftly shut down the leaking section of main. The latter involves having personnel on call at all times to respond to emergencies, knowing where all valves are, and having a valve exercise program so the valves are sure to operate when needed.

Chlorine residual should be maintained throughout the system to prevent any bacterial regrowth within the system and kill any bacterial contamination that might enter the system. The chlorine residual test (DPD) is quick and simple and can easily be performed at points in the system other than the regular sampling points if there is any question of water quality.

Cross-connection control, defined as a physical connection through which a supply of potable water could be contaminated or polluted, should receive the attention of every system operator. Although the chances of having a cross-connection incident may be relatively small, the consequence of a serious incident can be devastating. Cross-connection control is discussed in chapter 14.

The ultimate proof of the bacteriological safety of the water in the distribution system comes through frequent sampling. Samples collected to meet state requirements should be considered a minimum. Additional samples should be collected following construction and repair work as well as in response to customer complaints that could be the result of system contamination. A distribution system can become contaminated from an outside source, and it is best to discover the problem as soon as possible.

Bibliography

Bacterial Regrowth in Distribution Systems. 1988. Denver, Colo.: American Water Works Association Research Foundation.

Maintaining Distribution-System Water Quality. 1985. Denver, Colo.: American Water Works Association.

Pocket Guide to Water Sampling—Inorganic Contamination. 1991. Denver, Colo.: American Water Works Association.

Pocket Guide to Water Sampling—Lead and Copper. 1992. Denver, Colo.: American Water Works Association.

Pocket Guide to Water Sampling—Microbiological Contamination. 1990. Denver, Colo.: American Water Works Association.

Pocket Guide to Water Sampling—Organic Contamination. 1990. Denver, Colo.: American Water Works Association.

Water Quality. 1996. Denver, Colo.: American Water Works Association.

Chapter 5

Distribution System Design

There are many considerations involved in planning and designing a water distribution system. Some of the factors that may affect the design are the source or sources of water, population density, economic conditions of the community, geographical location, and history and practices of the water system.

Water Source Effects on System Design

The type and location of the water source have considerable effect on the design, construction, and operation of a water distribution system. The general types of systems classified by source are

- surface water
- purchased water
- groundwater supply
- rural water

Surface Water Systems

It is rare for groundwater to be available in large enough quantities to support a large community, so many medium-size and essentially all large water systems use surface water sources (Figure 5-1). One of the prime features of a surface water system is that the water often enters from one side of the distribution system. The situation that this creates is that large-diameter transmission mains are usually required to carry water to the far sides of the distribution system.

There are some exceptions, but in general, surface water is of good quality and plentiful. This in turn attracts industries that require process water for cooling, cleaning, and incorporation into a product. The availability of good-quality water at a reasonable price generally promotes rapid growth of the community, which in turn causes frequent expansion of the water distribution system.

Groundwater Systems

Although groundwater is generally available in most areas of the United States, the amount available for withdrawal at most locations is limited. If groundwater is generally available and the water requires no special treatment, some water systems are able to install several wells at various locations in the distribution system. These water systems may require few if any transmission mains because water flows from several directions through the piping grid.

If groundwater is available at only one location, all of the wells may be located at

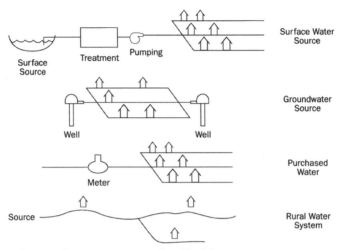

Figure 5-1 Types of water systems classified by source

one side of the distribution system, so the piping design is similar to that of a surface water system. A similar situation arises if the groundwater must receive treatment for contaminant removal or aesthetic improvement. In this case, water from several wells is piped to a central treatment facility, and then pumped to the distribution system.

Purchased Water

Many small water systems that started out using water from their own wells eventually had to change to either a surface water source or purchased water when their community outgrew the capacity of the groundwater source. Other communities have switched to purchased water when it was found that their groundwater source was contaminated and treatment for contaminant removal was not economically practical.

Examples of large numbers of purchasing systems are in the Chicago, Ill., and Detroit, Mich., areas where hundreds of surrounding communities draw water from a few large treatment plants using water from the Great Lakes. Some of these systems rechlorinate the water as it enters their systems, but otherwise no treatment is necessary.

Purchasing systems must usually provide a large amount of water storage because they depend on a single connection. If the connection should break, they could be without water for hours, or even days. Purchasing systems must maintain particularly tight water accountability because they are paying for all water metered to them, including unmetered uses and water wasted in leaks.

Rural Water Systems

A new class of water system has developed in recent years that has distribution system design and operating problems somewhat different than other water utilities. Rural water systems have developed in areas where both groundwater and surface water are nonexistent or of extremely poor quality. Many rural systems have been funded by government programs. The systems obtain water from remote sources, treat it if necessary, and then run long mains across the countryside to furnish water to individual farms, homes, and small communities.

In most cases, the water mains are plastic pipes installed by plowing them into the ground, and, in most systems, there is no intent to provide fire protection. The water main capacity is sufficient only to provide domestic water in limited quantities. Operators of rural water systems face many unique problems in operating and maintaining their systems.

Types of Water System Layout

The three general ways in which distribution systems are laid out include the following:

- arterial-loop system
- grid system
- tree system

Arterial-loop systems (Figure 5-2) are designed to have large-diameter mains around the water service area. Flow will be good at any point within the grid, because water can be supplied from four directions.

Grid systems (Figure 5-3) have most of the water mains that serve homes and businesses interconnected, and they are reinforced with larger arterial mains that feed water to the area. If the grid mains are all at least 6-in. (150-mm) diameter, flow is usually good at most locations because water can be drawn from two or three directions.

Tree systems (Figure 5-4) have transmission mains that supply water into an area, but the distribution mains that branch off are generally not connected, and many are dead ends. This is usually considered poor design because flow to many locations is through only one pipeline. Flow near the end of a long "branch" may be relatively poor. This design is poor also because a relatively large number of customers may be without water while repairs are made at a point near the connection of the branch to the transmission main. Customers at the ends of long branches may complain of poor water quality. This is caused by poor circulation of water in the system.

Unfortunately, few distribution systems are completely laid out in an ideal pattern. Most systems have been added onto as new housing or industrial areas were developed, and the original systems required reinforcement to carry the additional loads. Most distribution systems actually combine grid and tree systems.

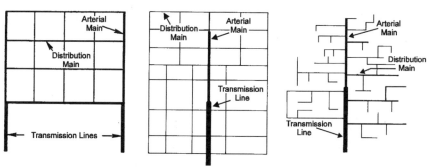

Figure 5-2 Arterial-loop system   **Figure 5-3** Grid system   **Figure 5-4** Tree system

Dead-End Mains

Residents usually like to live on dead-end streets because there is very little traffic. From a water supply standpoint, though, dead-end streets are undesirable because it is difficult to "loop" the piping system. A dead-end main can cause the following problems:

• The fire hydrants on the dead-end main draw from only one direction, so they may not provide very good flow.
• Domestic use on the main provides a very low flow rate, so water quality in the dead-end main often degrades to the point of prompting customer complaints about taste, odor, or rusty water. Many water systems have had to set up regular schedules of flushing dead-end mains to avoid customer complaints.

If a dead-end main is at least 6 in. (150 mm) in diameter and has sufficient flow and pressure, a fire hydrant should be installed at the end of the pipe. If the main does not have sufficient capacity to provide minimum fire flow, an approved flushing hydrant or blow-off should be installed for flushing purposes. Flushing devices should be sized to provide a flow velocity of at least 2.5 ft/s (0.75 m/s) in the water main.

Valves and Hydrants

Shutoff valves should be installed at frequent intervals in the distribution system so that areas may be isolated for repair without having to shut off too many customers. As a rule, at least two valves should be installed at each main intersection, and three is much better (Figure 5-5). Where there are long sections of main with no intersections, intermediate valves should also be installed at what would normally be one-block intervals. The *Ten State Standards* (Recommended Standards 1997) recommend a maximum spacing of 500 ft (152 m) in business districts, 800 ft (244 m) in residential areas, and 1 mile (1.6 km) in rural areas where future development is not expected.

Unless there are special circumstances, the best location for valves at a street intersection is opposite the right-of-way line for the intersecting street. This usually keeps them beyond the street paving and makes them easy to find. Mid-block valves should be located opposite an extended lot line, which is least likely to place them in a residential or business driveway.

Fire hydrants are best located at street intersections, and if the blocks are long, additional hydrants should be located near the middle of each block. Hydrant spacing should generally be between 350 and 600 ft (107 and 183 m), depending on the density and valuation of the area being served.

Water Main Sizing

Water mains must carry water for the following uses:
• domestic use in residential homes and apartments and irrigation of plants and lawns
• commercial uses, such as those at stores, public buildings, and industries
• fire flow

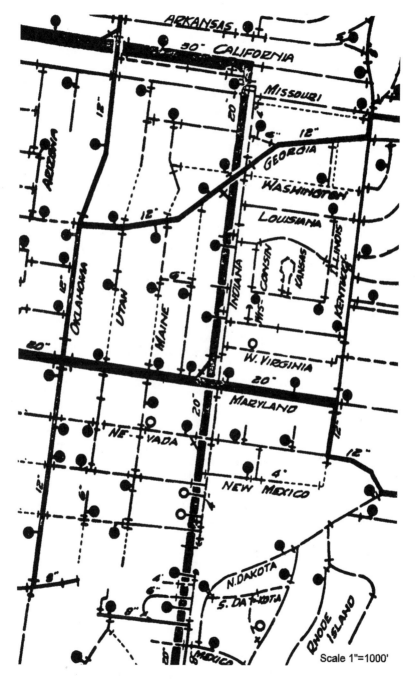

Figure 5-5 Portion of a typical distribution system map

Water Use Terms

The following terms are frequently used in determining pipe sizing for distribution system design:

Average day demand is the total system water use for 1 year, divided by 365 days in a year.

Per-capita water use is the average day demand divided by the number of residents connected to the water system. This figure varies widely from system to system, depending primarily on the quantity of water used for commercial and irrigation purposes. Nationally, the figure is estimated to be about 105 gallons per capita per day (gpcd) (397 L/d per capita).

Maximum day demand is the water use during the 24 hours of highest demand during the year.

Peak hour demand is the water use during the highest 1-hour period during the year, or sometimes during the history of the system.

Residential and Commercial Water Use

Residential flow is very small in comparison to the amount of water that can be carried in water mains of the size required for fire flow. In areas where there is no restriction on water use for sprinkling, the maximum hourly water use on a hot summer day may be two or three times the average rate, but this is still small in comparison to the capacity of mains required for fire flow.

Some industries and businesses, such as hospitals, incorporate large quantities of water in their products. Except under extreme emergencies, normal water service must be maintained to key facilities, such as hospitals, at the same time as fire flow is maintained in the area. In this case, the average water use of key facilities must be added to the fire flow requirements when designing mains.

Fire Flow Requirements

The primary factor in determining the size of water mains, storage tanks, and pumping stations for water systems serving a population of fewer than 50,000 is usually the fire protection requirements. The requirements for each community are set by the Insurance Services Office (ISO), which represents the fire insurance underwriters in the United States. The ISO determines the minimum flow that the water system must be able to maintain for a specified period of time in order to receive a specified fire protection rating. The fire insurance rates in the community are then based, in part, on this classification.

Many small, older, water systems were originally built with 4-in. (100-mm) diameter and smaller mains. These small lines will often provide adequate capacity for domestic flow, but fire hydrants located on them will not yield adequate flow to meet ISO requirements. The general requirements for a well-designed system are

- Mains in residential areas should have a minimum size of 6 or 8 in. (150 or 200 mm).
- Mains serving business, industrial, or other high-value areas should be at least 8 in. (200 mm), and may need to be larger to provide adequate fire flow.
- Mains smaller than 6 in. (150 mm) should be installed only when they are to be

used to provide circulation in a grid system. The general policy today is that water mains smaller than 6 in. (150 mm) should not have fire hydrants connected to them.

Additional information on fire flow requirements can be found in *AWWA Manual M31, Distribution System Requirements for Fire Protection.*

Water Pressure Requirements

The normal working pressure in the distribution system should preferably be between 35 and 65 psi (240 to 414 kPa). Higher pressures will significantly increase main and service leaks and will hasten the failure of water heaters and water-using appliances. In addition, customers do not like very high pressure because it will blow dishes out of their hands if faucets are opened quickly. The Uniform Plumbing Code requires that water pressure not exceed 80 psi (552 kPa) at service connections, unless the service is provided with a pressure-reducing valve.

The minimum pressure at ground level, at all points in the distribution system, *under all flow conditions*, must be 20 psi (140 kPa). In other words, the pressure should not drop below this pressure during fire flow conditions.

A water system supplying an area that has varying elevation must usually be divided into pressure zones to maintain reasonable pressure to customers. Water is furnished initially to the highest zone, and then admitted to the lower zones through pressure-reducing valves.

Water Velocity Limitations

The velocity of water flow in pipes is also a consideration in determining pipe sizes. The limit for normal operations should be about 5 ft/s (1.5 m/s). When the velocity is higher, the friction loss becomes excessive. Higher velocities can usually be tolerated under fire flow conditions.

Sizing to Maintain Water Quality

When sizing water mains there is a temptation to add a "safety" factor, enlarging the mains an additional size. This practice should be avoided because long detention times may result, which degrades water quality. The minimum size that can satisfy the fire and domestic demand should be selected.

Network Analysis

The sizing of water mains depends on a combination of factors, including system pressure, flow velocity, head loss resulting from friction, and the size of all mains that lead to a particular location. The calculation used for many years for analyzing flow in a distribution system involves use of the Hazen–Williams formula.

When a distribution system is to be expanded, it is usually necessary to analyze the entire system and to determine whether and how the system must be reinforced to properly handle the new loading. This analysis is now best performed by computer modeling techniques by consulting firms that specialize in this type of work.

Bibliography

AWWA Manual M31, Distribution System Requirements for Fire Protection. 1975. Denver, Colo.: American Water Works Association.

AWWA Manual M32, Distribution Network Analysis for Water Utilities. 1989. Denver, Colo.: American Water Works Association.

Cesario, L. 1995. *Modeling, Analysis, and Design of Water Distribution Systems.* Denver, Colo.: American Water Works Association.

Great Lakes–Upper Mississippi River Board of State Public Health and Environmental Managers. 1997. *Recommended Standards for Water Works.* Albany, N.Y.: Health Education Services.

Water Sources. 1996. Denver, Colo.: American Water Works Association.

Chapter 6

Water Main Pipe

Water main pipe must have sufficient strength to resist a variety of internal and external forces. Internal pressure includes not only the static pressure, which may be 100 psi (690 kPa) or higher, but also surge pressures. Surge, also called *water hammer*, is a sudden change in pressure caused by rapidly opening or closing a hydrant or valve, or starting or stopping a pump. The shock wave that travels through the pipe can amount to several times normal pressure.

External pressures include the weight of the earth fill over the pipe and the loading of traffic that may drive over it. The pipe must be capable of resisting crushing or excessive deflection due to the external loads.

Standards for all types of water system pipe have been established and are published by the American Water Works Association (AWWA) to ensure adequate and consistent quality (see appendix E).

Pipe Selection

There are several factors other than pipe strength that should be considered when selecting the type of pipe to be installed in a distribution system. Some factors may make a difference in the type of pipe to be used, others may not.

Corrosion Resistance

The potential for both internal and external corrosion of the pipe should be carefully considered. One of the advantages of plastic pipe is that it will not corrode. Concrete pressure pipe is also corrosion resistant for most soil conditions. Ductile-iron and steel pipe both carry internal and external coatings that will resist corrosion under normal water and soil conditions. Where the soil is very corrosive, a plastic wrap material is available to cover ductile-iron pipe to improve exterior corrosion resistance.

Smoothness of the Pipe Interior

Pipe with smooth walls ensures the maximum flow possible. The measure of pipe smoothness is called the C value or factor. Typical values are listed in Table 6-1. Old, tuberculated cast-iron pipe is the worst, with a C value of 100 or even lower. With internal coatings now being used, the value for all types of new pipe is about the same, and the value should not change much over the years provided aggressive waters are not being transported.

Pipe Material	C Value
Asbestos cement	140+
Cast-iron pipe (old)	100
Cast-iron badly tuberculated	<100
Concrete pressure pipe	140+
Ductile iron—cement lined	140+
Plastic	140+
Steel	140+
Wood stave pipe	±120

Table 6-1 C value of various pipe materials

Compatibility With Existing Materials

If extensions or replacements are being made to an existing water distribution system, a change in the type of piping material should be made only after careful consideration. In addition to the other considerations listed here, the following types of questions should be asked to determine whether the system should continue to use the existing type material, or should change to a new type of pipe:

• Has the existing pipe been satisfactory from a maintenance standpoint? Will the new type being considered be better?
• Will different types of fittings, repair parts, and tapping equipment be necessary for the new type of pipe? In other words, if a new type of pipe is added to the system, will it be necessary to stock two types of parts and fittings?
• Will the new type of pipe be significantly easier or harder to install, repair, tap, or locate?
• Will any disadvantages be offset by significant savings to the water system?
• If the type of pipe is changed, will the pipe and fittings, such as tees, elbows, and saddles, be readily available?

Economy

Installation cost is a major part of the total cost of a project, whether the work is done by contract or by utility personnel. In other words, if one type of pipe is slightly less expensive to purchase than another, but the excavation and installation costs are the same for either one, the difference in pipe cost won't make a very big difference in the end cost of the project.

On the other hand, if there is a difference in the cost of installing one type of pipe over another, it could make a significant difference in the overall project cost. Some of the factors that should be considered are:

• weight of the pipe—pipe that is lightweight can be handled easier and faster
• ease of assembling joints—push-on joints can be assembled much faster than bolted joints
• pipe strength—if one type of pipe requires special bedding to withstand external pressures while another pipe does not, it could make a significant difference in the installation cost

In many cases, the design engineer will specify the bedding and installation process required for each type of pipe that will be allowed, taking into consideration the local conditions on the project. The contractors will then determine the type of pipe that is most economical to install and will submit their bids accordingly.

Local Conditions

Water mains must often be installed in less-than-ideal soil conditions, and careful selection of the type of pipe and joints can result in both a more satisfactory and less expensive job.

Winding or Uneven Terrain

Installing a pipeline along a winding road or through hills and valleys will often require use of many elbows to accommodate the deflection. In addition, each of these elbows must be restrained, both horizontally and vertically. Under these conditions, consider using a type of pipe that will allow greater deflection and has restrained joints. This type may save on installation costs and provide a more trouble-free line in the future. As an example, some utilities install river-crossing pipe in very rough terrain.

High Groundwater Level

Where groundwater is high and it is difficult to completely dewater the excavation, some types of pipe and pipe joints may be easier to satisfactorily install than other types. For example, under wet, muddy conditions, mechanical joints can generally be made up with a greater certainty of holding than push joints.

Other Considerations

Some other considerations that may have a bearing on the type of pipe selected for use in the water system or on a specific job are:

- state and local regulations
- weather conditions at the time of installation
- likelihood of earthquakes in the area
- whether or not fire protection is to be provided
- whether or not the pipe is to be exposed to the weather or sunlight

Types of Pipe Service

Water system piping can generally be divided into two classes, for both purposes of service and type of material used—transmission mains and distribution system mains.

Transmission Mains

Transmission mains are designed to carry large quantities of water from the source of supply, such as a well or treatment plant, and furnish water to the distribution mains. They usually run in a nearly straight line from point to point and have only a few side connections.

Service lines to homes and businesses are not normally connected to a transmission main, so ease of making service taps is not a major consideration in selecting the type of pipe to be used.

Distribution Mains

Distribution mains are the pipelines that carry water from the transmission mains and distribute it to the customers and fire hydrants throughout the water system. They have many side connections and are frequently tapped for customer connections.

Types of Pipe Materials

Some of the very early water systems in the United States had wooden water mains made by boring or burning a hole down the center of logs. The logs were usually reinforced, but did not withstand much pressure, so were primarily used for gravity flow to supply local fountains and wells where residents could obtain water to carry to their homes.

The principal types of pipe in use in water distribution systems today fall into the following categories:

- gray cast-iron pipe
- ductile-iron pipe
- steel pipe
- asbestos–cement pipe
- polyvinyl chloride pipe
- other plastic and fiberglass pipe
- concrete pipe

A summary of the features of currently used pipe materials and the type of joints available is provided in Table 6-2.

Gray Cast-Iron Pipe

The oldest known installation of cast-iron pipe (CIP) was in 1664 in Versailles, France. Cast iron was by far the predominant type of pipe installed in the United States and Canada for many years, and most of it is still in use.

The earliest pipe was made of gray iron that was cast in sand molds, so it is commonly called *sand cast pipe*. It was usually made in 12-ft (3.7-m) lengths, with a bell on one end and spigot on the other, designed for a lead joint. The outside diameter of the pipe is larger than centrifugally cast pipe, and often is not completely round. Sand-cast pipe can usually be identified by the rough texture of the metal.

In the 1920s, the centrifugal process of manufacturing CIP was developed. With this method, molten iron is poured into a rotating horizontal mold, and centrifugal force maintains the iron around the walls of the mold until it solidifies. The outside walls of this pipe are smooth and uniform in size, and the desired strength can be developed with thinner pipe walls than sand-cast pipe because the iron is more homogeneous. Although gray CIP is strong and provides a long service life, it is brittle and can break. Most main breaks are straight-across cracks known as *beam breaks* and are quite often caused by stones or other hard objects improperly left in the bottom of the excavations when the pipe was laid.

Until the 1920s, distribution system pipe joints were made of poured lead (Figure 6-1). The process of pouring a lead joint was slow and required special skills. It was not unusual for the joints to leak, but because lead is rather flexible, the joints had some flexibility. The process of pouring a lead joint consisted of first tamping oakum into the bell, then pouring molten lead into the joint, and finally caulking the joint with a hammer and flat-end caulking iron.

Gray CIP is no longer manufactured in the United States.

ASBESTOS–CEMENT (A–C) PIPE

Common sizes	4 to 35 in. (100 to 890 mm) diameter
Normal max. working pressure	200 psi (1,380 kPa)
Advantages:	good flow characteristics
	light weight, easy to handle
Disadvantages:	small sizes have low flexural strength—requires special care in bedding
	easily damaged by impact
	difficult to locate underground
	requires special care in tapping
	asbestos fibers are weakened during field modifications
Type of joints:	individual coupling with ring gaskets

DUCTILE-IRON (DI) PIPE (CEMENT LINED)

Common sizes	4 to 64 in. (76 to 1,625 mm) diameter
Normal max. working pressure	350 psi (2,413 kPa)
Advantages:	durable and strong
	high flexural strength (resists breaking if bent)
	good corrosion resistance in all except very corrosive soil
	thinner walls than A–C or PVC, so more carrying capacity for the same outside diameter
	taps easily made directly into the pipe
Disadvantages:	quite heavy—must be handled with mechanical equipment
	must be covered with plastic or cathodically protected for protection in corrosive soil
Types of joints:	bell and spigot (lead)—no longer being used
	push-on and mechanical—general use for a flexible joint
	flanged—used where pipe is to be rigid in pumping stations
	flexible ball—used for river crossings
	restrained—used to resist thrust and in unstable ground

CONCRETE PIPE

Common sizes (reinforced)	12 to 168 in. (305 to 4,267 mm) diameter
Common sizes (prestressed)	16 to 144 in. (406 to 3,658 mm) diameter
Normal max. working pressure	350 psi (2,413 kPa)
Advantages:	durable with low maintenance
	good corrosion resistance, internal and external
	high external load capacity
	minimal requirements for bedding and backfilling
Disadvantages:	very heavy weight requires large lifting equipment for installation
	may require external protection in high-chloride soil
Types of joints:	bell and spigot with elastomeric gaskets
	other joint types available for fittings or thrust restraint

STEEL PIPE

Common sizes	4 to 120 in. (100 to 3,048 mm) diameter
Normal max. working pressure	just about any pressure by making the walls thick enough
Advantages:	light weight makes it easy to install with mechanical equipment
	high tensile strength; good choice where some movement may occur
	very flexible—requires significant bedding support
Disadvantages:	poor internal and external corrosion resistance unless properly lined and protected on the outside
	pipe can collapse if a vacuum should occur so air-and-vacuum relief valves are imperative on larger sizes
Types of joints:	mechanical sleeve—mostly for smaller pipe
	rubber gasket joints—for low-pressure applications
	welded joints—for high-pressure or large-diameter applications
	flanged joints—where valves and fittings are to be used
	expansion joints—allows movement due to pipe expansion

POLYVINYL CHLORIDE (PVC) PIPE

Common sizes	4 to 36 in. (100 to 914 mm) diameter
Normal max. working pressure	200 psi (1,379 kPa)
Advantages:	light weight makes it easy to install
	excellent resistance to corrosion
	high impact strength
Disadvantages:	difficult to locate underground
	requires special care during tapping
	susceptible to damage during handling
	requires special care in bedding
	damaged by exposure to sunlight (UV radiation)
Types of joints:	push-on joints

Table 6-2 Comparison of pipe materials and joints

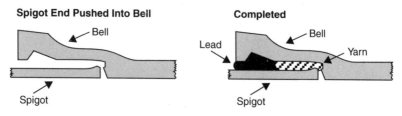

Figure 6-1 Leaded bell-and-spigot joint

Ductile-Iron Pipe

Ductile-iron pipe (DIP) outwardly looks the same as centrifugal gray CIP, and it is produced in the same type of mold. But by adding an inoculant, usually magnesium, to the molten iron, the molecular structure is changed so that the material is much stronger and tougher. Ductile-iron pipe can actually be bent to some degree without breaking, so it is not subject to the beam breaks that are common to CIP.

Bare DIP is subject to internal corrosion by aggressive water, the same as CIP, so most pipe is now lined with a thin cement-mortar coating that protects the metal and provides a smooth inner surface. The lining is between $1/16$ and $1/8$ in. (1.5 and 3 mm) thick, depending on the pipe size, and adheres to the pipe wall even when the pipe is cut or tapped. Cement-mortar is normally very durable, but it may be slowly attacked by very soft water, by high-sulfate waters, or by waters undersaturated in calcium carbonate. If the pipe is subject to any of these conditions, consider purchasing pipe with an epoxy or other lining.

The standard exterior coating used for DIP provides only moderate corrosion protection. In corrosive soils, supplemental corrosion protection should be provided.

Standard lengths for DIP are 18 and 20 ft (5.5 and 6.1 m). Standard pressure classes range from 150 to 350 psi (1,034 to 2,413 kPa).

Additional information on DIP may be obtained from the Ductile Iron Pipe Research Association (DIPRA) (see appendix D).

Ductile-Iron Pipe Joints

Several different types of joints are used today for connecting DIP and fittings. Details of more common types are illustrated in Figure 6-2 and described below.

Flanged joints are often used in exposed locations, such as treatment plants and pumping stations, where the pipe installation is to be rigid and the pipe must be restrained from movement. Each of the matching flanges has a machined surface and they are tightly bolted together with a gasket between them. Flanged joints should not be used underground because they have no means of flexing if there is ground movement.

Mechanical joints have special bells fitted with rubber gaskets. The joint is made tight by a bolted follower ring that squeezes the gasket into the bell. The joints are more expensive than push-on joints, but make a very positive seal and allow a fair degree of deflection of the pipe.

Push-on joints are now the most popular type of joint for most main installations because they are the least expensive and can be assembled quickly in the field. The joint consists of a special bell fitted with a greased gasket that is inserted in the field just before the pipe is joined. The spigot end of the joining pipe must be beveled so it will slip into the gasket without catching or tearing. The spigot end slips into the

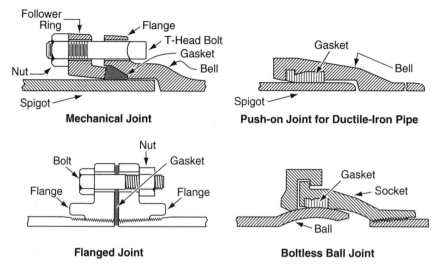

Source: Mechanical joint and Push-on joint adapted from ANSI/AWWA C111/A21.11.

Figure 6-2 Common types of ductile-iron pipe joints

gasket quite easily, and makes a very tight seal as internal water pressure compresses the gasket.

The design of push-on joints varies with different pipe manufacturers, and although they are similar, they are not necessarily interchangeable. The joints must be made up by pushing the pipes in a straight line, but after the spigot has been inserted the full distance, the pipe can be deflected from about 2 to 5°, depending on the pipe size.

Ball-and-socket joints are made to be restrained and deflect as much as 15°. The pipe is principally used for underwater intakes and river crossings, but it is also occasionally used for underground burial in very rough terrain. Both bolted and boltless ball-and-socket joint pipe are available.

Restrained joints of various types are also available from different manufacturers for use where it is necessary to ensure that the joints do not separate. Details of two types of restrained joints are illustrated in Figure 6-3.

Ductile-Iron Pipe Fittings

Before World War II, a wide variety of special fittings were available, such as reducing elbows, and tees with different sized outlets. But as manufacturing costs increased, manufacturers have cut back to making only a limited number of the most commonly used styles. Figure 6-4 illustrates some common styles that are available. Because of the limited choice of fittings, special connections must now be made up of a combination of fittings.

In addition to use on DIP, iron fittings are also commonly used on types of polyvinyl chloride (PVC) pipe having the same outside diameter as DIP.

Steel Pipe

Steel pipe has been used in water systems in the United States since 1852. It can be made to withstand almost any pressure by making the walls thick enough, so it is frequently used for high-pressure pipelines.

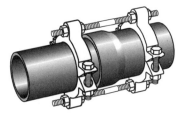 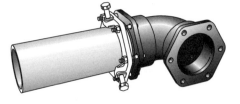

Pipe Bell Joint Restraint   **Mechanical Joint Pipe Restraint**

Courtesy of The Ford Meter Box Co., Inc.

Figure 6-3 Restrained joint

Steel pipe is fabricated by three methods. In the mill process, a long flat sheet is progressively rounded by a series of pressure rollers until a tube is formed, then the seam is welded shut. Large-diameter pipe is made by rolling flat plates to make short pieces of tube, and then several pieces are welded together to make lengths of pipe. In the spiral-weld method, a narrow piece of steel is fed from a coil to a machine that automatically welds it in a continuous spiral fashion. Steel pipe has been fabricated in diameters up to 30 ft (9 m).

Steel pipe is generally more competitive in price in sizes over 16 in. (400 mm). Unprotected steel is subject to corrosion, so both the interior and exterior must be protected. The interior is usually coated with cement mortar or epoxy as specified in AWWA Standards C205 and C210. AWWA Standards provide for

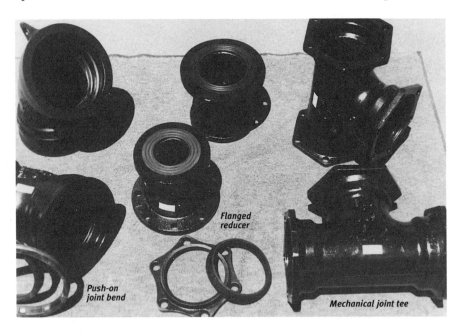

Figure 6-4 Typical iron pipe fittings   *Courtesy of U.S. Pipe and Foundry Company.*

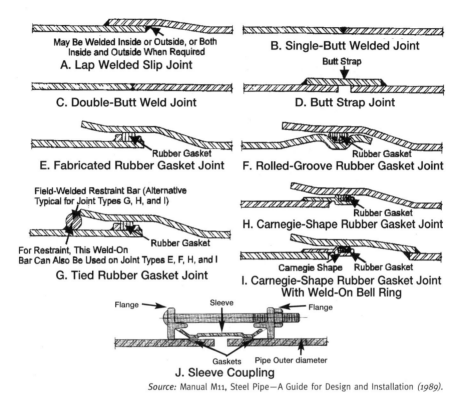

A. Lap Welded Slip Joint
May Be Welded Inside or Outside, or Both
Inside and Outside When Required

B. Single-Butt Welded Joint
Butt Strap

C. Double-Butt Weld Joint

D. Butt Strap Joint

E. Fabricated Rubber Gasket Joint
Rubber Gasket

F. Rolled-Groove Rubber Gasket Joint
Rubber Gasket

Field-Welded Restraint Bar (Alternative
Typical for Joint Types G, H, and I)

For Restraint, This Weld-On
Bar Can Also Be Used on Joint Types E, F, H, and I
Rubber Gasket

G. Tied Rubber Gasket Joint

H. Carnegie-Shape Rubber Gasket Joint
Rubber Gasket

**I. Carnegie-Shape Rubber Gasket Joint
With Weld-On Bell Ring**
Carnegie Shape   Rubber Gasket

Flange   Sleeve   Flange

Gaskets   Pipe Outer diameter
J. Sleeve Coupling

Source: Manual M11, Steel Pipe—A Guide for Design and Installation *(1989)*.

Figure 6-5 Common welded and rubber-gasketed joints used for connecting steel pipe

several types of plastic coatings, bituminous materials, and polyethylene tape that may be applied to the pipe exterior for protection against both abrasion and corrosion.

Cast-iron or ductile-iron fittings may be used on smaller sizes of steel pipe. For larger pipe, fabricated steel fittings are used. Various types of O-ring bell and spigot joints may be used with steel pipe, or the pipe lengths can be joined by welding as illustrated in Figure 6-5.

Additional information on steel pipe may be obtained from the Steel Tube Institute of North America (see appendix D).

Asbestos–Cement Pipe

Asbestos–cement (A–C) pipe was introduced in the United States around 1930. It is made of asbestos fibers, silica sand, and portland cement and is available in working pressures of 100, 150, and 200 psi (690, 1,030, and 1,380 kPa). Standard sizes are 4 to 42 in. (100 to 1,070 mm) and section lengths are 10 to 13 ft (3 to 4 m). Pipe sections are furnished with two plain ends and are coupled with an O-ring sleeve as illustrated in Figure 6-6.

Although A–C pipe resists mild corrosion, it should not be used in very aggressive soils or for carrying very soft water. The advantages of the pipe include low ini-

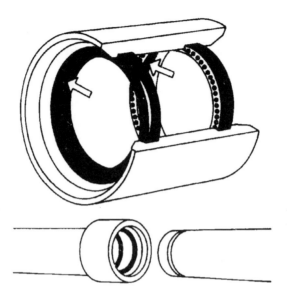

Figure 6-6 Method of connecting asbestos–cement pipe

tial cost, smooth interior walls, and light weight, which makes smaller sizes very easy to install.

Principal disadvantages are that it breaks easily if not handled and installed properly, the need for special care in tapping, and the need for special safety precautions during installation to prevent inhalation of asbestos dust. In recent years, the US Environmental Protection Agency (USEPA) has discouraged most uses of asbestos because of evidence that exposure to airborne asbestos fibers can greatly increase the chances of a person developing lung cancer. Studies by USEPA, AWWA, and other groups have concluded that the asbestos in water mains does not generally constitute a health threat to customers. But A–C pipe is rarely installed in the United States today, both because of the fear of working with asbestos materials and because PVC pipe has taken its place as an inexpensive, lightweight piping material.

Plastic Pipe

Plastic pipe was first introduced in the United States around 1940 and has seen rapid acceptance since the 1960s. There are many different types of plastic materials that can be manufactured to have various properties. The two important properties for plastic water main pipe are the ability to withstand both internal and external pressures and the absence of any harmful substances that would cause taste, odor, or potential adverse health effects to customers.

Plastic pipe is commonly made from polyvinyl chloride (PVC), polyethylene (PE), and composite plastic in the form of plastic material reinforced with fiberglass. The interior surfaces of all types of plastic pipe are very smooth, so it has a very good flow factor, and the material is almost completely corrosion free.

All plastic pipe used for potable water must be certified for conformance with National Sanitation Foundation International Standard 61 for potable water use. There must be a marking along the entire length of each section of pipe stating conformance with the standard.

Polyvinyl Chloride Pipe

Polyvinyl chloride is by far the most widely used type of plastic pipe. In sizes from 4 to 12 in. (100 to 300 mm), the pipe is manufactured with the same outside diameter as ductile-iron pipe, so DI tees, bends, and other fittings made of that material may be used for connections. Polyvinyl chloride fittings are also available. Polyvinyl chloride transmission pipe in sizes 14 in. (356 mm) and larger is available in outside-diameter sizes based on either iron pipe size or DIP size.

The light weight of PVC pipe makes it considerably less expensive to ship, handle, and install than DIP. The pipe is also easy to cut and has moderate flexibility to adapt to ground settlement.

The pipe is susceptible to the ultraviolet radiation in sunlight, so it should not be stored outside for prolonged periods. The pipe is also very susceptible to damage during shipping and installation. Gouges deeper than 10 percent of the wall thickness can cause pipe failure later. Although the pipe may be directly tapped in the same manner as DIP, it must be done with extreme care. Many water system operators find it safer to make taps through a saddle.

Additional information on PVC pipe is available from the Uni-Bell Plastic Pipe Association. Additional information on other types of plastic pipe is available from the Plastic Pipe Institute (see appendix D).

Polyethylene Pipe

Polyethylene pipe is available in nominal sizes through 63 in. (1,600 mm) diameter, typically with the same outside diameter as iron pipe sizes. Pressure class ratings range from 40 to 198 psi (276 to 1,365 kPa), except that the available maximum pressure rating is reduced for larger pipe sizes. Polyethylene pipe is not quite as strong as PVC at ambient temperatures, but it is very tough, ductile, and flexible, even at low temperatures. Polyethylene pipe will not fracture under the expansive action of freezing water.

Polyethylene pipe can be joined by thermal butt-fusion, flange assemblies, or mechanical methods. It cannot be joined by solvent cements, adhesives, or threaded connections. The most widely used method is butt-fusion, which uses a portable tool to hold the ends of the pipe or fittings in close alignment while they are heated and fused together, and then allowed to cool. The fusion temperature, interface pressure, and cooling time are rather critical so thermal fusion should only be performed by persons who have received training in use of the equipment, according to the recommendations of the manufacturer. Thermal fusion is covered in ASTM Standard D2657.

Fittings are also available for joining by thermal fusion. Special flanged and mechanical joint adapters are available for connecting PE pipe to other types of pipe and fittings.

Polyethylene pipe is covered in AWWA Standard C906-90, *Polyethylene Pressure Pipe and Fittings, 4 in. Through 63 in., for Water Distribution.*

Fiberglass Pipe

Fiberglass pipe is available for potable water use in sizes from 1 in. through 144 in. (25 mm through 3,600 mm) diameter, in five pressure classes ranging from 50 psi through 250 psi (345 kPa through 1,724 kPa). There are also several different stiffness classes available that are incorporated into the design, depending on the exterior loading that will be applied to the pipe. Advantages of the pipe include corrosion resistance, light weight, low installation cost, ease of repair, and hydraulic smoothness. Disadvantages include susceptibility to mechanical damage, low modulus of elasticity, and lack of a standard jointing system.

One method of manufacturing the pipe is called *filament winding*. A continuous glass-fiber roving saturated with resin is wound around a mandrel in a carefully controlled pattern and tension. The inside diameter (ID) of the pipe is fixed by the mandrel diameter and the wall thickness is governed by the pressure and stiffness class desired.

The other manufacturing method is centrifugal casting. The resin and fiberglass reinforcement are applied to the inside of a mold that is rotated and heated. The outside diameter of the pipe is determined by the mold and the ID varies depending on the wall thickness. Fittings are made by filament winding, by spraying chopped fiberglass and resin on a mold, or by joining cut pieces of pipe to make mitered fittings.

There are several different methods used by the various manufacturers for joining pipe sections and fittings. One method is to butt the sections together and wrap the joint with fiberglass material and resin. The other methods include a variety of tapered bell-and-spigot joints that are bonded with adhesives. Pipe, fittings, and adhesive for joining usually are not interchangeable between pipe from different manufacturers.

Fiberglass pipe is covered in AWWA Standard C950-95, *Fiberglass Pressure Pipe.*

Permeation of Organic Chemicals Into Plastic Pipe

If gasoline, fuel oil, or other organic compounds have saturated the soil around plastic pipe, some molecules of the compounds can pass through the pipe walls in a process called *permeation*. This can give the water a disagreeable taste, but more important, it could pose a significant health threat to customers using the water. Continued exposure to the organic compounds can also soften the pipe and eventually lead to pipe failure.

Plastic pipe should not be installed in locations known to have soil contamination or where soil contamination is likely, such as near old petroleum storage tanks.

Concrete Pipe

Concrete pipe combines the high tensile strength of steel and the high compressive strength and corrosion resistance of concrete to produce pipe that is very durable at reasonable cost.

The pipe is generally available in diameters ranging from 10 to 252 in. (250 to 6,400 mm) and in lengths from 12 to 40 ft (3.7 to 12.2 m).

The four types of concrete pipe construction commonly used in the United States and Canada are

- prestressed concrete cylinder pipe
- bar-wrapped steel-cylinder pipe (formerly called pretensioned concrete cylinder pipe)
- reinforced concrete cylinder pipe
- reinforced concrete noncylinder pipe

Prestressed Concrete Cylinder Pipe

The two types of prestressed concrete cylinder pipe are illustrated in Figure 6-7. Manufacture of the pipe starts with the assembly of a steel cylinder with the bell and spigot ends welded to it. The cylinder is first hydrostatically tested to verify water-tightness, and then a cement–mortar core is placed on the interior by a centrifugal process or vertical casting.

After the core has cured on lined-cylinder pipe, hard-drawn steel wire is helically wrapped around the cylinder. On embedded-cylinder pipe, a concrete coating is placed around the steel cylinder, and after it has cured, it is wrapped with steel wire. Wrapping the cylinder with wire produces a compression of the concrete and steel core, which greatly strengthens the pipe. The pipe is finally coated with cement mortar for corrosion protection and is ready for use after the coating has cured.

Bar-Wrapped Steel-Cylinder Concrete Pipe

Bar-wrapped pipe is manufactured similarly to prestressed pipe except that, after the mortar lining has cured, the steel cylinder is wrapped with hot-rolled steel bar. The exterior is then protected with a cement–mortar coating (see Figure 6-8).

Reinforced Concrete Cylinder Pipe

Reinforced concrete cylinder pipe differs in that, instead of wrapping the reinforcing wire around the steel cylinder, the reinforcing is cast into the wall of the pipe (see Figure 6-9). Use of this design is gradually declining in favor of prestressed or bar-wrapped pipe.

Reinforced Concrete Noncylinder Pipe

Noncylinder pipe has reinforcing, but does not have a steel cylinder. Pressure is limited to about 55 psi (380 kPa), so use of this type of pipe in water systems is generally limited to intake lines.

Uses of Concrete Pipe

As shown in Figures 6-7 through 6-9, concrete pipe joints are made up with an O-ring that is compressed as the spigot is pushed into the bell. The metal parts are then protected from corrosion with a covering of mortar.

Some of the advantages of concrete pipe are that it can be designed to withstand high internal pressure and external loads, and it is resistant to both internal and external corrosion under normal water quality conditions. Among the principal disadvantages are that the relatively great weight makes shipping expensive and that exact pipe lengths and fittings required for an installation must be carefully laid out in advance. It is necessary for the concrete pipe supplier to provide a detailed layout of the pipe project to minimize field adjustments.

Additional information on concrete pipe is available from the American Concrete Pipe Association and the American Concrete Pressure Pipe Association (see appendix D).

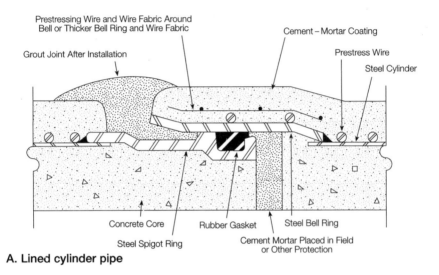

A. Lined cylinder pipe

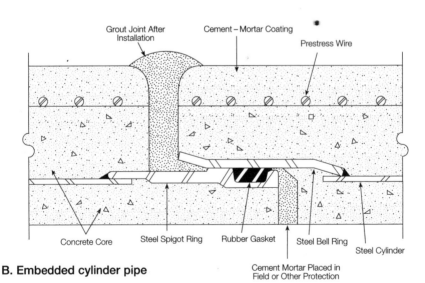

B. Embedded cylinder pipe

Drawings furnished by American Concrete Pressure Pipe Association.

Figure 6-7 Two types of prestressed concrete cylinder pipe

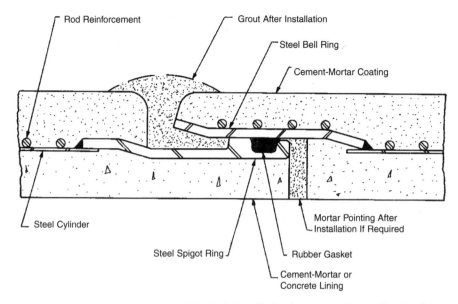

Drawing furnished by American Concrete Pressure Pipe Association.

Figure 6-8 Bar-wrapped steel-cylinder concrete pipe

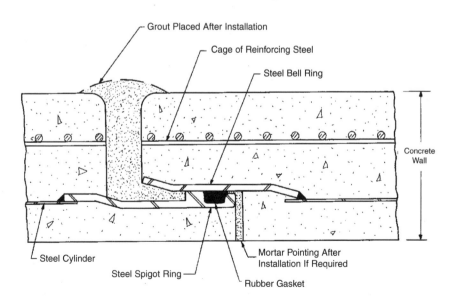

Drawing furnished by American Concrete Pressure Pipe Association.

Figure 6-9 Reinforced concrete cylinder pipe

Bibliography

American National Standard for Polyethylene Encasement for Ductile-Iron Pipe Systems. ANSI/AWWA C105/A21.5-93. 1993. Denver, Colo.: American Water Works Association.

ANSI/NSF International Standard 61, Drinking Water Components—Health Effects. 1995. Ann Arbor, Mich.: NSF International.

ASTM Standard D2657, Standard and Practice for Heat-Joining Polyolefin Pipe and Fittings. 1990. West Conshohocken, Pa.: American Society for Testing and Materials.

AWWA Manual M9, Concrete Pressure Pipe. 1979. Denver, Colo.: American Water Works Association.

AWWA Manual M11, Steel Pipe—A Guide for Design and Installation. 1989. Denver, Colo.: American Water Works Association.

AWWA Manual M16, Work Practices for Asbestos–Cement Pipe. 1978. Denver, Colo.: American Water Works Association.

AWWA Manual M23, PVC Pipe—Design and Installation. 1980. Denver, Colo.: American Water Works Association.

AWWA Manual M41, Ductile-Iron Pipe and Fittings. 1996. Denver, Colo.: American Water Works Association.

AWWA Manual M45, Fiberglass Pipe. 1997. Denver, Colo.: American Water Works Association.

AWWA Standard for Cement–Mortar Protective Lining and Coating for Steel Water Pipe—4 In. and Larger—Shop Applied. ANSI/AWWA C205-89. 1989. Denver, Colo.: American Water Works Association.

AWWA Standard for Fiberglass Pressure Pipe. ANSI/AWWA C950-95. 1995. Denver, Colo.: American Water Works Association.

AWWA Standard for Grooved and Shouldered Joints. ANSI/AWWA C606-87. 1987. Denver, Colo.: American Water Works Association.

AWWA Standard for Liquid Epoxy Coating Systems for the Interior and Exterior of Steel Water Pipelines. ANSI/AWWA C210-92. 1992. Denver, Colo.: American Water Works Association.

AWWA Standard for Polyethylene (PE) Pressure Pipe and Fittings, 4 In. Through 63 In., for Water Distribution. ANSI/AWWA C906-90. 1990. Denver, Colo.: American Water Works Association.

AWWA Standard for Prestressed Concrete Pressure Pipe, Steel-Cylinder Type, for Water and Other Liquids. ANSI/AWWA C301-92. 1992. Denver, Colo.: American Water Works Association.

AWWA Standard for Reinforced Concrete Pressure Pipe, Noncylinder Type, for Water and Other Liquids. ANSI/AWWA C302-87. 1987. Denver, Colo.: American Water Works Association.

AWWA Standard for Reinforced Concrete Pressure Pipe, Bar-Wrapped Steel-Cylinder Type, for Water and Other Liquids. ANSI/AWWA C303-87. 1987. Denver, Colo.: American Water Works Association.

AWWA Standard for Reinforced Concrete Pressure Pipe, Steel-Cylinder Type, for Water and Other Liquids. ANSI/AWWA C300-89. 1989. Denver, Colo.: American Water Works Association

Piping Handbook. 1992. New York: McGraw-Hill Companies.

Chapter 7

Distribution System Valves

Types of Valves

Most of the valves used in water system operations fall into one of the categories illustrated in Figure 7-1. Many of these types are used only for special purposes. The valves most commonly found in a water distribution system are gate valves, butterfly valves, check valves, and control valves. Valves used in conjunction with water service lines are discussed in chapter 12, Water Services.

Gate Valves

Gate valves are designed only to start or stop flow. They should not be used for throttling flow for prolonged periods because vibration of the gates will eventually wear and damage the valve.

The gate, or disk, of the valve is raised and lowered by a screw, which is operated by a handwheel or valve key. When fully open, the gates are pulled up into the bonnet, which provides almost unrestricted flow and very little head loss. When closed, the gates seat against two faces of the valve body. The principal causes of a gate valve not seating tightly are that the faces have become worn or an object has lodged under the gate.

Types of Gate Valves

Gate valves used in water systems are of two general types, rising stem and nonrising stem (NRS). Rising stem valves (Figure 7-2) are commonly called *outside screw and yoke* (OS&Y) because they have an exposed screw extending above the valve bonnet. This type of valve is commonly used in pump stations where it is an advantage to immediately tell whether a valve is open or shut by looking at the position of the screw.

Outside screw and yoke valves can't be used where dirt might get into the screw, so all valves that are to be buried must be of the NRS type. The screw on NRS valves threads down through the gate mechanism, and the operating shaft is sealed at the top of the valve bonnet. New designs of gate valves are available that use a resilient seat of rubber or synthetic material. These valves operate more easily and have more positive shutoff than older style valves. Figure 7-3 shows a cutaway of a resilient-seated NRS valve.

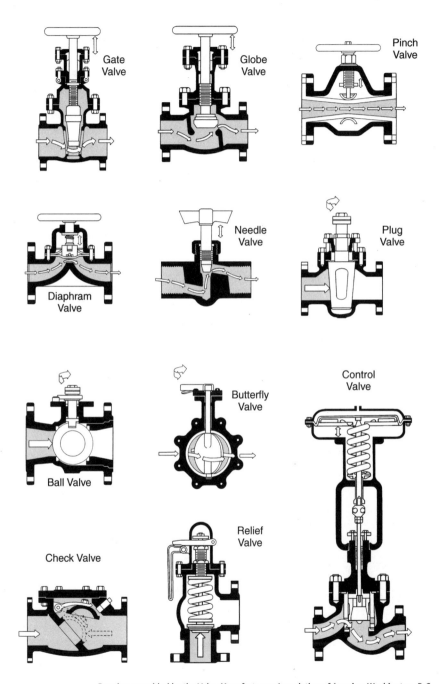

Drawings provided by the Valve Manufacturers Association of America, Washington, D.C.

Figure 7-1 Types of water utility valves

The stem seals on older valves used packing much the same as the packing used on some pump shafts, and over a period of years, the packing may have to be lubricated or adjusted to keep the seal from leaking at the stem opening. Newer valves use an O-ring seal that should not normally require maintenance (Figure 7-4).

Gate Valves Used in the Distribution System

Most of the gate valves used in a water distribution system are to isolate sections of the system, but some other types of specialty valves are also frequently used.

Hydrant auxiliary valves are internally the same as other gate valves, but the valve body has a special flange connection on one side for direct connection to a fire hydrant. This type of valve is pictured in chapter 10, Fire Hydrants.

Tapping valves are also internally the same, but have a special flange for connection to a tapping tee and for connection of a tapping machine as discussed further in chapter 11, Distribution System Operation and Maintenance.

Horizontal gate valves are much like other gate valves except they are designed to lie on one side. They are generally available in sizes over 16 in. (400 mm). One advantage to this design is that the operating mechanism does not have to lift the weight of the gate. Horizontal gate valves must also be used where a large-diameter main is buried with relatively little cover because the operating mechanism of a vertical valve would otherwise extend above the ground surface.

Some designs of horizontal valves are equipped with special tracks in the valve body. Rollers on the disk ride in the tracks to support the weight of the disks (Figure 7-5). Bronze scrapers are provided to move ahead of the rollers to remove any

Courtesy of Mueller Company, Decatur, Ill.

Figure 7-2 An outside screw and yoke gate valve

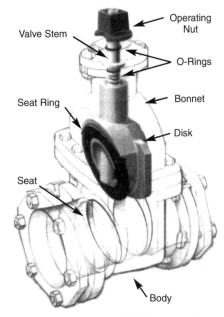

Courtesy of Mueller Company, Decatur, Ill.

Figure 7-3 Cutaway view of a resilient seated gate valve

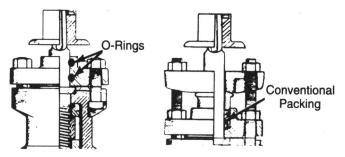

Courtesy of Terminal City Iron Works Ltd.

Figure 7-4 O-ring and conventional packing used on gate valves

foreign matter from the tracks. Another style is the rolling-disk valve, in which the disks themselves serve as rollers.

Bypass valves are often included within large gate valves. If a large gate valve has pressure on only one side, the pressure against the gates may make it difficult, if not impossible, to open the valve. A bypass valve is used to let water into the unpressurized main to equalize the pressure on the two sides of the gates so the valve may be operated.

Gate Valve Connections

Valve connections commonly used for distribution system gate valves are illustrated in Figure 7-6. Screw end connections are most often used in sizes up to 2 in. (50 mm). Flanged connections are most often used in exposed pumping station piping. Mechanical joints and push-type joints are used for buried water mains.

Gate valves are covered in AWWA Standard C500-93, *Metal-Seated Gate Valves for Water Supply Service,* and C509-94, *Resilient-Seated Gate Valves for Water Supply Service.*

Butterfly Valves

A butterfly valve has a disk that is rotated on a shaft. When in the open position, the disk is parallel with flow, and when closed, it seals against rubber or synthetic elastomer bonded either on the valve body or on the edge of the disk. Because the disk of a butterfly valve remains in the flow path when the valve is open, the valve creates a somewhat greater pressure loss than a gate valve, but it is generally not significant in comparison to other line losses.

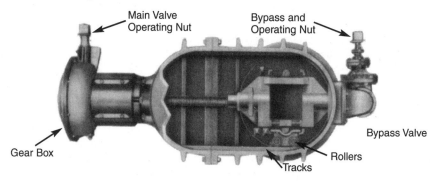

Figure 7-5 Horizontal gate valve   *Courtesy of Mueller Company, Decatur, Ill.*

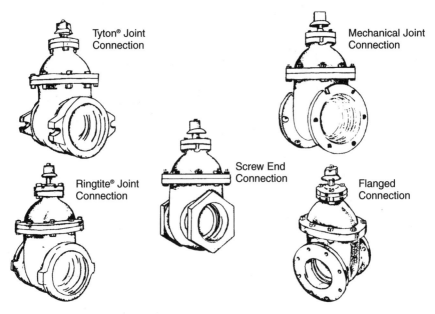

Figure 7-6 Common types of valve connections

Butterfly valves have the advantage of operating easily and quickly because the pressure on the two halves of the disk is relatively balanced and only one-quarter turn is necessary to fully open or shut them. On the other hand, care must be taken not to close a valve too quickly because it could produce a serious water hammer.

For use as water distribution system isolation valves, butterfly valves are less expensive than gate valves, particularly in larger sizes. The one consideration that should be made in considering their use is that, if the water main should ever have to be cleaned using pigs or swabs, the valves would present a serious obstacle.

Butterfly valves are primarily designed for on–off service. They can be used for occasional throttling, but if used for prolonged high-pressure throttling, the disk will vibrate until it is eventually damaged.

The types of connections commonly available for butterfly valves are illustrated in Figure 7-7. The wafer type valves are installed by "sandwiching" them between two flanges. The short laying length of valves installed in this manner is often an advantage in pumping station piping systems. The mechanical joint and push-joint connections are intended for burial in water distribution systems.

Butterfly valves are covered in AWWA Standard C504-94, *Rubber-Seated Butterfly Valves.*

Check Valves

Check valves are designed to allow flow in only one direction. The most common use in a water system is on the discharge of pumps to prevent backflow when the pump is shut down. Several types of check valves are illustrated in Figure 7-8. A foot valves is a special type of check valve installed at the bottom of a pump suction so the pump will not lose its prime when the power is turned off.

Wafer   Lug wafer   Mechanical joint   Flanged

Figure 7-7 Common body types of butterfly valves   *Courtesy DeZurik, a Unit of SPX, Sartell, MN.*

Depending on how and where a check valve is installed, there could be a problem with the valve slamming shut, potentially creating a serious water hammer. A variety of devices are available on some check valves to dampen the closing, including external weights, springs, and automatic slow-closing motorized drives.

Old check valves should be periodically inspected for wear. A worn valve on a pump discharge might stick in the open position, which could conceivably drain a whole water system backward through the pump if not noticed immediately. And worse, if the valve should finally slam shut, the water hammer force could be sufficient to break piping and move the pump off its foundation.

Check valves are covered in AWWA Standard C508-93, *Swing-Check Valves for Waterworks Service, 2 In. (50 mm) Through 24 In. (600 mm) NPS.*

Slanting Disk Check Valve   Rubber Flapper Swing Check Valve   Double Door Check Valve

Cushioned Swing Check Valve   Foot Valve

Reprinted with permission of APCO/Valve & Primer Corp., 1420 S. Wright Blvd., Schaumberg, IL 60193 from APCO Valve Index by Ralph DiLorenzo, Exec. V.P., Copyrighted 1993.

Figure 7-8 Types of check valves

Pressure Regulating and Relief Valves

Throttling the flow of water requires a design that will withstand the high pressure forces that are created. Pressure-reducing valves, altitude valves, and pressure relief valves are all of similar globe-type valve design.

Pressure Reducing Valves

It is generally desirable to maintain the pressure in residences and businesses under 60 psi (414 kPa). Higher pressures cause more main failure, more leakage, and reduced life of appliances. As illustrated in Figure 7-9, a water system located in hilly country must usually establish several system pressure zones. The pressure-reducing valves operate automatically to throttle flow and maintain a lower pressure in the lower distribution system zones.

A pressure-reducing valve has two upper operating chambers sealed from each other by a flexible reinforced diaphragm (Figure 7-10). The operating chambers receive pressure from the system and are adjusted to modulate the valve stem up and down to maintain the desired discharge pressure. The valve in the lower chamber constantly moves up and down to pass the correct quantity of water into the lower pressure system.

Altitude Valves

A ground-level reservoir is usually filled through an altitude valve. An altitude valve is similar in design to a pressure-reducing valve and can be adjusted to allow water to fill a reservoir at a controlled rate, and is activated by the water pressure from the reservoir to close automatically when the reservoir is full.

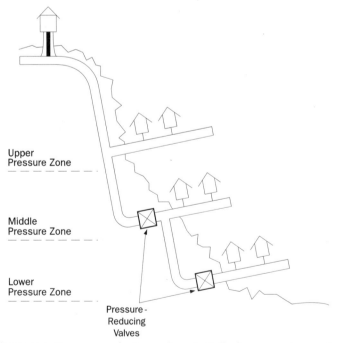

Figure 7-9 Pressure-reducing valves installed on a water system with three pressure zones

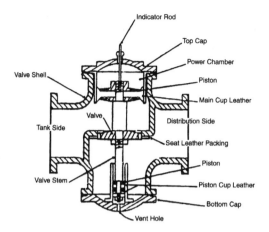

Figure 7-10 Principal parts of an altitude valve

Altitude valves are also used to control flow to an elevated tank when the tank is not high enough and would overflow under full system pressure. As illustrated in Figure 7-11, a double-acting valve restricts flow in both directions and automatically closes when the tank is full. A single-acting valve restricts flow into the tank and closes when the tank is full, but unrestricted flow is allowed from the tank through a check valve.

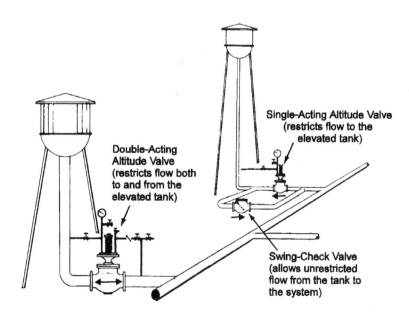

Courtesy of GA Industries, Inc.

Figure 7-11 Altitude control valves

Pressure Relief Valves

A rapid increase in pressure in a water system is called *surge* or *water hammer*. The pressure wave that moves rapidly down a pipe can damage valves, burst pipes, or blow pipe joints apart. Water hammer can also damage customer water services and plumbing fixtures. Common causes of water hammer include starting or stopping a large pump, or opening or closing a valve or fire hydrant too quickly. Pressure relief valves can be installed at points on a water system to release some of the high-pressure water created by the water hammer.

Plumbing codes also require a small pressure relief valve to be installed on all water heaters and boilers to vent excessive pressure so the tank won't burst. A pressure relief valve is essentially just a globe valve with an adjustable spring to maintain pressure on the valve seat to keep the valve closed under normal pressure conditions.

Air-and-Vacuum Relief Valves

As illustrated in Figure 7-12, an air-and-vacuum relief valve consists of a float-operated valve that allows air to escape when the float is down. When water enters the container, the air vent valve is closed. If a vacuum occurs in the connection to the container, the relief valve will admit air to the system.

One common use of air relief valves is on the discharge of a well pump. The valve is installed on the discharge of the pump to vent air that has accumulated in the well column while the well is idle; otherwise, the air would be blown into the distribution system.

Air relief valves should also be installed at the high points in transmission pipelines. If pockets of air are allowed to accumulate at high points, the effective area of flow is greatly restricted, resulting in restricted flow and increased pumping costs.

Valve Operation and Installation

Because they are operated frequently, many of the valves located in treatment plants and pumping stations are power operated. Distribution system valves are usually operated infrequently, so are manually operated.

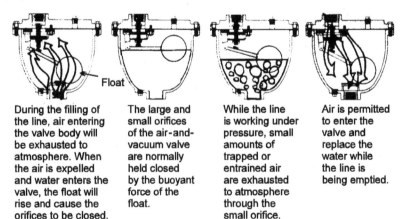

| During the filling of the line, air entering the valve body will be exhausted to atmosphere. When the air is expelled and water enters the valve, the float will rise and cause the orifices to be closed. | The large and small orifices of the air-and-vacuum valve are normally held closed by the buoyant force of the float. | While the line is working under pressure, small amounts of trapped or entrained air are exhausted to atmosphere through the small orifice. | Air is permitted to enter the valve and replace the water while the line is being emptied. |

Courtesy of GA Industries, Inc.

Figure 7-12 Air-and-vacuum release valves

Courtesy of M&H Valve Co.

Figure 7-13 Hydraulic valve actuator

Valve Operators

Several types of power operators are available for valves. Each has some advantages and disadvantages in terms of speed of operation, reliability, and ease of control.

Electric Operators

An electric valve operator uses a small electric motor to rotate the valve stem through a gear box. The motor is usually activated by a switch that turns on the motor, and the motor is turned off by a limit switch when the valve is fully open or closed. One advantage of electric control is that some units can be set to intermediate positions for throttling flow. A major disadvantage is that, if there is a loss of electrical power, the valve cannot be power operated unless standby electric service is provided. Some units have handwheels for manual operation in the event of power failure.

Hydraulic Actuators

Hydraulic valve actuators are frequently used in treatment plants and pumping stations (Figure 7-13). They may be operated by either water pressure or hydraulic fluid. The fluid is admitted to the operating cylinder by electric solenoid valves to operate the valve in each direction. One advantage of hydraulic operators is that the speed of operation can be varied from very fast to very slow by throttling the flow of fluid to the cylinder. In installations where it is absolutely essential to have the valves operable under all conditions, including complete loss of water pressure, a separate hydraulic system is provided from a tank that is maintained partially full of compressed air.

Pneumatic Actuators

Pneumatic actuators are similar to hydraulic actuators, except that they are operated with compressed air.

Distribution System Valves

Small- and medium-sized distribution system gate valves are generally direct

Valve Size	Number of Turns	Valve Size	Number of Turns
3 in.	7 ½	12 in.	38 ½
4 in.	14 ½	14 in.	46
6 in.	20 ½	16 in.	53
8 in.	27	18 in.	59
10 in.	33 ½	20 in.	65

Table 7-1 Approximate number of turns required to operate most water system valves

drive. Larger valves require a geared operator, so several turns of the valve key are required to make one turn of the valve stem. A gear-driven 20-in. (500-mm) valve may, for instance, require about 20 min for two workers to close by hand. The approximate number of turns required to operate most water system valves is shown in Table 7-1, but may vary by make or model.

Operators are urged to count and record the number of turns for each valve on their distribution systems. In this way, when the valves are exercised, it is possible to determine when they are fully opened and fully closed.

Manual Operation

A distribution system valve has a 2-in. (50-mm) square operating nut that is operated by hand with a valve key (Figure 7-14). A valve that has not been operated for a number of years will often have to be closed using a series of up and down motions to clear the stem threads and accumulation of corrosion on the gates. It is suggested

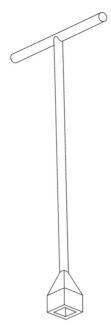

Figure 7-14 Valve key for water main valves

Courtesy of the Wachs Companies.

Figure 7-15 Valve being turned using an electric valve operator

that the valve be closed about 5 to 10 turns, and then opened two or three rotations, repeating this sequence until the valve is closed.

If a valve does not seat fully on the first try, it is often because some foreign matter has accumulated in the depression at the bottom of the valve body. This can often be cleared away by opening a downstream fire hydrant, and then cycling the valve up and down from the closed position so that high-velocity water flowing under the gates will scour the sediment. Using a cheater bar to force a valve that won't seat completely creates a serious potential of breaking the stem. Repairing a broken stem is relatively difficult and time-consuming, and if the stem is broken on a very old valve, there may be a problem finding the correct replacement parts.

Portable Power Operators

Several types of portable electric- and gasoline-powered tools are available for operating valves (Figure 7-15). They greatly speed the work of exercising valves, which will ensure that the valves will be operable when needed. If a water system has large valves in transmission mains, a power operator will save a great amount of time and energy in operating them. The power operator should preferably have a torque-limiting device to ensure that there is not excessive pressure applied to the valve stem. In any event, it is generally best to manually apply the last few turns of travel in both opening and closing valves.

Valve Boxes and Vaults

Buried valves are made accessible for operation either by installing a valve box over them or by building a valve vault around them. Valve boxes are made in two or more pieces that are adjustable to the particular depth of the valve. Figure 7-16 shows a typical valve-box installation. Note that the bottom of the box is externally supported so that it does not rest on the valve. This is particularly important if the valve box is to be placed under pavement because, if the box is supported directly on the valve, the pounding of traffic on the top of the box could damage the valve or adjacent piping.

A valve vault is constructed around a valve after it is installed (Figure 7-17). It is important that the bottom of the vault is on firm ground so the vault won't sink and cause the weight of traffic to exert excessive pressure on the water main at the points where the pipe goes through the vault walls (Figure 7-17).

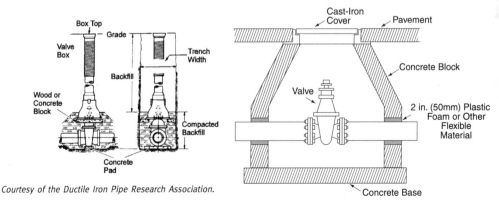

Courtesy of the Ductile Iron Pipe Research Association.

Figure 7-16 Valve-box installation   **Figure 7-17** Valve vault

Bibliography

AWWA Manual M44, Distribution Valves: Selection, Installation, Field Testing, and Maintenance. 1996. Denver, Colo.: American Water Works Association.

AWWA Standard for Metal-Seated Gates Valves for Water Supply Service. ANSI/AWWA C500-93. 1993. Denver, Colo.: American Water Works Association.

AWWA Standard for Resilient-Seated Gate Valves for Water Supply Service. ANSI/AWWA C509-94. 1994. Denver, Colo.: American Water Works Association.

AWWA Standard for Rubber-Seated Butterfly Valves. ANSI/AWWA C504-94. 1994. Denver, Colo.: American Water Works Association.

AWWA Standard for Swing-Check Valves for Waterworks Service, 2 In. (50 mm) Through 24 In. (600 mm) NPS. ANSI/AWWA C508-93. 1993. Denver, Colo.: American Water Works Association.

Water Transmission and Distribution. 1996. Denver, Colo.: American Water Works Association.

Chapter 8

Water Main Installation

It is important that water mains be installed properly. Careless handling of pipe and fittings and improper pipe installation can cause added maintenance, future repair problems, possibly even a threat to public health.

Pipe Shipment, Unloading, and Stringing

Most operations for shipping, unloading, and stringing pipe are basically the same regardless of the pipe material used. The various operations are discussed in general in this chapter. Additional details can be obtained from the pipe manufacturers and from the various pipe associations.

Pipe Shipment

Pipe to be used for small installations is generally delivered from a local warehouse. Large-diameter pipe and pipe for a large job may be shipped direct from the factory. Pipe is usually shipped by truck, although in some unusual circumstances it may be shipped by railroad or by barge. The advantage of truck delivery is that the pipe can be delivered direct to the jobsite. Some purchasers require the ends of pipe be covered to prevent an accumulation of dirt and bugs in the pipe while in transit or storage.

Pipe Unloading

All pipe should be unloaded carefully. Pipe may appear quite durable, but it should not be dropped or allowed to strike other pipe, rocks, or the pavement. Ductile-iron (DI) and steel pipe can be physically damaged by a sharp blow. Damage may affect both the lining and exterior coating. A relatively small gouge in polyvinyl chloride (PVC) pipe can cause a stress point that may result in pipe failure years later. Plastic pipe is particularly susceptible to damage in cold weather.

Before releasing the cables that secure the load to the truck, an inspection should be made of all blocking to make sure the pipes do not roll when the cables are released. Workers should never remain on the load or in front of it after the restraints are released.

If power equipment is not available, small-diameter pipe may be unloaded with skids and snubbing ropes as illustrated in Figure 8-1. Use of a derrick or backhoe for lifting can make unloading much faster and safer. No one should ever stand under a lifted load. If a forklift is used, the forks should be padded to prevent damage to the

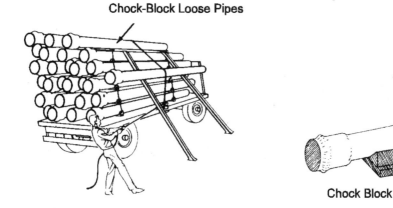

Figure 8-1 Unloading pipe with snubbing ropes

pipe or pipe coating. Plastic pipe should not be handled with an unpadded chain. It is best to use a nylon sling or pipe tong as illustrated in Figure 8-2.

Pipe Stacking

It is often most efficient to unload pipe directly along the proposed installation route so it will not have to be handled again. If the pipe must be stockpiled for later use, it should be carefully stacked in a manner that is well protected. Each manufacturer can furnish instructions for stacking a particular type of pipe, but in general, the following rules should apply:

• The stacking area should be an area of flat land, not subject to flooding.
• The bottom layer of pipe should be laid on timbers thick enough to keep the pipe bells from touching the ground.
• Blocks should be secured at each end of the timbers to keep the pipe from rolling.

Courtesy of the Ductile Iron Pipe Research Assocation.

Figure 8-2 Pipe being lifted with a pipe tong

- For DIP and concrete pipe, boards with blocks at each end should be placed between each layer of pipe.
- Pipe should be stacked with the bells of each layer in opposite directions, with the bells projecting beyond the barrels of the pipe below, taking particular care that they do not touch.
- Plastic pipe should be left in shipping units until needed, and should not be stacked higher than 3 ft (0.9 m).
- Plastic pipe should be protected from sunlight by covering it with a canvas or opaque plastic cover, and the cover should be installed in a manner that will allow air to circulate beneath it.
- If there is any potential of vandalism or children playing on the stack, the storage area should be secured with a fence.

Rubber gaskets should be stored in a location out of direct sunlight, out of possible contact with petroleum products, and safe from vandalism. In cold weather, it is desirable to keep the gaskets and gasket lubricant warm until they are ready for use.

Pipe Stringing

In rural areas, pipe is often distributed (strung) along the installation route in advance of excavation. In residential areas, it is generally best to string pipe as the excavation progresses, both to avoid the inconvenience to residents of having the pipe on the street or parkway, and because of the danger of vandalism or children injuring themselves playing around the pipe.

If possible, the pipe should be placed close to the ditch and on the side of the ditch opposite where the excavated dirt will be piled (Figure 8-3). This will make pipe handling the easiest during installation. The pipe must also be placed where it will be protected from traffic and the operation of heavy equipment.

The pipe should be laid with the bells in the direction of installation progress so the lengths won't have to be turned as they are lifted into the ditch. Each length must be prevented from rolling by driving substantial stakes or using blocks. If it is

Courtesy of Certainteed Pipe and Plastics Group.

Figure 8-3 Pipe strung along a work site

impossible to place pipe where dirt won't get into the ends, then the ends should be covered with a plastic bag or plug to prevent contamination.

Excavation

Excavation for water main installation is both expensive and dangerous. Preparations must be carefully made in advance so the job will run smoothly, efficiently, and safely.

Preparations

Before excavation can begin, a plan must be prepared for the project. The plan should show at least the following details:

- the location and depth of the main that is to be installed
- the location of valves, hydrants, and all fittings that can be anticipated
- the location and depth of all sewer and gas pipes, and electric, telephone, television, and street-light cables in the line of the new construction
- details of any other obstructions that must be protected or avoided

The plans must generally be submitted in advance to the state drinking water control agency for approval before work is started. If the work will at any point be on state highway or railroad property, the agency's approval will also be required. In some cases, county or city approval may be required. If the pipe installation or the operation of equipment will enter onto private property at any location, property access or usage rights may have to be obtained from the property owners.

Water and Sewer Line Separation

Adequate separation should always be maintained between water mains and sewer lines. The theory is that sewers are likely to leak and saturate the adjoining soil with wastes. If at the same time there is an adjoining leak in a water main, and the main becomes depressurized, the wastes could be drawn into the main.

The general rule is that there should be a horizontal separation of at least 10 ft (3 m) between water and sewer lines, and that the water line should be at least 1 ft (0.3 m) above the sewer. Each state has regulations specifying water and sewer separation and these should be reviewed before progressing with construction.

Notifying Property Owners and the Public

Owners of property adjoining distribution system work should be notified in advance with details of the work to be done and approximately when work will take place opposite their properties. Some property owners may be inconvenienced by having their driveways unusable for a day or two and their parkway in a mess for a week or two. It is certainly not a time when property owners would want to have parties at their homes, so they should be given ample notice to make personal plans. The property owners should also be given assurances that the work will progress as rapidly as possible and that the work area will be properly restored.

The general public should also be advised in advance of the work that will be done and why it is being done. This is a good opportunity to put a positive twist on an inconvenience. The public can be told how progressive you are in expanding your system and how the community will benefit with improved fire flow and water pressure after this small inconvenience is over. The story can be told in local newspapers and other media in advance, and signs warning drivers and pedestrians of the upcoming work can be posted at the site beginning a week or so before work is to begin.

Plans must also be made in advance to have adequate signs, barricades, flashing lights, and other safety equipment available to protect both workers and the public. State and federal regulations on the methods of placing warning equipment for various classes of streets and highways should be reviewed to be sure that protection of the construction site will be in compliance.

Recording Site Conditions Before Construction

If the work site is in an urban area, it is a good idea to take a series of photographs along the construction route just before the work is started, and the dates they are taken recorded. Particular attention should be given to recording the condition of sidewalks, fences, trees, and bushes. If there are later claims that the site was not properly restored, the photos can serve as proof that, for example, the property owner's fence was already broken before the job was started. Or conversely, that there was more damage done than was realized, and it should be restored to the original condition.

It should be kept in mind that site damage can sometimes occur at some distance from where the work is to take place. For example, careless machine operators can break sidewalks or damage trees and bushes on the opposite side of the street while they are maneuvering their equipment.

Identifying Serious Conflicts

In general, it is best to decide in advance how best to avoid difficult conflicts between the proposed main and other utilities. One common problem is an intersection with a crossing sewer at the same elevation. The grade of a sewer usually cannot be changed, so the grade of the water main must be altered. This will require either special fittings or a gradual change in grade on either side of the crossing. If the exact grade of the sewer cannot be determined by probing or measurements at nearby manholes, it is usually best to make a preliminary excavation to make accurate measurements.

Trenching

By far the most expensive part of pipe installation is the excavation, so it is important that it be done as economically as possible.

Most trenching for water main installation is done with hydraulic backhoes. These machines are easy to operate, quite maneuverable, and provide excellent control. The machine should preferably be sized proportionally to the size of pipe being installed. A machine that is too large will probably do more damage than is necessary, and a machine that is too small will do the job too slowly.

Concrete and asphalt roads and driveways should be scored in advance using an air hammer or diamond-edged power saw. This will minimize damage to surrounding pavement and keep the amount of pavement replacement to a minimum. It is often most economical to employ a firm specializing in pavement cutting to do this work.

As a rule, large pieces of asphalt and concrete should not be used for trench backfill. It is most efficient to have a truck waiting for direct loading when large quantities of pavement are to be removed to eliminate having to rehandle it. If asphalt is removed using a rotomill, the debris may be small enough that it can be used in the upper part of the trench backfill.

Trench Width

The best bucket width to use will be based in great part on pipe size, trench depth, and local experience concerning soil conditions. On the one hand, the trench width should be a minimum, both to aid rapid progress of the job and to minimize site damage and restoration. But the trench must be wide enough to maintain trench wall support and allow workers to work properly.

Trench width should generally be no more than 1 to 2 ft (0.3 to 0.6 m) greater than the pipe diameter. All that is needed is enough room for workers to make up the pipe joints and tamp the backfill under and around the pipe. It is particularly important to maintain trench width as narrow as possible under paved areas because this will minimize the traffic load that will be transmitted down through the backfill and exerted on the pipe. Recommended trench widths for small-diameter pipe are listed in Tables 8-1 and 8-2. If a much wider trench must be used or if unusually heavy surface loads may be exerted on the pipe, the pipe manufacturer or a design engineer should be consulted for special installation recommendations.

When pipe is to be laid on a curve, a limited amount of deflection can be obtained at each pipe joint. The trench width must, of course, be wider around a curve, but particular care should be taken not to over-dig the outside wall of the circle because the pipe must be blocked against a firm surface to prevent outward movement.

Trench Depth

In warm climates, the depth at which mains are buried is generally dictated by the depth necessary to sufficiently spread surface loadings and protect the pipe from damage. The minimum cover for mains is typically 2.5 ft (0.8 m), and 18 in. (0.5 m) for water services.

In colder areas, the mains are placed at a depth that is locally considered the

Nominal Pipe Size, in.	(mm)	Recommended Trench Widths, in.	(m)
3	(80)	27	(0.69)
4	(100)	28	(0.70)
6	(150)	30	(0.76)
8	(200)	32	(0.81)
10	(250)	34	(0.86)
12	(300)	36	(0.92)
14	(350)	38	(0.96)
16	(400)	40	(1.00)
18	(450)	42	(1.07)
20	(500)	44	(1.12)
24	(600)	48	(1.22)
30	(750)	54	(1.37)
36	(900)	60	(1.52)
42	(1,050)	66	(1.68)
48	(1,200)	72	(1.83)
54	(1,350)	78	(1.98)
60	(1,500)	84	(2.13)

Table 8-1 Recommended trench widths for ductile-iron mains

	Trench Width	
Pipe Diameter, *in. (mm)*	Minimum, *in. (m)*	Maximum, *in. (m)*
4 (100)	18 (0.46)	29 (0.74)
6 (150)	18 (0.46)	31 (0.79)
8 (150)	21 (0.53)	33 (0.84)
10 (250) and greater	12 (0.31) greater than outside diameter of pipe	24 (0.61) greater than outside diameter of pipe

Table 8-2 Recommended trench widths for PVC pipe

maximum depth of frost. Although a water main can withstand having frost around and below it as long as the water is always in motion, the danger of having mains too shallow is that water services will freeze at the point of connection.

Consideration should also be given to the fact that frost penetration is usually the deepest under pavement and driveways that are kept clear of snow. If the weather turns very cold with no snow cover, frost can penetrate quite deep within just a few days.

If adequate burial depth of a main is not possible, the main can be insulated. Closed-cell styrofoam insulation, 2 in. (50 mm) thick and 2 to 4 ft (0.6 to 1.2 m) wide, placed a short distance above the pipe, has been successfully used to reduce the danger of pipe freezing.

Excavation

When excavating a pipe trench, the excavated material should be piled on the pavement side of the trench. This protects the trench and workers from traffic, and keeps the equipment that will be backfilling the trench on the pavement where its operation will do minimal damage.

The excavated material (spoil) must be placed far enough away from the trench so that it will not fall back into the excavation, and a space should be maintained for workers to walk along the side of the trench. Consideration must also be given to the weight of the excavated material close to the trench and the possibility of its contributing to trench wall failure (cave-in). The general rule is to place the spoil at least 2 ft (0.6 m) back for trenches up to 5 ft (1.5 m) deep, and about 4 ft (1.2 m) back for deeper trenches. Keeping the area adjacent to the trench clear also minimizes the danger of someone inadvertently kicking dirt down on a worker in the trench, or of someone tripping and falling into the trench.

The bottom of the trench should be dug as closely as possible to the exact grade that has been specified. The trench should provide a continuous, even support for the pipe. If there are found to be high points after the pipe has been placed in the trench, the excess dirt will have to be excavated by hand. If there are low points, they should be filled with granular material or other special fill that will provide good support for the pipe.

The excavation depth is often checked using a "story pole." A string is installed on stakes along the side of the ditch slightly ahead of excavation, with its elevation a given number of feet above the ditch bottom as determined by the plans. A marked pole is used to periodically check the excavation depth by resting the pole on the trench bottom and checking to see whether the mark near the top of the pole lines up with the string.

It is usually best not to excavate much ahead of pipe laying. The most important reason for this is that the longer a trench stands open, the more likely it is to have a cave-in. Other reasons are the likelihood of flooding if it should rain and the dangers to curious children and the interested public. An open trench is particularly dangerous after workers have left the site and worse after dark. Most contractors try to have very little open trench left at the end of the day, and then guard it well with barricades, lights, and warning tape. Local regulations often require that the trench be completely filled or protected in a specific way overnight.

Rock Excavation

The excavation for a water main trench may encounter loose boulders, ledge rock (such as hardpan or shale), or solid rock. The possibility that a main cannot be buried to the required depth without rock excavation must be determined before the job is started because it makes quite a difference in how the job progresses. The easiest method is to take periodic test borings or make quick excavations with a backhoe along the route.

If blasting is required, it is usually best done by a firm specializing in the work because it has both the special expertise and insurance required. A detailed record should be kept of the dates of blasting in the event of any claims for damage resulting from the work.

Poor Soil Conditions

Some material considered unacceptable to surround a water main include coal mine debris, cinders, sulfide clays, mine tailings, factory wastes, and garbage. This material should be excavated to well below the grade line of the main and hauled away for disposal in an approved manner. The excavation must then be filled with suitable material that has been trucked in to the site.

Groundwater

If the elevation of groundwater in the area is above the level of the trench bottom, water will enter the ditch. Trying to assemble pipe under water is usually not successful, and could result in leaking joints because of silt, leaves, or other material inadvertently caught under the joint gasket. Working in saturated soil is also dangerous because of the greatly increased possibility of cave-ins. In some areas, groundwater levels fluctuate during the year, so selecting the dry time of year for construction may avoid groundwater problems.

If pipe must be installed below the groundwater table, the accepted practice is to dewater the ground in advance of the excavation by installing a system of well points to below the level of trench bottom. The points are connected to a manifold and pumping system and operated until the ground is safe to excavate. It is important to check with local and state regulatory authorities to see if there are any special requirements on disposal of the pumped water. This type of dewatering can greatly increase the cost of a main installation and must be carefully considered before the job is started.

Causes of Trench-Wall Failure

Soil is generally classified as clay, till, sand, or silt. Firm clay and till with low moisture content can usually be excavated easily and safely. Dry sand requires special care in excavation because it can slip and run easily. Wet till is generally unpredictable and has a high potential for caving in.

Just because soil appears firm and stable does not ensure that the walls of an excavation will not cave in. Some of the primary causes of failure include:

• the pressure of water contained in the soil
• the load of construction equipment working near the edge of the trench
• the load of excavated soil that has been piled close to the edge of the trench
• trench walls that are too steep for the type of soil
• cleavage planes in the soil, usually caused by the previous installation of another utility, such as a gas main or sewer

Trench wall failures occur most often in winter and early spring when ground moisture is higher. Failures usually give little warning and occur almost instantaneously, but some of the warning signs that workers can look for are:

• cracks in the ground surface parallel to the trench, located about one half to three quarters of the trench depth away from the trench edge
• soil crumbling off of the trench wall
• settling of the ground surface near the trench
• sudden changes in the color of excavated soil, indicating that a previous excavation was made in the area

Preventing Cave-in

Lack of shoring or shoring failure is the leading cause of death and injury in underground construction. Appropriate shoring is now required by Occupational Safety and Health Administration (OSHA) requirements and similar laws enacted by each state. Failure to comply with these laws can result in stiff penalties. Regulations generally require trench wall protection for all trenches deeper than 4 or 5 ft (1.2 or 1.5 m).

The five basic methods of preventing cave-in are sloping, shielding, shoring, sheeting, and use of collapsible metal shoring.

Sloping is the excavation of the trench walls at an angle, based on the cohesive strength of the soil. The angle varies with the type of soil, the amount of moisture in the soil, and surrounding conditions, such as vibration from machinery. The approximate angles of repose for various soil types are shown in Figure 8-4.

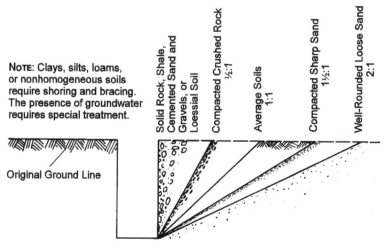

Figure 8-4 Approximate angles of repose for various types of soil

Figure 8-5 Pipe being installed using a shield

Shielding is the use of a steel box in the ditch to protect workers. The box is open at the bottom and top, and is pushed or pulled along the trench as work progresses as a constant shield against caving of the trench walls (Figure 8-5). The box is also often called a *trench shield, portable trench box, sand box,* or *drag shield.*

The shield does not prevent cave-in. It must fit loosely in the trench in order to be moved and is designed only to protect workers in case a cave-in should occur. As the shield is moved forward, the last pipe length is usually backfilled immediately to prevent cave-in.

Shoring is basically a framework of wood, metal, or both, installed to prevent caving of trench walls. As illustrated in Figure 8-6, a shoring assembly has three main parts. The uprights are placed directly against the trench walls. Then horizontal stringers are installed to support the uprights. The stringers are often called *whalers* because they are similar to the horizontal members in the hulls of wooden ships. Trench braces or trench jacks are finally placed to keep the stringers separated and tight against the trench walls.

Shoring should always be installed from the top down, and removed from the bottom up, for maximum protection of workers. It is often necessary to leave the shoring

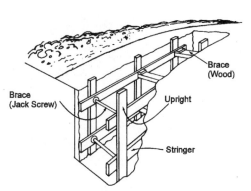

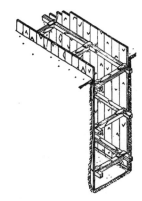

Figure 8-6 A shoring assembly

Figure 8-7 A tight sheeting installation

in place as the trench is backfilled, and in some cases, it may be necessary to leave the uprights in place and just cut them off near the ground surface. Ropes are usually fastened to jacks and stringers so they can be removed from the surface and workers won't have to enter the excavation as protection is removed.

Sheeting is the process of installing tightly placed planks against the trench wall when soil conditions are very poor. If the excavation must be very deep in poor soil, steel sheet piling may have to be driven into the ground before excavation can begin. As illustrated in Figure 8-7, the sheeting is supported and later removed in about the same manner as shoring.

The sizes of shoring and sheeting members and the sizes and number of braces depend on trench depth and other local conditions. State regulations should be consulted for further details.

Collapsible shoring assemblies are lightweight panels of steel or aluminum that are available in various panel sizes and with spreaders designed for standard bucket width trenches, such as 24, 30, 42, and 48 in. (0.6, 0.8, 1.1, and 1.2 m). The assemblies can usually be handled by two or three workers (Figure 8-8), and they fold for easy transporting in a small truck. Standard assemblies can be stacked for use in a trench as deep as 12 ft (3.7 m).

Pipe Laying

As the trench is excavated, the pipe must be inspected and carefully installed on the bottom of the trench.

Pipe Inspection Prior to Installation

After the trench is prepared, but before the pipe is placed in the ditch, the pipe should be inspected. It takes only a couple of minutes, but is well worth the time as compared to the work required to later remove a defective pipe section. All pipe is inspected as it leaves the factory, but there are several opportunities for damage as the sections are stored and handled before installation. Some of the things to look for are a split in the spigot end, damage to the exterior, and damage to the lining. Another way of checking metal pipe is to tap it gently with a hammer. If the pipe

Figure 8-8 Collapsible shoring assembly   *Courtesy of Ultra Shore Products.*

does not ring, it may be cracked and should be rejected and inspected further before being used.

The pipe should also be relatively clean as it is laid. It should be inspected for oil, dirt, grease, animals, and other foreign matter. If mud has accumulated in the pipe while it was strung out, the pipe may have to be washed out with a hose. If there is any appreciable amount of foreign matter in the pipe, it should be swabbed with a strong hypochlorite solution before it is installed.

Pipe Placement

Pipe lengths should never be tossed or rolled into the trench from the top. They should be lowered by hand with ropes or with mechanical equipment. If the pipe is lowered using a sling, it is usually necessary to do some hand excavation to remove the sling. If a pipe tong is used for handling the pipe, removal is greatly simplified.

Pipe having bell ends is usually laid with the bells facing in the direction that work is progressing, but this is not mandatory. Contractors often find it easier to work with the bells facing uphill if the slope is steeper than 6 percent.

When work is not in progress, the open end of the pipe should be plugged to prevent dirt, animals, and water from entering. Although a small piece of plywood is often used for this purpose, a pipe plug made for the type of pipe joint is much better.

Pipe Bedding

The trench bottom must be leveled so that the barrel of the pipe will have firm support along its full length. A leveling board is usually used to check for high spots or voids. As illustrated in Figure 8-9, it is important that undue weight is not placed on the pipe bells. Normal practice is to hand excavate "bell holes" at each bell location both for this purpose and to provide a free area around the bell for joint assembly.

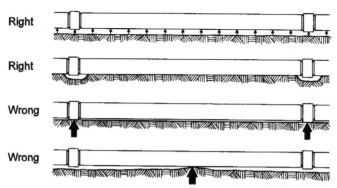

Courtesy of J-M Manufacturing Company, Inc.

Figure 8-9 Correct and incorrect pipe bedding

If there are many small rocks in the soil or the soil is unstable, it is often specified that special bedding material be placed on the trench bottom. In this case the trench is overexcavated, and a few inches of granular material is spread on the bottom of the trench before the pipe is placed.

After the pipe has been placed, the load-bearing capacity of the pipe should be increased by compacting the backfill beneath the pipe curvature (haunching). As illustrated in Figure 8-10, a pipe that is supported only on the center of the bottom has a great amount of pressure exerted from above the pipe, which is tending to deform the pipe. If the bedding is compacted up to the springline (center) of the

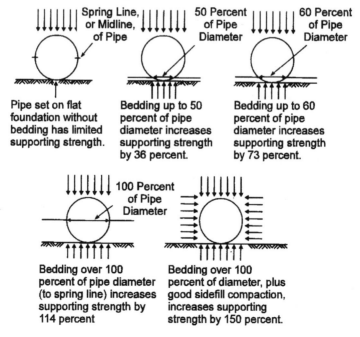

Figure 8-10 Effect of bedding on a pipe's load-bearing strength (for rigid pipe)

pipe, the support is greatly increased, and if compacted bedding is placed completely around the pipe, supporting strength is increased by 150 percent.

Pipe Jointing

One of the most important procedures in making up all types of joints is that the pipe bell, spigot end, and gasket must be kept clean. All sand, dust, tar, and other foreign matter must be carefully wiped from the gasket recesses of the bell, and the spigot must be smooth and free of rough edges. A small piece of a leaf caught under the gasket can cause a leak that will prevent the new pipeline from passing the pressure test.

Push-on Joints

The four general steps required for making up push-on joints are illustrated in Figure 8-11. One particularly important point is that the spigot end must be pushed

1. • Thoroughly clean the bell socket and plain end.

   • Inspect the gasket for any damage.

   • Follow the manufacturer's recommendation on whether the socket should be lubricated.

   • Insert the gasket into the socket.

   • In cold weather, it may be necessary to warm the gasket to facilitate insertion.

2. • Apply lubricant to the gasket and plain end.

   • Protect the lubricant from contamination.

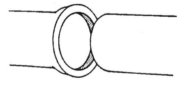

3. • Be sure the plain end is properly beveled. Sharp edges can damage the gasket.

   • Keep pipes in line when making up the joint. Deflection should take place only after the joint is assembled.

4. • Push the plain end into the socket.

   • When pushing pipe with a backhoe or jack, use a timber header across the end of the pipe.

Source: AWWA Standard for Installation of Ductile-Iron Water Mains and Their Appurtenances *(1993).*

Figure 8-11 Assembling a push-on joint

completely "home" into the bell. All full lengths of pipe have a painted line near the spigot end. This line should be all the way to the face of the bell when the joint is complete.

The spigot end of all push-on joint pipe has a beveled end that allows it to easily slip into the gasket. If a pipe is cut to make a short length, the cut end must be beveled so that it will not cut or jam in the gasket. The bevel on DIP can be made with a portable electric grinder or a special grinder made for the purpose. The bevel can be made on PVC pipe with a rasp file or with a special beveling tool. After the end of a cut piece is beveled, a measurement should be made of the "home" mark on a full pipe length, and a similar mark placed on the cut end using a felt-tipped marker. This will ensure that the pipe is inserted the full distance when it is installed.

If a push-on joint is to be deflected, it must first be inserted with the two pipes in line, and then the deflection can be made. If an attempt is made to push the pipe in at an angle, it may jam or not make up a tight joint.

Small-diameter pipe can be pushed home using a pry bar and block of wood as illustrated in Figure 8-12. Larger pipe joints are usually made up using a come-along or by pushing with the bucket of a backhoe.

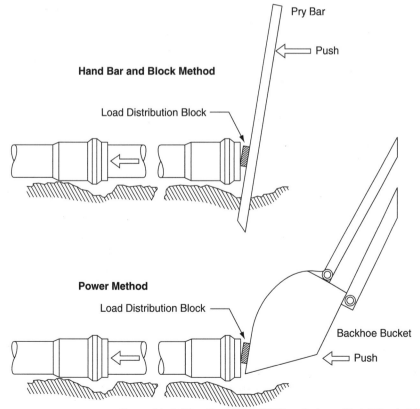

Source: Adapted from Manual M23, PVC Pipe—Design and Installation (1980).

Figure 8-12 Assembling small-diameter push-joint pipe

1. • Clean the socket and plain end.
    • Lubricate the gasket and plain end with soapy water or an approved lubricant.
    • Install the gland and rubber gasket.

2. • Keep the pipes in line during joint assembly.
    • Insert the plain end into the socket.
    • Press the gasket evenly into the bell.

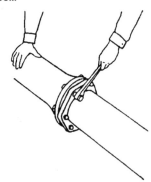

3. • Push the gland toward the socket.
    • Insert the bolts and hand-tighten the nuts.

4. • Alternately tighten nuts on opposite sides to maintain the same distance between the gland and the flange.
    • Tighten the nuts to the correct torque.

Source: AWWA Standard for Installation of Ductile-Iron Water Mains and Their Appurtenances *(1993).*

Figure 8-13 Assembling a mechanical joint

The assembly of concrete pipe joints is similar, except that the round gasket is mounted in a groove on the spigot end before insertion. Concrete pipe joints must be made up completely tight all around the pipe. If there is to be any deflection, it must be achieved by the use of special fittings.

Mechanical Joints

Mechanical joint fittings are made up as illustrated in Figure 8-13. Although these joints are more expensive and take longer to assemble than push-on joints, they make a very secure seal and allow quite a bit of deflection.

Connecting to Existing Mains

A new main can be connected to an existing main by either inserting a tee or by making a pressure tap.

Tee Connections

One method of connecting a new main to an existing main is by inserting a tee in the old main. Doing this means that the existing main will be out of service for a period of several hours if all goes well—longer if all does not go well. If this is acceptable, the first thing to do is to determine whether the valves on either end of the section hold securely. If they do not, they may have to be repaired before proceeding.

A method of inserting a standard tee using two rubber-joint sleeves is illustrated in Figure 8-14. The outside diameter of the old main should be carefully measured and sleeves purchased having the correct gaskets for the pipe size. If the old main is cast iron, the pipe will usually have to be cut in three places in order to break it out. A valve should also be ready to install on the outlet of the new tee so the main can be flushed and put back in service as quickly as possible.

Pressure Taps

Most connections to old mains are currently made with a pressure tap that avoids having to take the old main out of service. As illustrated in Figure 8-15,

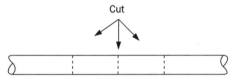

1. • Cut pipe in three places and break pieces out

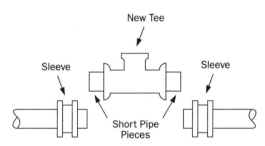

2. • Assemble tee with two short pieces of pipe.
   • Slide sleeves onto existing pipe.

3. • Place tee in line and slide sleeves back to cover joints.

Installing Tapping Sleeve

Setting Up Drilling Machine

Courtesy of Mueller Company, Decatur, Ill.

Figure 8-14 Steps in using short pieces of new pipe and rubber-joint sleeves to install a tee

Figure 8-15 Preparing to tap a large connection

the first step in the process is to clean the old main and install a split tapping tee. A special tapping valve having a flange on one side and a mechanical joint fitting on the other is then bolted to the tee, and the drilling machine is fastened to the valve outlet.

The drilling machine extends through the open valve to cut a circle of material from the main using a shell cutter (Figure 8-16). The drill is then retracted, the valve closed, the drilling machine removed, and the connection is completed.

Thrust Restraint

Water in motion can exert tremendous pressure if it is suddenly stopped or there is a change in the direction of flow. The thrust against tees, valves, bends, reducers, and fire hydrants can cause a leak or completely push fittings apart if they are not suitably restrained or blocked. The pressure can be several times normal if there is a surge or water hammer in the system caused by such things as quickly closing a hydrant.

Plastic pipe is particularly smooth so is very vulnerable to slipping out of a push joint if not adequately restrained. It has also been found that polyethylene bags placed around DIP for corrosion control provide almost no soil friction, so the pipe can slide within the bag if not well restrained.

Typical horizontal blocking is illustrated in Figure 8-17. The block can be made of poured concrete or other material that will not disintegrate over time. Wood should not be used for blocking. The block should be centered on the thrust force and should cradle the fitting, but not cover the joint fittings. It is important that the ditch not be overdug at changes in pipe direction, otherwise there will be no firm, undisturbed soil to block against.

Similar blocking should also be placed when pipe is laid around a curve. Even though the curve is made by deflecting the pipe joints and appears quite gradual, the fresh backfill around it may not be adequate to prevent the line from pushing out-

Courtesy of T.D. Williamson, Inc.

Figure 8-16 Coupon cut from main

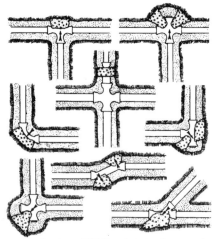

Courtesy of J-M Manufacturing Company, Inc.

Figure 8-17 Common concrete thrust blocks

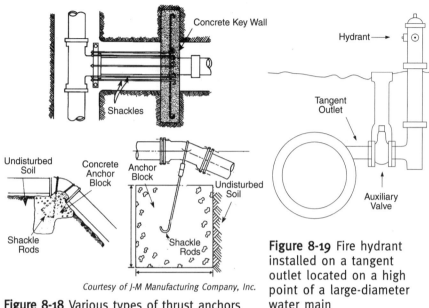

Figure 8-18 Various types of thrust anchors

Courtesy of J-M Manufacturing Company, Inc.

Figure 8-19 Fire hydrant installed on a tangent outlet located on a high point of a large-diameter water main

ward if there is water hammer. Polyvinyl chloride pipe is particularly vulnerable to movement if not firmly blocked against the outer wall of the trench.

When there is no undisturbed earth behind a horizontal bend or tee to place a block against, and for vertical bends, tie rods or thrust blocks made of large masses of concrete may have to be used (Figure 8-18). Several companies are now offering restraining fittings that have set screws or clamps that can be used in place of blocking.

Air Relief

When a water main is laid over uneven ground, a bubble of air will be trapped at each high point as the main is filled. If the bubbles are allowed to remain in the pipe, the flow of water will be restricted much as though there is a partly closed valve at these points. For small-diameter mains, opening one or more hydrants will generally create enough velocity to blow the bubbles out of the main. For large mains, however, there is no practical way of flushing the bubbles out.

One method of releasing air from large mains is to locate a fire hydrant at each high point. To be completely effective, the hydrant should be connected to a tangent tee that draws from the top of the main (Figure 8-19). The only problem with this method is, if there is entrained air in the water, the bubbles will gradually re-form over a period of time, so the air will have to be manually released periodically from each hydrant.

A method for releasing air automatically is to install an air relief valve at each high point. The valve is often located in a pit to facilitate maintenance, and the air is vented through a screened pipe that extends above the ground level (Figure 8-20).

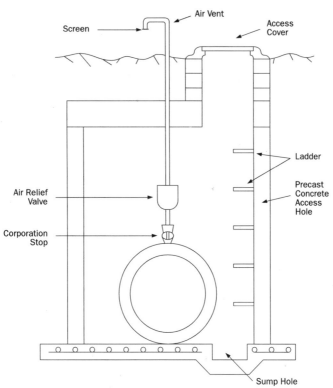

Figure 8-20 Installation of an air relief valve at a high point on a large-diameter water main

Bibliography

Arasmith, Skeet. 1992. *Water Distribution System Construction*. Albany, Ore.: ACR Publications.

AWWA Manual M11, Steel Pipe—A Guide for Design and Installation. 1980. Denver, Colo.: American Water Works Association.

AWWA Manual M23, PVC Pipe—Design and Installation. 1980. Denver, Colo.: American Water Works Association.

AWWA Standard for Installation of Asbestos–Cement Pressure Pipe. ANSI/AWWA C603-96. 1990. Denver, Colo.: American Water Works Association.

AWWA Standard for Installation of Ductile-Iron Water Mains and Their Appurtenances. ANSI/AWWA C600-93. 1993. Denver, Colo.: American Water Works Association.

AWWA Standard for Underground Installation of Polyvinyl Chloride (PVC) Pressure Pipe and Fittings for Water. ANSI/AWWA C605-94. 1994. Denver, Colo.: American Water Works Association.

Water Transmission and Distribution. 1996. Denver, Colo.: American Water Works Association.

Work Practices for Asbestos–Cement Pipe. 1989. Denver, Colo., American Water Works Association.

Chapter 9

Backfilling and Main Testing

After water main pipe and fittings have been installed in the trench, the excavation must be backfilled with suitable material and the pipe tested for leaks, flushed, disinfected, and tested for bacteriological quality before the public may be allowed to use water from the new section of the system.

Backfilling the Trench

Backfill material placed around and over the newly installed pipe serves several purposes besides just filling up the excavation. The most important is that it distributes the surface loads. For example, the downward pressure from a heavy truck passing over a pipe in a shallow trench with uncompacted fill could damage the pipe because the load is transmitted directly downward. If the backfill is properly compacted, the load is transmitted outward to the trench walls and the pipe will not be damaged.

Another important function of properly placed backfill is to provide lateral restraint of the pipe to keep it from moving in the event of water hammer in the system.

Placing Backfill

Only clean sand or selected soil should be used for the first layer of backfill. It should contain no peat, stones, roots, construction debris, or frozen material and should have enough moisture to permit thorough compaction. If the excavated soil is not suitable for the first layer that will surround the pipe, other backfill material should be brought in.

Initial Backfill Layers

The first layer of backfill should be placed equally on both sides of the pipe, up to about the center of the pipe. This material should then be compacted, a process often called *haunching*.

A hand tamper often used for haunching is shown in Figure 9-1, but the work goes much faster if a pneumatic tamper is available. Compacting the soil under and on each

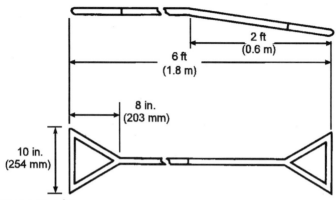

Figure 9-1 Hand tamper

side of the pipe up to the center of the pipe (springline) provides valuable support so the pipe will withstand the weight that will later be placed on it from above.

Backfill practices above the springline vary depending on the type of pipe used, local soil conditions, and regulatory requirements. In general, another layer of good-quality material should be placed over the pipe and again compacted to protect and secure the pipe. This layer should be at least 6 in. (150 mm) over the top of the pipe for pipe up to 8 in. (200 mm) in diameter, and thicker for larger pipe as recommended by the pipe manufacturer.

Backfilling the Remainder of the Trench

The backfill material used to fill the remainder of the trench does not have to be selected, placed, or compacted as carefully as the first two layers. In general, the excavated material may be used unless the job specifications or regulatory agency direct otherwise. If soil backfill is not compacted in some manner, the trench will continue to settle for years. There are four methods of dealing with settling.

If the construction is in a rural area where the ground surface does not have to be restored immediately, the easiest method of backfilling is to carefully place the soil in the trench to prevent voids, and then finish with a neat mound of excess fill over the top of the trench. The ditch will then be settled by rain and gravity over a period of time. If the ditch settles to below grade someone could be injured from stepping into it, so someone must accept responsibility for patrolling the ditch periodically for several years to provide more fill as necessary.

The next easiest method of settling the backfill is by using water. If the backfill material is granular and drains well, just flooding the ditch may be sufficient. If the backfill is clay, however, settling must be done by jetting. This is usually done by using a 1½-in. (100-mm) galvanized pipe connected to a fire hose, with the pipe repeatedly pushed all of the way to the level of the pipe in the trench. If done thoroughly, this method will provide compaction of the backfill to within 5 percent of the maximum density. On the negative side, this method requires a very large quantity of water, particularly in a wide trench, so if there is a scarcity of water, or the water must be purchased at a rather high rate, it may not be practical.

If compaction of the fill is necessary but it is not practical to do it with water, the fill is usually placed in the trench in layers and tamped with power equipment. Pneumatic or gasoline-engine tampers may to used by a crew working up and down the trench line, but this should be used only where there is no danger of trench wall cave-in caused by the vibration. A boom-mounted tamper is also available that is operated from a crane so workers do not have to be in the ditch. This method provides a fair degree of compaction depending on the type of soil, but there will usually be some settling of the earth at the surface over a period of years.

In areas such as street crossings where the surface must be repaved as soon as possible, it is usually quickest and most economical to backfill the entire trench in the area with granular backfill, such as sand or fine stone. Most engineers and local authorities now specify this because it virtually eliminates future settling of the pavement.

Pressure Testing the Main

After the trench has been at least partially backfilled, the new main must be tested to determine whether there are any leaks. The test may be performed one section at a time between valves, or the installer may wait and test the entire job at one time.

Many years ago, when only lead joints were used on cast-iron pipe, it was always assumed that there would be leaks. The only thing the installer could do was hope that it would not be too much. Now, an installation of all mechanical, push-on, or other rubber-gasket joints will have virtually no leakage unless something is defective.

Testing Procedure

The following general procedures apply to testing of all types of pipe:
- If poured concrete blocking was used, allow at least 5 days before testing. If high early strength concrete was used, this time can be shortened.
- Make sure the valves at all connections with existing mains are holding completely tight.
- Fill the new main with water and be sure that air has been released at all high points. If chlorine tablets have been installed in the pipe as work progressed, be sure to fill very slowly so the tablets will not be dislodged.
- Close all fire hydrant auxiliary valves.
- Connect a pressure pump to a corporation stop in the main. The pump must have a pressure gauge and connection to a small tank of makeup water.
- Apply partial pressure and again check that all air has been removed from the system. Allow the pipe to stand with pressure on it for at least 24 hours to stabilize.
- Pump up the pressure as specified in the applicable AWWA standard. The minimum is usually 1.5 times the operating pressure, or 150 psi (1,030 kPa) for a period of 30 minutes.
- Examine the piping and fittings for visible leaks or air that was not previously released.
- Again pump up the pressure and wait for at least 2 hours.
- During the waiting period, pump up the pressure as required to maintain the minimum test pressure. Pump from a calibrated container and record the quantity of makeup water used.
- Compare the amount of leakage (the quantity of water required to bring the pressure back up) with the suggested maximum allowable leakage in the appropriate AWWA standard.

Rapid loss of pressure will usually be due to an open valve, a cracked or broken pipe, or a joint that slipped out after it was made up. These leaks are usually relatively easy to locate by continuing to apply pressure until the water comes to the surface.

One possible cause of a slow drop of pressure is that all of the air was not completely removed before testing began. In this case, the amount of apparent leakage will usually be less on each subsequent repeat test.

A slow leak is often difficult to locate. If the initial test was on a long section of main, it will probably be necessary to locate a small leak by performing tests on small sections between valves to narrow down the location. Leak detection equipment can then be used to locate the leak. Another alternative is to continuously subject the main to the highest pressure that can be safely applied, and wait for the water to come to the surface.

Flushing and Disinfection

All new sections of water main must be thoroughly flushed, disinfected, and tested for bacteriological quality before the water can be used by customers.

Flushing

Flushing is primarily required to remove any mud and debris left in the pipe from the installation. If the workers were not careful in plugging the end of the main when it was unattended, the flushing might also produce dead animals and other foreign matter.

One or more fire hydrants should be used for flushing so that a velocity of at least 2.5 ft/s (0.8 m/s), and preferably 3.5 ft/s (1.1 m/s), is obtained in the pipe. This velocity should be maintained long enough to allow two or three complete changes of water, and for the water to run visibly clean.

Table 9-1 lists the number of hydrants required to adequately flush smaller mains. If a hydrant is not to be installed at the end of a new main, a temporary blow-off connection should be provided. For very large mains where there are insufficient hydrants or plant capacity to supply the water needed for flushing, the new pipe should be cleaned with polypigs.

Disinfection

New water mains and equipment must be disinfected with some form of chlorine. Two methods typically used include tablets and chlorine solution.

| Pipe Diameter | | Min. Required Flow Rate* | | No. of Hydrants |
in.	(mm)	gpm	(L/s)	Open**
4	(100)	100	(6)	1
6	(150)	200	(13)	1
8	(200)	400	(25)	1
10	(250)	600	(38)	1
12	(300)	900	(57)	2
16	(400)	1,600	(100)	2

*Based on 2.5 ft/s (0.76 m/s) at 40-psi (280-kPa) pressure.
**Based on hydrant with one 2-1/2 in. (63-mm) outlet.

Table 9-1 Flow rates and number of hydrants required for flushing mains

Pipe Diameter		No. of Tablets
in.	(mm)	per Pipe Length
4	(100)	1
6	(150)	1
8	(200)	2
10	(250)	3
12	(300)	4
16	(400)	7

Table 9-2 Number of 5-g calcium hypochlorite tablets required to produce a chlorine residual of 25 mg/L in 20-ft (6-m) pipe lengths

Tablet Method

With the tablet method, calcium hypochlorite (HTH) tablets are placed in each section of pipe and fire hydrant as the work progresses, and they will dissolve when the new pipe is filled with water. The tablets are usually glued to the top of the pipe with an epoxy resin, in sufficient quantities to produce a chlorine residual of 25 mg/L after they have dissolved. The number of tablets required for each 20-ft (6-m) pipe section is listed in Table 9-2.

After the main has been filled with water, the chlorine solution should be maintained in the pipe for at least 24 hours. Because the tablets are placed only at the end of each pipe section, it is advisable to periodically bleed off a small amount of water at the end of the line to move the chlorine solution to new locations in the piping.

When tablets are used for disinfection, the velocity of the water filling the pipe must be kept below 1 ft/s (0.3 m/s), or the tablets will be dislodged and washed to the end of the pipeline. When the tablet method is used, workers must take particular care to keep the pipe clean during installation because the main cannot be flushed before it is disinfected. If it is anticipated that working conditions will make it difficult to keep the pipe clean, the tablet method should not be used so that the line may be flushed before being disinfected.

Hypochlorite Disinfection

Although chlorine gas may be used for disinfecting water mains, it requires special equipment and is dangerous to use, so is recommended for only large water main installations where it can be done under supervision of someone experienced with the equipment. Calcium hypochlorite and sodium hypochlorite (bleach) are generally used for disinfecting smaller mains.

A concentrated chlorine solution is usually injected through a corporation stop that has been installed close to the valve that connects to the existing water system. The chlorine is administered by either the continuous feed or the slug method.

In the continuous feed method, water is slowly admitted to the new pipeline while chlorine solution is forced in through the connection using a chemical feed pump or booster pump. The water flow rate can be gauged by measuring the flow of water from a fire hydrant at the end of the line. The chemical feed rate should be such that it will produce a concentration of about 50 mg/L when mixed with the incoming water.

The feed should continue until a residual of at least 25 mg/L can be measured in the flow at the end of the line. The flow should then be stopped and the chlorine solution allowed to remain in the pipe for at least 24 hours. During this time, all valves and hydrants on the line should be operated to make sure they are also properly disinfected. The quantity of HTH required to produce a 50-mg/L concentration is listed in Table 9-3.

In the slug method, a long slug of water having a very high dose of chlorine is initially created, and then it is slowly moved through the pipeline. The concentration should be at least 300 mg/L, and the slug should be moved at a speed that will provide at least 3 hours of contact as it moves through the pipeline. Fire hydrants and side connections must be operated as the slug passes to make sure the chlorine reaches all parts of the piping. This method is primarily used for larger pipelines for which the continuous feed method is impractical.

At the end of the contact period, the chlorinated water should be flushed from the pipeline and disposed of in an environmentally responsible manner. The high chlorine concentration will probably kill grass, so the flow should be carried to a disposal site through hoses. State and local regulatory agencies should be contacted in advance to determine whether they have any special requirements that must be met. In some cases, they may require that the water be dechlorinated before it is released to a waterway.

Bacteriological Testing

After a new pipeline has been disinfected and flushed, it should be refilled with water from the distribution system and tested for bacteriological quality. This test takes at least 24 hours from the time of sampling. When planning the pipe installation, this time should be included. The tests must meet requirements of the state regulatory agency, and customers must not be allowed to use the water until the results of the testing have been received. The state agency should be contacted in advance for sample bottles and instructions on sampling procedures.

If the results of the sampling are reported as negative, it means that no coliform bacteria were present in the sample and the system has been adequately disinfected.

If the results are reported as positive, the agency will usually suggest resampling. If the results of the second set of samples are still positive, disinfection of the pipeline will have to be repeated, and more samples will have to be processed to make sure the pipeline has been properly disinfected.

Nominal Pipe Diameter		Amount of Hypochlorite per 100 ft (30.5 m) of Pipe	
in.	(mm)	lb	kg
4	(100)	0.04	0.018
6	(150)	0.09	0.04
8	(200)	0.17	0.08
10	(250)	0.26	0.12
12	(300)	0.38	0.17
14	(350)	0.51	0.23
16	(400)	0.67	0.30
18	(450)	0.85	0.39
20	(500)	1.05	0.47

Table 9-3 Quantity of HTH required to produce 50 mg/L chlorine residual

Site Restoration and Inspection

The construction site should be promptly restored to its original condition. Disturbed grass should be replaced with sod or seeded and watered if necessary to get good initial growth, street pavement and curbs should be replaced in kind, and ditches and culverts should be checked for proper drainage.

All construction debris must be removed from the site, and private driveways, walks, fences, lawns, and bushes must be returned to their original conditions.

Damaged roots can cause some trees to die, sometimes several years later. If there is a question on damage to trees, a qualified tree expert should be consulted. In some cases, pruning and feeding may help to save damaged trees.

As soon as all restoration is considered complete, a responsible person should make a detailed final inspection of the entire jobsite, and make note of anything that was missed. This is also a good time to complete as-built drawings of the construction, showing any changes from the original plans, and noting exact measurements to fire hydrants and valves. It is also a good idea to make a final check of all valves to make sure they are in the full open position, and to flow test all new hydrants and record the results in the system records.

Bibliography

AWWA Manual M20, Water Chlorination Principles and Practices. 1973. Denver, Colo.: American Water Works Association.

AWWA Standard for Disinfecting Water Mains. ANSI/AWWA C651-92. 1992. Denver, Colo.: American Water Works Association.

Chapter 10

Fire Hydrants

Fire hydrants are so seldom used for fighting fires in small communities that it is easy to forget how important they are. Hydrants that operate properly and provide adequate flow can make the difference between losing or saving valuable property and even lives in the event of a serious fire.

Hydrant Uses

Fire hydrants have a number of uses in a water distribution system. The most obvious is for public protection fighting fires. But there are several other uses that should be addressed in the process of operating and maintaining a water distribution system.

Fire Fighting

It is important to a community to have fire hydrants that are properly spaced and fed by an adequate distribution system. As mentioned, adequate fire hydrants can make the difference between losing and saving buildings that catch fire, and having a good system in place can result in substantial savings in fire insurance for residents.

In most communities, the water utility has the responsibility for installing and maintaining hydrants. In some cases the fire department will assume responsibility for maintaining and flow-testing hydrants. Water distribution system operators have both moral and legal responsibilities to keep hydrants in good working order.

Other Hydrant Uses

Other frequent uses for fire hydrants include:

- flushing water mains to clear the pipes of rust and sediment
- furnishing large volumes of water for flushing sewers to clear them of accumulated solids
- filling tank trucks for rural fire fighting, street washing, tree spraying, and other uses
- construction uses, such as furnishing water for settling dust during demolition and mixing mortar for construction before a permanent water service is installed

In general, uses other than for fighting fires should be discouraged both because water is wasted in the process and use of hydrants by inexperienced persons could cause damage to the hydrants. This is particularly true in very cold weather when a hydrant may freeze during or after use.

Unauthorized use of fire hydrants should be absolutely prohibited, and all police and public works employees should be instructed to immediately report any use that they notice that may not be authorized. If hydrant use by anyone other than experienced system workers is necessary, it should be allowed only under specific conditions. In general, it is best to issue a hydrant use permit both for record purposes and to be sure that all specific conditions are understood. The conditions specified by many water utilities include the following:

- Only a standard hydrant wrench may be used for operating hydrants—repeated use of a pipe wrench on the five-sided nut will round off the nut so a hydrant wrench will no longer work.
- Very old hydrants should not be used by inexperienced persons—hydrants often will not seat well when closed and may be inadvertently left running. Also, an inexperienced person might break the stem while forcing it in an attempt to get the hydrant to stop leaking.
- Hydrants on busy streets should not be used unless absolutely necessary—their use could unnecessarily cause traffic tieups or accidents.
- Unless there is some specific reason why it is necessary, hydrants on the end of dead-end mains should not be used—there is usually sediment accumulation in dead-end mains that will be needlessly stirred up.
- Hoses should not be left attached overnight or when the user is not present—if firefighters should have to use the hydrant, they will be delayed by having to remove the hose.
- If use from a hose will require that the water be intermittently turned on and off (for example, for mixing batches of mortar), an auxiliary hose valve should be used (Figure 10-1). The hydrant should be opened at least halfway and left in that position until the use is completed—repeated opening and closing of the hydrant valve may damage the hydrant and may flood the underdrain system so the hydrant will not drain properly.

Some water utilities have eliminated the problems caused by tank trucks being filled from random points on the system by establishing one watering point and insisting that all tankers be filled at that location. The watering point is usually located at the city yards where the operation can be closely observed. It is set up to make the operation simple and eliminate any possibility of a cross connection. It is also convenient to meter the water at this point and charge the users for the amount of water taken.

Charging for Water Used From Hydrants

From the standpoint of water use accountability, it is a good idea to meter water taken from fire hydrants. Many water utilities have one or more special hydrant meters (Figure 10-2) available for contractors to use when they require water for construction. The contractor must be informed that the hydrant should be flushed before the meter is installed the first time so that accumulated sediment will not lodge in the meter. The meter must also be protected from vandalism and freezing and removed at night. Some water system operators also assemble a metering system for small hoses using a regular home-type water meter.

Besides recording the exact amount of water used by contractors, using a meter also discourages them from wasting water. When the water is not metered, there is a strong tendency by workers to let the water run rather than shut it off between uses.

Courtesy of USA Blue Book.   Courtesy of Schlumberger Industries Water Division.

Figure 10-1 Hydrant hose valve   **Figure 10-2** Fire hydrant meter

The problem with metering hydrant flow is that the meters receive considerable abuse when they are thrown in the back of a truck with the picks and shovels at the end of each day. For this reason, many utilities find it easier to just estimate the water use and charge a lump sum for a hydrant use permit to cover both the cost of water and the water system's labor in monitoring the use by the contractor.

Problems Caused by Hydrant Operation

The most common problem caused by hydrant operation is that it stirs up sediment that has accumulated in the mains. This is sure to cause "rusty water" complaints by customers unless the section of main is thoroughly flushed until the water is clear. This problem can be somewhat reduced by having a regular hydrant flushing program to minimize the amount of sediment buildup.

Once an area of the system has been stirred up from a major hydrant use, such as for fire fighting, it may be possible to bleed off some of the discolored water by opening some hydrants to partial flow. The velocity in the mains, however, must be kept low enough to not stir up more sediment. When the water is discolored, customers should be informed that the water is safe to drink, but they should not wash clothes until the discoloration has cleared.

If any customers have washed clothes, they will probably complain that their white clothes came out yellow or brown. Products are available, packaged in small bottles, that will usually remove the discoloration when the clothes are rewashed with the chemical. Many water systems keep a supply of these bottles at the city hall or other location to give to customers when they have this problem.

Another problem that can be caused by hydrant use is water hammer. If a hydrant on a large main is closed very quickly, the pressure buildup caused by abruptly stopping the large quantity of water traveling through the main can be several times normal pressure. This could result in moving the hydrant backward if it is not firmly blocked, or other system damage, including blowing out adjoining-home water services. All hydrant users should accordingly be warned to open and close hydrants slowly.

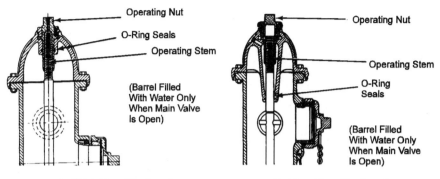

A. Wet-Top Hydrant

B. Dry-Top Hydrant

Figure 10-3 Wet- and dry-top hydrants

Courtesy of Mueller Company, Decatur, Ill.

Types of Fire Hydrants

The four general types of fire hydrants available include dry barrel, wet barrel, warm climate, and flush.

Dry-Barrel Hydrants

Dry-barrel hydrants are used in locations with freezing weather and are equipped with a main valve and a small drain valve in the base that allows the barrel to drain when the main valve is closed. An additional advantage of dry-barrel hydrants is that there is no flow of water from a broken hydrant because the main valve is underground.

Dry-barrel hydrants are further classified as wet top or dry top. Wet-top hydrants (Figure 10-3A) are constructed so that the threaded end of the operating mechanism is not sealed from water when the hydrant has water in it. Dry-top hydrants (Figure 10-3B) have this mechanism sealed to reduce the possibility of the threads becoming fouled from sediment or corrosion.

The three general types of main valves used in dry-barrel hydrants are illustrated in Figure 10-4. In a standard compression hydrant, the valve closes with water pressure against the seat, which assists in providing a good seal.

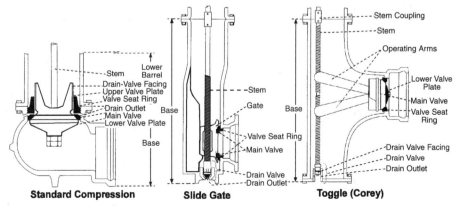

Standard Compression

Slide Gate

Toggle (Corey)

Figure 10-4 Common types of hydrant main valves

The principal parts of an older-style dry-barrel hydrant are shown in Figure 10-5. As shown in this illustration, early hydrants were made with a single-piece barrel that extended from the foot piece to the bonnet. A disadvantage to this design is that, if the hydrant is broken (usually by being struck by a vehicle), the hydrant must be dug up to the foot piece to replace the barrel. In such an accident, the operating stem is also usually bent beyond repair, and must be replaced. If the hydrant is broken when there is frost in the ground, it requires considerable effort to make the repair; sometimes the hydrant must be taken out of service until the ground thaws.

In recent years, all manufacturers have been using the breakaway, or traffic hydrant design, which uses a flanged coupling just above the ground line as illustrated in Figure 10-6. In most cases, all that is broken when a hydrant is struck is the cast-iron safety flange and the safety coupling on the operating stem. The hydrant can usually be easily restored to service using a new flange and coupling.

The design of dry-barrel hydrants is covered in AWWA Standard C502-94, *Dry-Barrel Fire Hydrants*.

Wet-Barrel Hydrants

As illustrated in Figure 10-7, wet-barrel hydrants are filled with water all the time, so are not suitable for locations with freezing weather. The hydrant itself has no main valve, but each nozzle has a separate valve. The design of wet-barrel hydrants is covered in AWWA Standard C503-97, *Wet-Barrel Fire Hydrants*.

Warm-Climate Hydrants

A warm-climate hydrant has the main valve located at the ground line so that the lower barrel is always full of water and under pressure. The main valve controls flow from all outlet nozzles, and there is no drain mechanism.

Flush Hydrants

Flush hydrants are used where a regular hydrant would be objectionable, such as on airport taxiways or in pedestrian malls. The entire standpipe and head are below ground and are accessible through a cover flush with the surface (see Figure 10-8).

Flushing Hydrants

Small-diameter hydrants are available for installation on the end of a small pipeline, solely for the purpose of flushing the line (Figure 10-9). Flushing hydrants are not intended for fire use. They are generally available with 2-in. pipe thread inlet and a standard $2\frac{1}{2}$-in. nozzle so a fire hose may be used to divert discharge flow, if necessary.

Auxiliary Valves

Every fire hydrant should have an auxiliary valve installed between the hydrant and the main so each hydrant may be individually turned off for repair. The type of auxiliary valve most often used is directly connected to the hydrant by a flange. One of the advantages to this arrangement is that the valve cannot separate from the hydrant. Another advantage is that it places the valve at the same location in relation to each hydrant, thus they are easy to find.

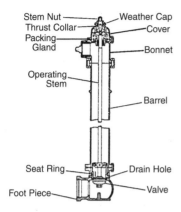

Figure 10-5 Solid-barrel hydrant

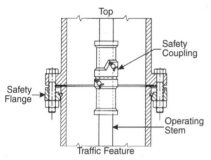

Courtesy of AMERICAN FLOW CONTROL, a Division of American Cast Iron Pipe Company.

Figure 10-6 Detail of one type of breakaway flange and stem coupling

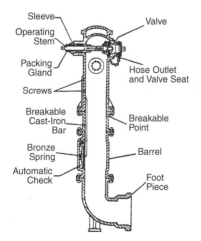

Figure 10-7 Wet-barrel hydrant

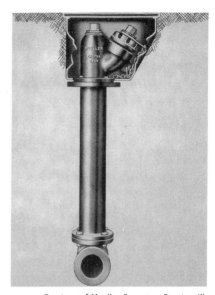

Courtesy of Mueller Company, Decatur, Ill.

Figure 10-8 Flush hydrant

Courtesy of Kupferle Foundry Company.

Figure 10-9 Flushing hydrant

Hydrant Installation

Fire hydrants must be handled and installed carefully. Carelessness can result in future maintenance problems or even failure of a hydrant when it is needed.

New Hydrant Inspection

Before installing a hydrant, make sure that it meets local standards. Most hydrants installed in the United States open counterclockwise and have operating nuts that measure 1¹/₄ in. (32 mm) from flat to point. But some water systems got started with other standards and have chosen to stay that way for uniformity. There are also many communities that have a special thread (other than National Standard) for the 2¹/₂-in. (63.5-mm) ports. It is much easier to check that these are all correct before installation than to find out after the hydrant is in place.

The depth of burial should also be carefully computed and checked to make sure the hydrant to be installed will stand the correct distance above the ground. The break-flange should be located about 2 in. (51 mm) above the ground surface. Hydrants are generally purchased to coincide with the water main depth of burial required by the utility. But, occasionally a main may be a little shallower, or may be considerably deeper, due to the need to go over or under an obstruction, such as a sewer.

If the main is considerably deeper than normal at the hydrant location, it is usually best to angle the hydrant lead up to the normal depth using angle fittings. If the main is much shallower than normal, it may be necessary to order a special hydrant with a shorter barrel. If the main is only 1 ft (0.3 m) or so deeper than normal, the regular hydrant can be installed and then the upper section can be raised later using extension kits that are available in 6-in. (150-mm) increments.

And finally, the new hydrant should be opened and closed to ensure that no damage occurred during shipping or storage. If hydrants must be stored outside in freezing weather, they should be placed with the inlet facing down to prevent rain and snow from entering and freezing.

Installation Location

Fire hydrants are usually located at street intersections so that hose can be strung in any direction for fighting a fire. Hydrant spacing typically ranges from 300 to 600 ft (90 to 180 m). Mid-block hydrants are usually best located opposite a lot line, as they are least likely to conflict with a driveway and will be least objectionable to the property owners.

Hydrants should be located far enough back from a roadway to minimize the danger of being struck by vehicles. The minimum setback from the face of a curb should be about 2 ft (0.6 m), which is generally beyond large-vehicle overhang and far enough back to place the auxiliary valve behind the curb. On the other hand, they should be close enough to the paving so that a hard suction can be connected between a pumper truck and the hydrant without danger of the truck getting stuck in mud or snow.

In areas with heavy snowfall, consideration should also be given to locations where the hydrant will be least likely to have snow piled on it during snow removal.

Hydrants should not be located close to buildings. Fire fighters usually will not position their truck in a location where a building wall will fall on the truck if the building collapses.

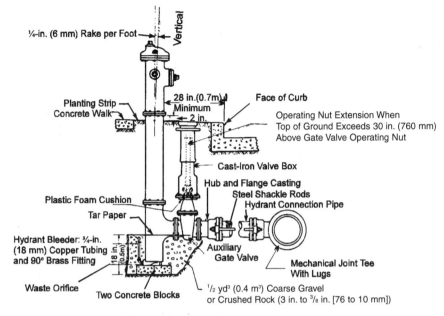

Figure 10-10 Hydrant auxiliary valve installation

Installation Procedures

Fire hydrants must be set on a firm footing that will not rot or settle. A flat stone or concrete slab is ideal (Figure 10-10). As the hydrant is set, a carpenters level should be used to ensure that it is plumb in all directions.

The hydrant must also be securely blocked or restrained from movement because the force against it will be tremendous if the valve is closed quickly. If possible, the excavation for the hydrant should be made carefully so there will be undisturbed earth directly behind the foot piece. Solid concrete blocks can be tightly wedged between the hydrant and earth, or a small quantity of concrete can be mixed on the job and poured into the void. If poured concrete is used, care must be taken not to block the drain hole.

If the ground behind the hydrant is soft or otherwise unsuitable for blocking, the hydrant must be restrained in some other fashion. One method of restraint that works well is to install at least two lengths of threaded rod between the auxiliary valve and the tee on the main. If mechanical joint fittings are being used, the rod can be substituted for two of the bolts and double nuts used to tighten the joints. If push-on joints are being used, the rod can be fastened through bell clamps.

To facilitate quick removal of the water from the hydrant barrel when the main valve is shut, a pocket of coarse gravel or crushed rock should be placed in the excavation before the hydrant is set. The top of the gravel should be slightly above the drain opening and should be covered with heavy polyethylene or tar paper to prevent the gravel from being clogged with dirt.

If the hydrant barrel will not fully drain, because of a high water table, common practice is to plug the drain hole. If there is any danger of ground frost at the location, special note must be made of these hydrants so that they will be pumped out by hand after every use.

Testing New Hydrants

New hydrants installed in conjunction with installation of a new water main should not be tested during main testing. All hydrant auxiliary valves should be closed during the pressure test. After main testing is completed, the following hydrant test procedures should be followed:

1. Open the auxiliary valve, remove a cap, and fill the hydrant with water.
2. Replace the cap, but leave it loose to let air escape, then tighten it.
3. Apply a pressure up to a maximum of 150 psi (1,000 kPa) by using a pressure pump connected to one of the nozzles. If it is not practical to apply higher pressure, system pressure will suffice.
4. Check for leakage at flanges, outlet nozzles, and at the operating stem.
5. Tighten any loose bolts and correct any leakage.
6. Flush the hydrant to remove any foreign material.
7. For dry-barrel hydrants, shut the main valve, immediately remove one cap, and place the palm of a hand over the nozzle. If the barrel is draining properly, a noticeable vacuum can usually be felt. If there is still a question of proper drainage, a string with a small weight attached can be dropped down the barrel and inspected to determine whether it comes out wet.

Hydrant Maintenance

Maintenance of fire hydrants must be a continuing program. The lives and property of residents depend on hydrants working properly when needed. Water system operators should also keep in mind that fire hydrants are often the only visible signs of the water utility seen by most customers, so hydrant appearance can go a long way in promoting the utility's public image. Shabby hydrants immediately bring to mind a poorly run utility.

Hydrant Operation

Fire hydrants are designed to be operated by one person using a 15-in. (380-mm) long wrench. A length of pipe (cheater) should not be used on the wrench. If a hydrant cannot be operated with a standard wrench, it should be repaired or replaced. Some very old hydrants may not seat completely on the first try, but will usually respond to reopening and closing the valve several times. A person operating a hydrant must always make sure that the valve is tightly shut and the barrel has drained before leaving the site.

Hydrant Painting

Fire hydrants should be painted colors that are easily visible to the fire department. Red, orange, and yellow are generally the most visible, although not always the favorites of property owners who would prefer less visible hydrants. If darker colors are used, do not allow bushes or other vegetation to obscure the hydrants.

Many water systems now color code their hydrants to indicate the capacity and assist the fire department in deciding which hydrants are the best to connect to. Most

Hydrant Class	Usual Flow Capacity at 20 psig (140 kPa [gauge])* gpm	(L/mm)	Color**
AA	1,500	(5,680)	Light Blue
A	1,000 to 1,499	(3,785 to 5,675)	Green
B	500 to 999	(1,900 to 3,780)	Orange
C	Less than 500	(Less than 1,900)	Red

*Capacities are to be rated by flow measurements of individual hydrants at a period of ordinary demand. See AWWA Standard for Dry-Barrel Fire Hydrants, C502-94, for additional details.
**As designed in Federal Standard 595B, General Services Administration, Specification Section, Washington, D.C.

Table 10-1 Standard hydrant color scheme to indicate flow capacity

systems just paint the hydrant top or caps the code color. The color code scheme suggested by AWWA is shown in Table 10-1.

Hydrant Inspection and Repair

All fire hydrants should be inspected regularly to ensure that they operate satisfactorily. Many water systems in northern regions do their hydrant inspection in the fall to make sure that the barrels are drained, the hydrants are cleared of vegetation, and snow flags are installed if necessary. Some systems also do another inspection in the spring. It is advisable to inspect hydrants after every use. This is particularly important in freezing weather to make sure the barrel has drained completely (Figure 10-11).

Figure 10-11 Hydrant pump   *Courtesy of Kuranda USA.*

Some water utilities have inspection crews equipped to make repairs immediately if any problems are found. Other systems have crews that perform only inspection and, if they find that repairs are necessary, submit repair requests to follow-up repair crews. If, during inspection, a hydrant is found to be inoperable, an out-of-service sign should be hung on it or a plastic bag placed over it and the fire department notified that the hydrant is not operable.

Inspection procedures for dry- and wet-barrel hydrants and maintenance tips are included in AWWA Manual M17, *Installation, Field Testing, and Maintenance of Fire Hydrants*. The AWWA publication *Hydrant Maintenance Field Guide* is also an inexpensive, pocket-sized reference that is handy for use by field crews.

Hydrant Records

A record card, sheet, or computer record should be maintained for every hydrant in the water system. Basic information that should be recorded at the time of installation includes the make, model, depth of burial, location measurements to various markers, information on the auxiliary valve, and flow performance at the time of installation.

An entry should then be made on the record each time the hydrant is inspected, and notes made of any repairs that are made. It is important that the records be accurately maintained because they could serve as proof of a good hydrant maintenance program in the event that the utility is charged with negligence if a hydrant should fail to operate properly in an emergency.

Bibliography

AWWA Manual M17, *Installation, Field Testing, and Maintenance of Fire Hydrants*. 1989. Denver, Colo.: American Water Works Association.

AWWA Manual M31, *Distribution System Requirements for Fire Protection*. 1998. Denver, Colo.: American Water Works Association.

AWWA Standard for Dry-Barrel Fire Hydrants. ANSI/AWWA C502-94. 1994. Denver, Colo.: American Water Works Association.

AWWA Standard for Wet-Barrel Fire Hydrants. ANSI/AWWA C503-97. 1997. Denver, Colo.: American Water Works Association.

Conducting Flow Tests Reference Card. 1993. Laminated card. Denver, Colo.: American Water Works Association.

Fire Hydrant and Water Maintenance Training Package. 1991. Denver, Colo.: American Water Works Association.

Hydrant Maintenance Field Guide. 1993. Denver, Colo.: American Water Works Association.

Standard for Fire Hose Connections. Quincy, Mass.: National Fire Protection Association.

Chapter 11

Distribution System
Operation and Maintenance

The operation and maintenance of a water distribution system requires many varied duties and skills. The piping system must be carefully operated to keep an adequate supply of water available for all consumer uses, while maintaining utmost diligence to protect public health.

Distribution System Inspection

As a municipality expands, the demands on the system change. Increases in everyday customer water use and greater numbers of customers will increase the velocity of flow in mains and result in increasing head loss. In addition, the capacity of older mains may decrease due to tuberculation and corrosion.

Pressure and Flow Tests

The pressure can be checked at points on the distribution system by attaching a pressure gauge to a fire hydrant (Figure 11-1A). After the gauge is attached, the hydrant

Figure 11-1 Hydrant pressure gauge (A) and chart recorder (B) *Courtesy of USA BlueBook.*

107

should be opened several turns to be sure the drain valve is closed, and air must be bled through the petcock before a reading is taken. It is usually advisable to take readings during periods of high and low water use to determine the difference. Maximum water use on most water systems is usually around supper time on a summer evening.

A more satisfactory way of recording pressure fluctuations is to install a chart recorder on a hydrant for at least 24 hours (Figure 11-1B). To prevent vandalism of the recorder, a barrel is placed over the hydrant. The fire department must be informed that the hydrant is out of service.

If there are no hydrants at locations that require pressure testing, it is possible to attach a pressure gauge to a sill cock on a customer's building. To do this, obtain customer permission first, and be sure no water will be used in the building during the test.

A wide variation in pressure between readings taken at night and at maximum use times of the day is a sure indicator that the system is being stressed from normal usage and will probably be considerably worse when fire flow is required.

It is also advisable to periodically check the capacity of key locations on the system by conducting fire flow tests. The testing will indicate whether the system should be reinforced with new transmission mains or would benefit from cleaning the mains. It will also indicate other problems, such as valves inadvertently left closed after a main repair.

A permanent record of pressure and flow test information should always be kept at each location so that comparisons can be made with future tests to identify any changes in the system operation.

Flow-testing procedures are detailed in AWWA Manual M17, *Installation, Field Testing, and Maintenance of Fire Hydrants*, and in the AWWA video *Conducting Hydrant Flow Tests*.

Watching for Leaks

Because most of a water distribution system is hidden underground, system operators must be particularly vigilant in looking for signs of trouble. Every water system should have a regular program of inspecting and exercising valves and fire hydrants. Besides verifying that they are operational, it is also an opportunity to check for problems such as hydrants that are blocked or partially obscured by vegetation, and valve boxes that have stones in them or have the lid covered or missing.

Police and other municipal workers should be encouraged to help the water distribution crews by watching for, and reporting, unusual water on the street or parkway that could be from a water leak. All reports should be investigated as soon as possible, and the person who made the report thanked for taking the trouble to call even if the problem turns out to be something else. Police and other municipal workers should also be asked to particularly watch for signs of vandalism, damaged equipment, and unauthorized use of hydrants, and report the information to the distribution system supervisor.

Cleaning and Lining Mains

Most water distribution systems have some accumulation of sediment that has settled in the bottom of the mains. How much sediment exists is a function of the quality of the water source, treatment, and the type of piping. In most cases, the sediment can be adequately removed by periodically flushing the main. If old piping is badly corroded, it may be necessary to clean and line the pipe to maintain good water quality and to provide good flow.

Water Main Flushing

Water mains are primarily sized for fire flow, which means that the velocity of flow under normal use by customers is generally very low. As a result, it is common for sediment caused by corrosion products and precipitated iron in the water to accumulate in the mains and then to be stirred up by heavier-than-normal water flow, such as opening a fire hydrant. The sediment can also be stirred up by a reversal of flow, such as would occur from closing a key valve on a transmission main.

Depending on water quality and the type of piping in the system, some water systems have very few problems while others have a continual problem with discolored water caused by sediment. Although it may be bacteriologically safe, customers are reluctant to drink discolored water. The sediment may also discolor washed clothes and can be a source of annoying taste and odor. Slime growth is also a problem in some systems, but this can usually be controlled by maintaining an adequate chlorine residual in the distribution system.

Operators of systems with sediment problems usually find that it is best to set up a regular flushing program that will keep the mains relatively clean and minimize customer "dirty water" complaints. Flushing can also help prevent obstructions. Some water system operators find it most convenient to combine main flushing and hydrant testing in the fall after the heavy water use of summer is over. Other system operators flush in spring to rid the system of sediment that has accumulated during the winter, before flow rates increase in the summer sprinkling season.

Many water systems have particularly bad sediment accumulation in dead-end mains, and some system operators have found it necessary to flush these mains as often as weekly in order to avoid customer complaints.

It is not normal practice for a larger water system to flush the entire distribution system, but areas that have been found from experience to draw customer complaints may be placed on a regular flushing program. If flushing of a large area of the system is necessary, the conventional procedure is to start at the well or treatment plant and work outward, flowing each hydrant in turn until the water is relatively clear.

Another relatively new flushing technique is called *unidirectional flushing*. With this method, all of the valves to connecting mains are closed so that a section of main about 2,000 ft (610 m) long draws from a relatively clean source and discharges from a single hydrant at the end. The unidirectional flow increases the velocity of the water, causing a scouring that is said to be particularly effective in removing sediment and biofilm. Each unidirectional run must maintain a minimum velocity of 5 ft/s (1.5 m/s) to provide favorable results.

Flushing late at night will provide better flow rates, will cause less traffic disruption by water on the street, and will result in fewer customer complaints. In addition, customers will not see how bad the water sometimes looks when it is flushed. Flushing should be preceded by various announcements warning customers of when flushing will take place and suggesting that they not wash clothes if the water is discolored. The announcements can be made in local media, and many utilities also place "water main flushing this week" signs on key roads in the area.

The flow rate required for effective flushing is at least 2.5 ft/s (0.76 m/s), which translates to about 250 gpm (830 L/min) in a 6-in. (150-mm) main. A flow of 3.5 ft/s or 350 gpm (1.1 m/s or 1,170 L/min) is even better. When larger mains are to be flushed, the required flow rate should be calculated in advance.

Figure 11-2 Flow diffuser   *Courtesy of USA Blue Book.*

Methods of diffusing flow must also be considered for each site so as not to damage public or private property. Various types of flow diffusers are available to break up and divert the flow to prevent damage to lawns (Figure 11-2).

Water Main Cleaning

Old, unlined cast-iron water pipe often develops tuberculation that gradually constricts flow and causes water discoloration due to the corrosion products (Figure 11-3). It is possible to clean these pipes using one or more of the following cleaning techniques, but in most cases, the cleaning process is not a permanent solution. Unless the cleaned pipe is lined or the corrosiveness of the water is reduced, experience has shown that regrowth of the incrustation is rather rapid. It is also occasionally necessary to clean pipe other than old cast iron if there are accumulations of slime or deposits from iron bacteria.

Smooth Pipe   Tuberculated Pipe

Courtesy of J-M Manufacturing Company, Inc.   *Courtesy of Girard Industries.*

Figure 11-3 Effect of tuberculation

Figure 11-4 Pressure relief valve installed on a hydrant

Courtesy of Baburek Metal Preserving Company.

Cleaning Preparations

A pipe-cleaning operation requires very careful preparation. The mains to be cleaned must be carefully mapped, and all hydrants and valves tested for proper operation. Customers must be notified of the times that their water will be turned off, and police and fire departments notified of the work to be done.

A way of dealing with possible water hammer must also be considered. If for instance, a valve is operated too rapidly, or a cleaning pig suddenly is caught and stops moving, a very serious pressure surge can result. The best method of relieving excessive pressure is to install a pressure relief valve on a fire hydrant located near the point where pressure is being applied to the cleaning instrument (Figure 11-4).

Air Purging

Small mains up to 4 in. (100 mm) in diameter can sometimes be successfully cleaned by air purging. All services must be shut off and a blowoff valve opened at the end of the section. Spurts of air from a large compressor are then forced in with the water at the upstream end, and the air–water mixture will usually remove all but the toughest scale.

Swabbing

Polyurethane foam plugs, called *swabs*, may be forced through a pipe by water pressure to remove slime, soft scale, and loose sediment. Swabs are made of soft foam for use in mains with severe tuberculation or where there may be changes in the cross section of the pipe. They will not significantly remove hardened tuberculation, and they wear out quickly. Hard foam swabs are used in newer mains and where only minor reductions in diameter are expected.

An experienced crew can swab several thousand feet of main a day if the job is properly planned. Swabs should be operated at the speed recommended by the manufacturer. If they travel too fast, they remove less material and wear out faster. A pitot tube should be used to measure the flow on the end of the pipe section, and the water entering the section throttled to obtain the optimum speed of the swab.

Preparations include turning off all water services on the pipe section, closing the valves on any connecting mains, and making provisions for inserting and retrieving the swab. The time should be noted when the swab is launched so the approximate exit time can be anticipated. If the travel time becomes too long, the swab is probably stuck, in which case the flow should be reversed to push it back to the starting point. Enough swab runs should be made so that the water runs clear within 1 min following the run.

Pigging

Pipe-cleaning pigs are stiff, bullet-shaped foam plugs that are forced through a main using water pressure. They are harder, less flexible, and more durable than swabs. Although they are able to remove tougher encrustation, their limited flexibility reduces their ability to change direction and they are more likely to be caught at a constriction in the piping.

Pigs of different grades are classified as bare pigs, cleaning pigs, or scraping pigs. Bare pigs are made of high-density foam and are usually sent through a tuberculated main first to determine whether there are any obstructions. Cleaning pigs have tough polyurethane ribs applied in a crisscross pattern, and they will remove most types of encrustation and growths from the main. A bare pig is sometimes sent behind an undersized cleaning pig to maintain the water seal. Scraping pigs have spirals of silicon carbide or hardened steel wire brushes that will remove hard encrustation and tuberculation. Cleaning and scraping pigs that are somewhat smaller than the pipe diameter are usually sent through first to gradually remove layers of encrustation.

Launching Pigs

There are no easy methods of launching pigs. Three methods of launching pigs are illustrated in Figure 11-5. One method requires that the top of a hydrant be removed, and a special adapter connected to the hydrant base. A separate source of water is required to force the pig into the main, and then as it enters the main, it is pushed by system pressure. The other two methods require that a section of main be

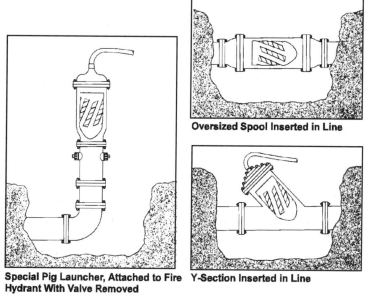

Oversized Spool Inserted in Line

Special Pig Launcher, Attached to Fire Hydrant With Valve Removed

Y-Section Inserted in Line

Courtesy of Girard Industries.

Figure 11-5 Launching methods for pipe-cleaning pigs

removed to install the launcher. In some cases, it is also possible to remove the gates from a gate valve and insert the pig into the main through the body of the valve.

If a pig should become lodged in a main, the main must be exposed and opened to remove the pig. To facilitate locating a pig in this situation, a small radio transmitter called a *sonde* can be installed in the pig and the signal can be picked up by a pipe locator. There are numerous pitfalls in the operation of pigging, so it is recommended that a first-time water utility crew work with someone experienced in using the equipment and performing the operation.

Other Cleaning Methods

Badly encrusted mains may also be cleaned using metal scrapers consisting of a series of units having high-carbon spring-steel blades. The sections are free to rotate and the unit is pushed through the main by water pressure acting against pusher cones.

If deposits in a main are particularly thick or dense, mechanical cleaning with a power drive is usually required. The work is generally done by a special contracting firm using a unit similar to a sewer rodding machine to pull a cutter through the main.

Following any of the pipe cleaning procedures, the main must be thoroughly flushed and then disinfected before it is returned to service.

Lining Water Mains

Cleaning a tuberculated water main can usually restore the interior to close to that of a new pipe, but if the quality of the water remains the same, the tuberculation will recur at a very rapid rate. In some cases, it may be possible to slow the corrosion rate by altering the water quality or adding corrosion inhibitors. In most cases, it is best to coat the pipe interior to prevent further corrosion. Although this process is quite expensive, the cost must be compared to the cost of totally replacing the pipe. In a rural area, it may be less expensive to simply replace the pipe. But in an urban area, with all of the problems of working around trees, driveways, other utilities, and obstructions, it will usually be less expensive to line the existing pipe. One exception would be if the existing pipe is undersized and should be replaced with a larger main anyway.

In the cement–mortar lining process, after the main has been cleaned, a thin layer of cement mortar is applied to the pipe walls. As illustrated in Figure 11-6, small-diameter pipe is lined by remote-controlled equipment pushed through the pipeline. Larger-diameter pipe can be lined with a machine that allows an operator to enter the pipe on a carriage to control the operation.

If there are customer services on the main, the buildings must be served with water from a temporary piping system during the lining operation. This is usually accomplished by installing a temporary 2-in. (50-mm) pipe on the ground surface and making connections to each service line. After the lining operation has been completed, it is necessary to dig up each service connection to remove the mortar from the corporation stops and reconnect the water services to the main.

Another lining method involves sliplining the cleaned main with high-density polyethylene pipe. The plastic pipe is either pushed or pulled through the pipeline in a folded configuration, and then expanded into place using heat. As with cement lining, it is then necessary to individually expose each service connection to remove the blockage caused by the lining.

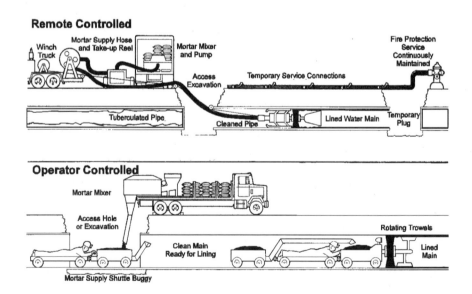

Figure 11-6 Pipe-lining operations   *Courtesy of Mainlining Service, Inc.*

Locating Pipe and Detecting Leaks

Electronic equipment is now available at reasonable costs that allow all water systems to locate piping and detect leaks.

Locating Pipe

Electronic locators are used for locating metallic water mains, service pipes, valve boxes, and access covers. The units will also locate metallic gas pipe and telephone and television cables, but it is generally best to let other utilities locate their own pipes and cables to ensure accuracy and avoid liability.

Ground-Probing Radar

Radar is now used for many purposes and would be very useful for all utilities if it could be easily used to detect all underground pipes and cables. Unfortunately, at the present time, the units that are available work only under certain soil conditions, require special expertise to interpret the results, and are expensive. Perhaps radar equipment will someday be developed for use by all water systems.

Metal Detectors

Units similar to military mine detectors have flat detection coils on the ends of their handles (Figure 11-7). When the coil is near a metal object that is relatively close to the ground surface, there is a change in audible tone or meter reading. Relatively inexpensive units can save a lot of time locating metal access covers, valve boxes, and meter-pit covers that have been paved over, have grass growing over them, or are covered by snow.

Some valve boxes and meter pits are now made entirely of plastic. To make one of these detectable by an electronic locator, fasten a small piece of metal or a small magnet to the underside of the cover.

Magnetic Locators

A magnetic locator consists of a single unit that monitors the earth's magnetic field. When it is brought near any object containing iron or steel, there is an imbalance in the magnetic field, which the locator translates into a change in sound or meter reading. A unit will generally detect an 8-in. (200-mm) ductile-iron pipe 8 ft (2.5 m) deep. It will not detect noniron metals, such as aluminum cans, copper water service pipe, or cables.

Radio Transmission Units

Another type of locator uses a radio transmitter and receiver. Commonly called a *line tracer, continuous metal locator,* or *pipe and cable locator,* it consists of two units: a radio transmitter that sends out a signal and a receiver with a loop antenna that receives a maximum signal only in the plane of the loop. It will locate any continuous pipe or cable made of any type of metal. The transmitter introduces a signal into the metal, either by a direct connection or by placing the transmitter above the line (Figure 11-8).

Pipe and cable locators will locate copper and galvanized service pipes over a considerable distance. But when used for new DIP with rubber joints, the signal may travel for only a few pipe lengths because the signal does not conduct well from one pipe to the next.

M-95 Valve and Box Locator from
Fisher Research Laboratory, Los Banos, Calif.

TW-770 Digital Line Tracer from
Fisher Research Laboratory, Los Banos, Calif.

Figure 11-7 Electronic metal detector

Figure 11-8 Electronic pipe detector

Nonmetallic Pipe Locators

The best way of locating nonmetallic pipe is to have a metallic tape or tracer wire buried in the ditch at the time the pipe is installed. If a metal tape is used, it is usually buried about 1 ft (0.3 m) below the surface so it will be easily detectable and will act as a visual warning to anyone excavating in the vicinity of the pipe. The tape or wire can be easily located with a pipe and cable locator by either direct or inductive signal.

Unfortunately, few installers have had the foresight to install tracers, so there are many water systems with nonmetallic pipe and no location records. One way of locating nonmetallic mains and services is to use a unit that uses a transmitter to send small shock waves through the water. The pipe is then located using a receiver that detects the vibration in the soil above the pipe. In most soils, pipe can be located at least 250 ft (76 m) from the transmitter, and may work over as long as a mile (1.5 km) under ideal conditions. This type of unit will usually not work well in dry, loose soil or very wet ground.

Locating Leaks

Besides wasting water, leaks from mains and service lines can cause a number of problems, including property damage and personal injury. There have been numerous cases in which large sections of pavement have caved in after being undermined by hidden water leaks. Large leaks occasionally cause flooding that flows into basements of adjacent buildings. Also icing caused by water leaks in freezing weather can cause very serious traffic problems. Relatively small leaks can waste a surprisingly large quantity of water, as indicated by Table 11-1.

Pipe Leak Size	Water Loss*			
	Per Day		Per Month*	
	gal	(L)	gal	(L)
●	360	(1,360)	11,160	(42,241)
●	3,096	(11,720)	95,976	(363,270)
●	8,424	(31,890)	261,144	(988,430)
●	14,952	(56,593)	463,512	(1,755,392)
*Based on approximately 60-psi (410-kPa) pressure.				

Table 11-1 Water loss versus pipe leak size

In areas with clay or other dense soil, leaks generally come to the surface or find their way into a sewer. A leak detection program, therefore, includes asking police and other municipal employees to watch for unusual water on the street or parkway, and getting sewer maintenance workers to watch for and report sewers with unusually high flow. If unusually high sewer flow is suspected to be due to a water leak, the flow can sometimes be traced upstream until a section is found with heavy flow in one manhole and low flow in the next, indicating that the leak must be entering somewhere between them. Leak locations can also occasionally be identified by a sunken piece of pavement or a particularly lush growth of grass in an area.

If the ground is sand or gravel, locating small leaks can be difficult because the water is directly dissipated. One method that may work under some conditions is to use an infrared thermometer gun. The gun can instantly read the temperature of the ground surface at a distance of about 3 ft (1 m), so by reading the temperature of the ground over a water line, a subtle change in temperature caused by the leaking water may be noted.

Listening Devices

Listening devices can be used to locate leaks by detecting the sound caused by escaping water. In general, the smaller the leak, the higher the pitch the sound will be. One mechanical device that has been used by water system operators for many years is the aquaphone, which is like the receiver of an old-fashioned telephone with a metal spike protruding from where the telephone wire should go. The spike can be placed against a metal pipe, meter, or fire hydrant and sounds are amplified surprisingly well. Aquaphones continue to be used because they are inexpensive, trouble free, and fit in a worker's pocket.

The problem with simple amplifiers is that they amplify all sounds equally, including traffic, wind, and any other noises in the area. More accurate sound detection of leaks can be accomplished using an amplifier that can reduce the band of unwanted sound frequencies and enhance the frequency band of escaping water. More complete leak detection kits, such as the one shown in Figure 11-9, include equipment for listening for sounds on the ground surface as well as probes and direct contact devices to connect to hydrants, valves, and service boxes.

Firms specializing in contractual leak detection use even more sophisticated equipment. A leak technician checks for leaks on a section of main by feeding sound picked up by transducers into a computer (called a *correlator*) for analysis. The computer takes into account pipe size, pipe material, and other factors that affect the speed at

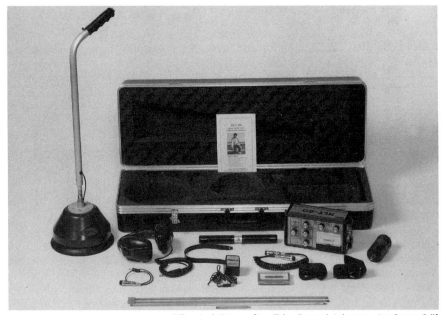

XLT-20 Leak Detector from Fisher Research Laboratory, Los Banos, Calif.

Figure 11-9 Portable electronic leak detection kit

which sound travels through the pipe. As illustrated in Figure 11-10, sound information obtained from two listening points can pinpoint a leak location quite accurately.

Leak Surveys

The simplest type of leak detection survey is to just listen for sounds of leaks on selected hydrants, and then follow up with a more complete survey in suspected areas. A very complete survey collects sound information from all hydrants, valves, and water services.

Leak surveys are best conducted at night when there is less traffic noise and lower flow in the mains. If it appears that a leak may be on a water service, the service should be shut off at the curb stop to determine whether there is a change in the sound. If there are wide gaps in the system with no hydrants or valves, metal rods may be driven down to contact the main and a listening device connected to the top of the rod.

If the suspected location of a leak is under pavement, it is often prudent to check further before completely opening the roadway. A small hole is drilled down to the main, and if there really is a leak at the location, the water will usually come to the surface through the hole.

Copper pipe transmits sound best, followed in order by steel, cast or ductile iron, plastic, asbestos–cement, and concrete. Unfortunately, mains with rubber gaskets will often not transmit sound much beyond the pipe length having the leak.

Water Audits

A water audit is a combination of analyzing flow measurements and listening for leaks. The first step is to check all master meters measuring water entering the distri-

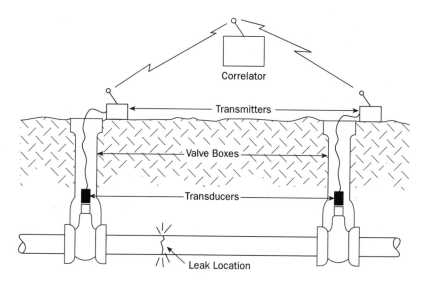

Figure 11-10 Pinpointing a leak from data provided by two transducers

bution system to make sure they are accurate. Any large industrial meters on customer water services are also checked, and all unmetered uses must be identified.

The system is then divided into districts, and temporary flowmeters are installed in mains at the entry point to each district. The night use in all districts is then compared, and the districts with the highest use that cannot be accounted for are targeted for further study. In some cases, a targeted district may be further broken down into smaller areas for individual flow study. Finally, the areas that are suspected of having leaks are checked using listening devices.

Emergency Repairs

The degree of emergency in making distribution repairs varies by how serious the problem is, where the problem is, and the weather conditions. A large main break must obviously be taken care of as quickly as possible. A small service leak can often be guarded and repair deferred a day or two if necessary in summer, but in winter it may have to be repaired immediately to prevent dangerous icing conditions. Various other degrees of emergency also exist. The bottom line is that the distribution crew must be prepared and organized to quickly, efficiently, and safely perform in the worst-case situation.

Emergency Repair Preparations

In the event of a major emergency, every minute counts, so the better organized the work crew is, the sooner workers will arrive at the site and start repairs. The starting point is to make sure workers are available to respond at all times. If everyone on the distribution crew has gone on vacation and there is a major main break, the system could be completely drained before someone is found to shut valves to isolate the leak. For this reason, most water utilities have a system where at least two key personnel are always on call at night and on weekends. The duty is rotated, and the persons on duty must be accessible by phone. In many cases, the person on call is allowed to take the emergency service truck home so that a response can be made without delay. It should be that person's responsibility to be sure the truck has a full fuel tank and all equipment is ready for use at the end of each day.

The best method of achieving immediate response is to have at least one service truck equipped with the essential tools and equipment required for emergency response. Among the items that should be included are valve keys, picks and shovels, hand tools and special wrenches, commonly used repair sleeves, barricades and warning signs, ladder, bucket, boots, rope, flashlights, hardhats, and other safety gear. A dewatering pump, generator with floodlights, and can of gasoline for the pump and generator should also be carried. Other important items are copies of maps and records showing main, valve, hydrant, and service locations. A valve-box locator will also facilitate finding valve boxes, particularly if there is snow on the ground.

Some means must be established to make sure the items to be carried on the truck are not borrowed and inadvertently not returned. Among the methods used is to have a special place on the truck for each item, or to paint all of the tools for the emergency truck a special color.

Having a regular program of valve and hydrant exercising and inspection is also part of preparing for an emergency. Being able to quickly locate valves and having them operate easily can greatly facilitate shutting down a main break. Systems without a valve inspection program often have to shut several valves before they can find a combination that will work properly and shut tightly, which significantly delays the repair work.

It is best to consider various emergency scenarios, and plan equipment and procedures for each one. If, for instance, repair parts are not kept in stock for all sizes and types of water pipe in the system, a supply house or other water utility must have the parts and be accessible at any time. It is also wise to have interconnections in place with adjoining water systems and agreements on when water may be used.

Special thought and planning should be given to providing employees with proper personal safety equipment and equipment that might be required for confined space entry, trench wall stabilization, and public safety. Water quality testing and sampling as part of an emergency repair procedure needs special attention and training.

Repair Procedures

The first three tasks in repairing a main break are (1) locate the valves that must be closed to isolate the section, (2) notify the customers that their water service will be off for a period of time, and (3) call the local "dig safe" system to have the other utilities locate their pipes and cables at the location to be excavated. If enough workers are available, one crew can start closing valves while another crew is notifying customers. The customers should be advised to draw some drinking water, provided with an estimate of how long the water will be off, and advised not to wash clothes if the water is discolored after it is turned back on.

Common practice is to close all but one valve as quickly as possible and leave the last one partially open until the last minute before repair is to be made. If possible, a leak should be repaired without completely shutting off pressure to reduce the possibility of dirty water flowing into the main through the break. Maintaining some pressure in the main also reduces the possibility of water draining from customer services. After all preparations have been made for installing the repair sleeve, the last valve that has been kept partially open can be closed further so that water continues to flow from the break at a nominal rate.

The excavation for repairing a water main or service leak should normally be parallel to the pipeline and located to one side to allow a worker to stand next to the pipe while making the repair. The excavation should not be made too small in an attempt to save time. If the pipe is buried 5 ft (1.5 m) or more deep, the opening must be about the size of a grave excavation in order for a person to work properly. It usually helps to dig a sump hole a little deeper than the bottom of the rest of the excavation, and locate it in a corner as far away from the main break as possible. The pump suction hose can then be placed in the sump to keep the excavation as free of water as possible.

Repair sleeves of the type shown in Figure 11-11 are most commonly used to repair beam break or to plug holes in corporation stops. Sleeves should be kept on hand to fit the outside diameter of each type of pipe installed on the system.

Installation of a sleeve includes first scraping and wire brushing the exterior of the main to remove as much corrosion and dirt as possible. The pipe and repair sleeve should then be disinfected by spraying or daubing with 5 percent sodium hypochlorite (ordinary store bleach). The sleeve is then installed around the pipe adjacent to the break, slid into position, and rotated to make sure the skived edge is not folded under. Particular care must be taken to prevent foreign matter from being caught between the pipe and gasket.

Although the sleeve nuts can be tightened with a large pair of pliers, this requires an unnecessarily long time, especially because it is prudent to do the job and leave the ditch as quickly as possible. As illustrated in Figure 11-12 several types of long sockets and special wrenches are available for use to quickly tighten the sleeve bolts.

After the sleeve is tightened, pressure should be restored by partially opening one valve to make sure there is no leakage before the excavation is backfilled. The line should then be flushed to remove any air and dirt that may have entered the pipe during the repair, and the line should be chlorinated to reduce the danger of contamination. If pressure has been completely shut off at any time during the repair, bacteriological samples should be collected for analysis to make sure the main has not been contaminated.

Figure 11-11 Pipe repair devices   *Courtesy of The Ford Meter Box Company, Inc.*

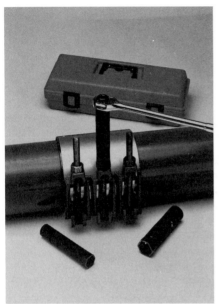

Courtesy of Wheeler Manufacturing;
Division of Rex International USA, Inc.

Figure 11-12 Ratchet wrench with a deep socket for tightening repair sleeve bolts

FIELD DATA FOR MAIN BREAK EVALUATION

DATE OF BREAK _____ TIME _____ A.M. _____ P.M.

TYPE OF MAIN _____ SIZE _____ JOINT _____ COVER ___ FT___ IN ___

THICKNESS AT POINT OF FAILURE _____ IN.

NATURE OF BREAK: Circumferential ☐ Longitudinal ☐ Circumferential & Longitudinal ☐
Blowout ☐ Joint ☐ Split at Corporation ☐ Sleeve ☐ Miscellaneous _____ ☐

APPARENT CAUSE OF BREAK: Water Hammer (surge) ☐   Defective Pipe ☐ Corrosion ☐
Deterioration ☐   Improper Bedding ☐   Excessive Operating Pressure ☐
Differential Settlement ☐ Temp. Change ☐ Contractor ☐ Misc. _____ ☐

STREET SURFACE: Paved ☐ Unpaved ☐   TRAFFIC: Heavy ☐ Medium ☐ Light ☐

TYPE OF STREET SURFACE _____ SIDE OF STREET: Sunny ☐ Shady ☐

TYPE OF SOIL _____ RESISTIVITY_____ ohms/cm
ELECTROLYSIS INDICATED: Yes ☐ No ☐   CORROSION: Outside ☐ Inside ☐
CONDITIONS FOUND: Rocks ☐ Voids ☐   PROXIMITY TO OTHER UTILITIES_____
DEPTH FROST ___ IN.   DEPTH OF SNOW ___ IN.

OFFICE DATA FOR MAIN BREAK EVALUATION

WEATHER CONDITIONS PREVIOUS TWO WEEKS
SUDDEN CHANGE IN AIR TEMP.? Yes ☐ No ☐ TEMP___°F RISE___°F FALL ___°F
WATER TEMP. SUDDEN CHANGE: Yes ☐ No ☐ TEMP___°F RISE___°F FALL ___°F
SPEC. OF MAIN _____ CLASS OR THICKNESS _____ LAYING LENGTH _____ FT

                    OPERATING   PREVIOUS BREAK
DATE LAID _____   PRESSURE _____   PSI REPORTED_____

INITIAL INSTALLATION DATA
TRENCH PREPARATION: Native Material _____ ☐ Sand Bedding ☐ Gravel Bedding ☐

BACKFILL: Native Material ☐ DESCRIBE _____ Bank Run Sand & Gravel ☐

Gravel ☐ Sand ☐ Crushed Rock ☐ OTHER _____ ☐

SETTLEMENT: Natural ☐ Water ☐ Compactors ☐ Vibrators ☐ OTHER _____ ☐

ADDITIONAL DATA FOR LOCAL UTILITY

LOCATION OF BREAK _____ MAP NO. _____
REPORTED BY _____
DAMAGE TO PAVING AND/OR PRIVATE PROPERTY _____
REPAIR MADE (Materials, Labor, Equipment) _____
REPAIR DIFFICULTIES (if any) _____
INSTALLING CONTRACTOR _____

Figure 11-13 Report of a water main failure

Record Keeping

A detailed record should be kept of every break or leak that is repaired. If it can be determined, the cause should be recorded, such as beam break, pipe split, blowout, joint leak, or failure due to corrosion. If any old pipe is removed during the repair, a piece of it should be tagged and kept for future reference on the condition of the pipe interior and exterior. A simple form for use in recording main breaks is shown in Figure 11-13.

Emergency Repair Safety

Safety for both workers and the public must not be ignored in the haste to stop the flow of water and restore service to customers. To put it in perspective, a few gallons of wasted water is nothing in comparison to a person's life. Time must be taken to direct traffic and keep onlookers, especially children, away from the excavation. Time must also be taken to properly install sheeting or shoring if necessary to protect workers from excavation wall cave-in.

Water System Corrosion

For the purpose of water works discussion, corrosion primarily refers to the deterioration of metal pipes, but also includes other types of pipe, such as the disintegration of A–C pipe under certain conditions. Plastic pipe is essentially immune to both internal and external corrosion.

Internal Corrosion

Internal corrosion of pipe is caused by corrosive water flowing through the pipe. In addition to the effects on unlined cast-iron and steel mains, corrosive water will also corrode the interiors of steel water tanks, metal water service lines, as well as building interior piping and appliances. Ductile-iron and steel pipe is now lined to prevent corrosion, and steel water tanks are generally protected by a coating or provided with cathodic protection.

In recent years, the potential adverse health effects of lead and copper leached from water service lines and customer plumbing has prompted federal regulations under the Lead and Copper Rule. The regulation requires all water systems to monitor for the presence of lead and copper in drinking water samples from customer taps and, if excessive levels are found, the system must add treatment to reduce the corrosiveness of the water. The treatment may consist of changing the water chemistry, such as altering the pH of the water, or by the addition of a chemical, phosphate, for example, that will form a protective layer inside the pipe.

External Corrosion

External corrosion is caused by either chemical or electrical conditions in the soil surrounding the pipe. The corrosiveness of soil can vary widely from one area of the country to another, sometimes even within the same community. In general, A–C and concrete pipe will suffer harmful corrosion only under very corrosive soil conditions. Ductile-iron pipe does not require protection under normal soil conditions, but if the pipe is to be installed in corrosive soil, a PE wrap should be loosely installed around the pipe to prevent corrosion. Steel pipe must have a heavy protective coating under all soil conditions, and is usually provided with cathodic protection.

Some conditions that are likely to increase the corrosiveness of soil include
• high moisture content
• poor aeration
• fine soil texture, such as clay or silty materials
• low electrical resistivity
• high organic content, such as in a swamp
• high chloride or sulfate content
• high acidity or high alkalinity
• presence of sulfide
• presence of anaerobic bacteria

Corrosion cells are typically created in metallic pipe by surface impurities, such as nicks, or impurities in the metal. The corrosion usually takes the form of pits in an otherwise relatively undisturbed pipe surface. The pits may eventually penetrate the pipe wall.

Another type of external corrosion is caused by direct current that leaves its intended circuit, collects on a pipeline, and discharges into the soil. The problem was primarily caused by trolley cars when they were operating in many older cities (Figure 11-14). Although there are no longer many trolley lines in operation, the same type of stray-current corrosion may occur from some other sources, such as cathodic current being applied to other nearby structures, for example, natural gas pipelines, as well as current from subway trains.

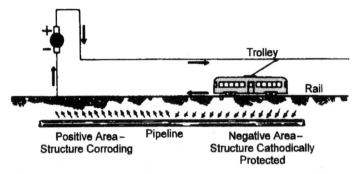

Positive Area –   Pipeline   Negative Area –
Structure Corroding   Structure Cathodically
                                           Protected

Figure 11-14 Stray-current corrosion resulting from an electric trolley car

Corrosion caused by stray current often appears as deep pits concentrated in a relatively small area of the pipe. Stray-current corrosion is rather complicated, so if it is suspected as affecting water distribution piping, it is best to seek professional assistance.

Bimetallic Corrosion

Bimetallic corrosion is most often seen in the plumbing systems of buildings. It is caused by the connection of two electrochemically different metals, such as a brass fitting to a galvanized iron pipe. The two metals form a corrosion cell (galvanic cell) that results in loss of the anodic metal (the iron pipe) and protection of the cathodic metal (the brass fitting).

The galvanic series for common waterworks metals is shown in Table 11-2. Each metal may be corroded by any metal below it in the series. The greater the separation between the metals, the more potential and rapid the corrosion process will be. If dissimilar metals must be connected together, an insulating coupling should be installed between them.

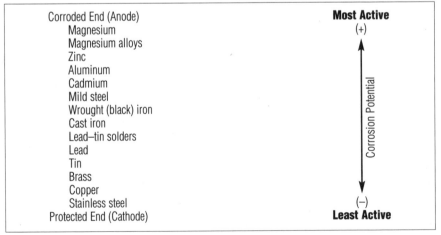

Corroded End (Anode)	**Most Active**
Magnesium	(+)
Magnesium alloys	
Zinc	
Aluminum	
Cadmium	
Mild steel	
Wrought (black) iron	
Cast iron	
Lead–tin solders	
Lead	
Tin	
Brass	
Copper	
Stainless steel	(−)
Protected End (Cathode)	**Least Active**

Table 11-2 Galvanic series for metals used in water systems

Bibliography

AWWA Manual M17, Installation, Field Testing, and Maintenance of Fire Hydrants. 1989. Denver, Colo.: American Water Works Association.

AWWA Manual M19, Emergency Planning for Water Utility Management. 1994. Denver, Colo.: American Water Works Association.

AWWA Manual M27, External Corrosion—Introduction to Chemistry and Control. 1986. Denver, Colo.: American Water Works Association.

AWWA Manual M28, Cleaning and Lining Water Mains. 1987. Denver, Colo.: American Water Works Association.

AWWA Manual M36, Water Audits and Leak Detection. 1999. Denver, Colo.: American Water Works Association.

Conducting Hydrant Flow Tests video. 1993. Denver, Colo.: American Water Works Association.

Corrosion Control for Operators. 1986. Denver, Colo.: American Water Works Association.

Distribution System Maintenance Techniques. 1987. Denver, Colo.: American Water Works Association.

Fire Hydrant and Water Main Maintenance Training Package. 1991. Denver, Colo.: American Water Works Association.

Jordan, J.K. 1990. *Maintenance Management.* Denver, Colo.: American Water Works Association.

Leaks in Water Distribution Systems. 1987. Denver, Colo.: American Water Works Association.

Maintaining Distribution System Water Quality. 1985. Denver, Colo.: American Water Works Association.

Chapter 12

Water Services

A water service is the pipeline that carries water from the utility's water mains to the consumer's building or other point of use.

Service Line Design

Water services are typically designed in two ways in regard to meter placement—with the meter located in a pit close to the main or with the meter located at the building.

Meters Located in Basements

In parts of the country that never experience freezing, meters can be located almost anywhere. Some utilities in the southern United States allow meters to be installed in garages or on the sides of buildings, as long as they are reasonably protected from damage and vandalism.

Where buildings have basements, the meter is usually located in the basement. As illustrated in Figure 12-1, the service pipe is usually placed under the footing so it will be below the frost line. The meter should be located as close as possible to where the pipe enters the building to avoid any temptation to the customer to install an illegal connection ahead of the meter. The curb stop is used for turning off the service for repair or nonpayment of bills. The curb stop with box is normally installed at a point in the parkway or on the property line. It should not be on the customer's property.

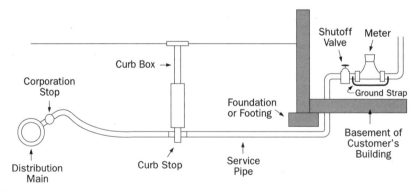

Figure 12-1 Small service connection with the meter located in a basement

126

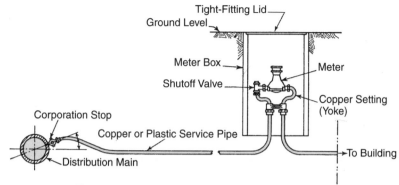

Figure 12-2 Small service connection with shallow meter box

In communities where the policy is to install meters in the basements of all building having basements, a special problem arises as to where to locate meters in buildings without basements. Some utilities require that meters for these buildings be installed in meter pits or boxes. Some utilities will allow the meter to be installed in a crawl space or utility closet, but this generally creates difficult meter reading and meter replacement problems.

Meters Installed in Meter Boxes

In warmer climates, where the water service does not have to be very deep, it is common to install all meters in meter boxes. The meter box is usually located in the parkway between the curb and sidewalk. The box may be a vitrified or concrete tile, or may be made of cast iron or plastic. Figure 12-2 illustrates a meter box installation.

In northern climates, where the service must be buried quite deep, the meter must be located in a larger enclosure, usually called a meter pit. As long as a pit has a tight-fitting cover, the meter can be raised relatively close to the surface to facilitate reading without danger of freezing because heat from the warmer ground at the bottom circulates within the pit (Figure 12-3).

One of the reasons many water systems originally standardized on installing meters in boxes instead of in buildings was to facilitate meter reading. Manual reading of the meters in pits is much faster than going inside each building for reading. Now, with the various types of electronic meter reading devices that can be installed on meters, this need no longer be an issue.

Other advantages of meter boxes are that the meters can be replaced without entering the building and there is less likelihood of customers tampering with the meters. Two major disadvantages of pits used in colder climates are that they may be difficult to locate and expose when covered with snow, and they are often filled with water that may have to be pumped out before the meter can be read.

Service Line Size

The size of the water service line necessary to properly serve a building generally depends on the following factors: the number of water-using appliances, water

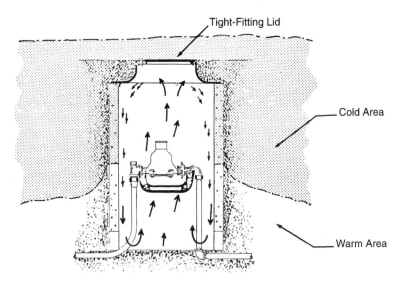

Figure 12-3 Cold-climate meter installation

pressure, and the distance between the main and the building. Average single-family homes are normally adequately served with a ³/₄-in. (20-mm) service, and larger homes having several bathrooms with a 1-in. (25-mm) service. If water pressure is low or the building is set far back from the main, the service size should be increased to compensate for friction loss in the piping.

The size of water service for larger buildings depends in part on the use pattern. Hospitals, for instance, use larger quantities of water, 24 hours a day. Some industries may have heavy use at some times, and almost none at others. Probably the ultimate in uneven use is in military barracks, where everyone wakes up at the same time in the morning and every shower and toilet is in use simultaneously. Additional information on sizing water services can be obtained from AWWA Manual M22, *Sizing Water Service Lines and Meters.*

Service Line Materials

The types of material used for small service lines include lead, galvanized iron, copper, and several types of plastic. Services over 2 in. (50 mm) in diameter are usually the same as water main materials.

Lead Pipe

Lead pipe has been used for transporting water since Roman times because it is relatively strong and long lasting. It is also flexible so it will not be affected by ground movement. The word *plumber* comes from the Latin word for lead, *plumbum.* The connection of lead pipe to fittings was done by partially melting the lead in a process called *wiping,* which required considerable skill by plumbers.

Use of lead for water services gradually decreased as other materials became available and the cost of lead became proportionally higher. Most older water systems still have many lead services in use. Lead services that must be repaired can be connected to newer type materials using a special mechanical fitting, but most utilities have established a policy that a lead service that has broken or is leaking must be completely replaced with new material. Many water utilities have also established a policy that, if a street is to be repaved, all lead services under the street must be replaced as part of the project. One reason for this is that some old lead becomes brittle and may leak if disturbed. Another reason for lead service replacement is new evidence that lead leached from plumbing could present a health risk, particularly to small children.

Galvanized Iron Pipe

Many older water systems allowed the use of galvanized iron pipe as a less expensive substitute for lead as a water service material. Because the pipe is rigid, it was usually connected to the corporation stop with a lead gooseneck a few feet long to provide flexibility at the connection to the main.

The life of galvanized pipe varies widely depending on water quality and soil conditions. Some very old galvanized services continue to provide good service, but if they are disturbed for any reason, they will usually start to leak. Repair of an old galvanized pipe is not usually successful in the long run, so most utilities insist that a leaking galvanized service pipe be completely replaced. There is also concern by many people over the possible adverse health effects of lead leached from the lead goosenecks, so some systems are replacing galvanized services for this reason.

Another problem with galvanized pipe is that direct connection of brass valves and other fittings often creates a galvanic action that hastens corrosion of the pipe at the connection.

Copper Tubing

Beginning shortly before World War II, copper tubing became popular as a replacement for lead and galvanized pipe for water services. The material is flexible, easy to install, corrosion resistant in all but the most corrosive soil, able to withstand high pressure, and not excessively expensive. Other advantages are that there is no serious reaction between the copper and connected brass valves and fittings, and the service lines are easy to locate with an electronic locator.

Very corrosive water may dissolve enough copper from copper tubing to cause stains on plumbing fixtures, but water systems that might have this problem generally must treat the water to reduce corrosivity for other reasons. Although copper tubing used in interior plumbing is usually joined with solder joints, copper that is buried is usually joined by either flare or compression joints (Figure 12-4).

Plastic Tubing

Plastic material used for water services must not soften and swell or become brittle and crack over time. It also must be a material that will not be attacked by underground rodents and will not leach harmful chemicals into the water. Three types of plastic are now generally used for water service—polyvinyl chloride (PVC), polyethylene, and polybutylene. All plastic pipe and tubing to be used for potable water must be tested by an approved laboratory to meet National Sanitation Foundation (NSF) International standards to ensure that chemicals will not leach from the

Flare Fittings

Compression Fittings
Courtesy of The Ford Meter Box Company, Inc.

Figure 12-4 Fittings for water service pipe

plastic and cause tastes or odors, or present a health threat. The NSF approval must be printed along the exterior of the tubing.

Plastic tubing has a very smooth interior, is relatively flexible, and very light-weight, which makes it easy to install. Valves and other accessories are connected to plastic tubing using brass fittings similar to those used for copper tubing.

Plastic tubing is covered in several AWWA standards in the C900 series.

Curb Stops and Boxes

Every water service should have a shutoff valve so that the service line may be easily turned off for repairs or nonpayment of the water bill.

Curb Stops

The valve commonly installed as the main shutoff for a water service is called a *curb valve* or *curb stop*. The type of valve that has been used for this service for many years is the inverted plug style (Figure 12-5). An inverted plug valve that has not been used for many years may be rather stiff, but can usually be made to

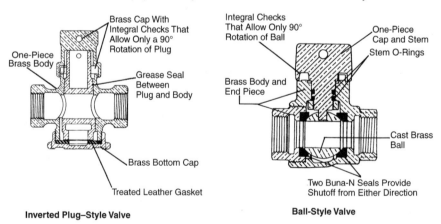

Inverted Plug–Style Valve

Ball-Style Valve

Courtesy of A.Y. McDonald Mfg. Co., Dubuque, Iowa.

Figure 12-5 Principal styles of curb stops

operate. There are problems in operating a very old valve on a lead or galvanized-iron service because the twisting action on the valve is likely to initiate a leak on the adjoining service pipe.

The newer style curb stop with a ball valve operates very easily, even after many years of nonuse. Curb stops are available with a variety of piping connections. The type with female pipe thread connections requires a connector to adapt to the type of pipe being used. Stops are also available with flare and compression couplings for direct connection to the service line.

If the water meter for a service is located in a box or pit, the curb stop is usually located just ahead of the meter so it will be accessible through the box. A standard curb stop or a special meter valve may be used.

Curb Boxes

If the meter is located in the building, the stop is fitted with a box so that it may be operated with a special valve key. There are two styles of boxes in general use in the United States (Figure 12-6). The arch-style box sits loosely over the top of the stop. The Minneapolis-style box has threads at the bottom that screw onto special threads on the top of a Minneapolis-style curb stop.

Each style has some advantages and disadvantages. If the arch-style box is used in loose soil, some soil may work up into the box from the bottom. It is also possible for the box to shift so that the key will not fit on the valve. On the other hand, if the box is disturbed, the service line will usually be unaffected.

The Minneapolis-style connection eliminates the possibility of filling with soil or mis-alignment. The one disadvantage is that if there is any serious damage to the box, such as its being inadvertently being pulled up by construction equipment, the service line will come right along with it.

Various styles of lids are available for curb boxes. Most of them use a pentagon nut that can only be operated by a special wrench to discourage unauthorized persons from removing the lid. It is particularly important to keep children from opening the lid, because if they do, their next motivation is usually to drop stones into the box. Water systems generally standardize on a particular style of box and insist that they be used for all new construction and repair.

Arch-pattern curb box and curb stop   Minneapolis-style curb stop

Courtesy of The Ford Meter Box Company, Inc,   *Courtesy of A.Y. McDonald Mfg. Co., Dubuque, Iowa.*

Figure 12-6 Styles of curb stops and boxes

Valve keys having a slotted end to engage the top of curb stops are available in various lengths to match the standard depth of services. A key is generally easiest to use if it projects to about waist height when it is being used. Most water systems inadvertently end up with some services that are much deeper than normal, usually because fill dirt was added to the properties after the services were installed. It is therefore good practice to have one extra-long key available.

Water service valves and fittings are covered in AWWA Standard C800-89, *Underground Service Line Valves and Fittings.*

Water Service Taps

If the pressure in a water main can be easily turned off, a connection for a water service can be made by drilling a hole in the pipe and either threading the hole to insert a fitting or placing a saddle with fittings over the hole (dry tap). It is, though, usually far more convenient to make the connection while the main is pressurized (wet tap). Besides being much more convenient, a wet tap is also preferred because there is less chance of contamination entering the main.

Water services have traditionally been connected to the water main through a

Corporation stops with different pipe connections
Courtesy of The Ford Meter Box Company, Inc.

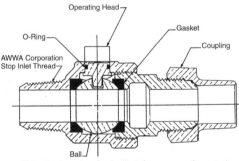

Principal parts of a ball-style corporation stop
Courtesy of A.Y. McDonald Mfg. Co., Dubuque, Iowa.

Figure 12-7 Corporation stops

special brass valve called a corporation stop (Figure 12-7). The valve serves two functions. It provides a means of connecting to the main, and allows the water to be turned off until the service line is completed and ready for use. It also provides a means of turning off the connection if the service is ever discontinued or is to be completely replaced with new piping.

When small taps are to be made on ductile-iron pipe, they are usually made by direct insertion. A hole is drilled in the pipe, threads are made in the hole, and the corporation stop is screwed into the hole as illustrated in Figure 12-8. Corporation stops that are to be used for direct insertion have a thread called an *AWWA thread*, which has more of a taper than standard pipe thread so that it will quickly tighten as it is screwed into the pipe. Corporation stops are available with either plug- or ball-type valves, and with various end connections.

Direct insertion may also be used for connecting service to asbestos–cement (A–C) and PVC mains, but the work must be done very carefully. Because of the steep taper in the corporation stop threads, excessive tightening of the valve as it is

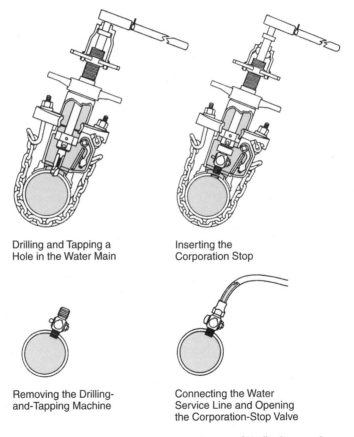

Drilling and Tapping a
Hole in the Water Main

Inserting the
Corporation Stop

Removing the Drilling-
and-Tapping Machine

Connecting the Water
Service Line and Opening
the Corporation-Stop Valve

Courtesy of Mueller Company, Decatur, Ill.

Figure 12-8 Steps in making a service tap

Courtesy of The Ford Meter Box Company, Inc.

Figure 12-9 Some styles of service clamps

inserted can either damage the pipe or strip the threads. For this reason, many operators prefer to install all services on A–C and PVC pipe through a saddle.

Pipe manufacturers suggest that all taps larger than 1 in. (25 mm) made on any type of pipe 6 in. (150 mm) or smaller should be made through a saddle. Manufacturer's recommendations should be consulted if a direct tap is to be made in a larger-diameter main.

Various types of service clamps or saddles are available, with each size designed for only a limited range of pipe outside diameter (Figure 12-9). If a saddle tap is to be made on old pipe, the diameter of the pipe should be measured before the clamp is ordered. A saddle tap is made by installing the corporation stop on the clamp, and then drilling a hole in the main through the open valve as illustrated in Figure 12-10. Special service connectors for PVC pipe are also available that incorporate a built-in drill and valve as a complete unit (Figure 12-11).

Tap Location

It is generally recommended that the best location for the tap on a main is at an angle of about 45° down from the top of the main. A tap at the top of the main is more likely to draw trapped air into the service line, and a tap near the bottom of the pipe is likely to draw in sediment. The service pipe should be laid in an S-curve down from the tap so that there is plenty of slack to allow for earth settlement and pipe expansion and contraction.

Service Pipe Installation

Water service pipes must be installed below the deepest frost line anticipated for the area. They are particularly prone to freezing at night when water is not moving. The most likely places for a service to freeze is where there is no snow cover, such as under the street, sidewalk, or driveway.

In southern locations, pipe can often be installed deep enough using a trenching machine. In northern areas, a backhoe must usually be used to provide a trench that is deep enough. The pipe can be installed under paved areas by jacking a pilot pipe or by using a portable boring machine (Figure 12-12).

Plastic pipe has a relatively high coefficient of expansion so the pipe should be installed with ample slack as it is placed in the ditch. If it is installed completely taut, the pipe may eventually pull out of a fitting as it contracts.

A. With the service clamp attached to the main, the corporation stop is threaded into the clamp. The machine is then mounted on the corporation stop, and the stop is opened.

B. The drill penetrates the main without water escaping.

C. The drill bit is retracted, and the corporation stop is closed. The stop now controls the water.

D. The machine is removed, the service line connected, and the corporation stop reopened to activate water service.

Courtesy of Mueller Company, Decatur, Ill.

Figure 12-10 Using a service clamp to install a corporation stop

Courtesy of DMD Division, Dresser Industries, Inc.

Figure 12-11 Service connector made for use with PVC pipe

Courtesy of Underground Equipment & Supply.

Figure 12-12 Boring machine

Water Service Maintenance and Repair

Leak and Break Repair

As discussed in chapter 11, water leaks in dense soil will usually either come to the surface or find their way into a sewer. If there is a question of whether or not there is a leak on a water service, the sound can usually be heard by listening on a valve key placed on the curb stop or on the meter. If it appears that the leak may be on the building side or the curb stop, the valve can be closed to determine whether the noise stops and the water stops flowing. In a location with porous soil, small leaks may not come to the surface where they will be noticed, so meter readers should be particularly vigilant in listening for leaks as they make their readings or inspections of the meter installations.

The most common location of leaks on old services is at the connections to the curb stop. This may be due either to the twisting of the valve as it is operated, or because of pressure on the curb box after heavy equipment has driven over it. An old service may also develop a leak after the adjacent soil has been disturbed, such as in the installation of a new sewer or gas line. Special fittings are available for repairing old lead and galvanized iron pipe, but once the pipe has been disturbed, there is a good chance it will leak again. It is usually best to replace the entire service with new material. If this is not possible, at least the entire leaking section should be replaced.

Thawing Frozen Services

The best way of preventing frozen services is to insist that all service piping be installed to below the recommended maximum frost depth for that part of the country. The most common cause of a shallow service is that the installing contractor did not comply with local requirements. The best policy is to insist on an inspection of the installation by a city or water utility inspector before the trench is backfilled. Some utilities go so far as to make the contractor reexcavate the trench if it is backfilled before inspection, to make sure the proper depth is maintained.

Continuous snow cover typically allows relatively little frost penetration in areas where the snow has not been disturbed. But at the same time, during a very cold winter, there can be several feet of frost in the ground under streets and driveways. The most common services to freeze are those that run under roadways.

A copper, lead, and galvanized-iron service can usually be thawed by running an electrical current through it. A portable source of direct current, such as a welding unit, is connected to the main and the service at the building, and will usually generate enough heat in the line to release the ice blockage. Electrical thawing can be dangerous and should only be performed by someone with experience.

One of the problems that can arise in electrical thawing is a point of poor conductivity in the service line connections. Another potential problem is if the service is in contact with another conductor, such as a gas pipe, which will divert the current and could cause it to enter other adjacent buildings. The current may also damage O-rings or gaskets in the service fittings. Thawing is a service performed by the utility or a contractor on the customer's property, so a waiver should be signed by the property owner, and there must be confirmation by the insurer that the person doing the work has adequate liability insurance in effect to cover any possible consequences of the work.

Hot-water thawing is becoming more common because it is less dangerous and can be used for plastic pipe. As illustrated in Figure 12-13, a plastic tube carrying hot water is fed into the service line and pushed against the ice blockage. The same process can also be used with a steam generator, but it should first be determined if the extreme heat might damage plastic pipe.

If only a meter or small section of service is frozen in a meter pit, it is best thawed using a hair dryer or heat gun. A propane torch should be used with extreme caution for thawing because of the possibility of igniting explosive gases in the pit and the potential of damaging fittings by overheating them. If the line is heated too quickly, there is also the danger of generating steam, which may have no place to escape, and could rupture the meter or piping.

After a frozen service pipe has been thawed, the only way to prevent it from freezing again is to open a faucet to allow a small, continuous flow until the ground has thawed. In that this could be several weeks or months, some water util-

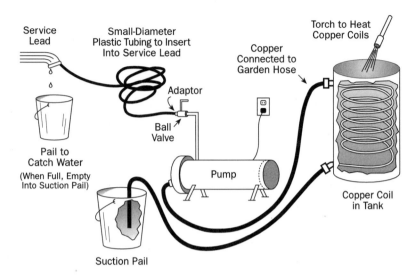

Adapted from drawing by Randal W. Loeslie, manager, G.F.-Traill Water Users, Inc., Thompson, N.D.

Figure 12-13 System for thawing plastic water line

ities will remove the meter or make allowance for the unusual water use when billing the customer.

Service Line Responsibility

Various municipalities and water utilities have different policies regarding responsibility for water services. If a policy does not exist, it is best to formally establish one so there will be no problem of convincing property owners of their responsibility when repairs are necessary. Each policy has advantages and disadvantages. Some of the more common policies are

- The entire water service is the responsibility of the property owner, from the main connection to the building. If any part of it leaks or breaks, it is their responsibility to pay for the repair.
- The portion of the service up to the property line is the water utility's responsibility and they will make any necessary repairs. The portion on private property is the responsibility of the property owner.
- The portion up to the curb stop or meter pit is the utility's responsibility and the remainder is up to the property owner.

Policies also vary on who does the work of installing a new service. A utility with its own tapping machine usually prefers to make the tap on the main to ensure that the work is done correctly, and the property owner is billed for the service. This is often combined with a tapping fee that covers all of the costs of establishing a new service, such as inspection, establishing a new billing account, the initial cost of the meter, and possibly reimbursement for a portion of the cost of the main installation.

Bibliography

AWWA Manual M22, Sizing Water Service Lines and Meters. 1975. Denver, Colo.: American Water Works Association.

AWWA Standard for Polyethylene (PE) Pressure Pipe and Tubing, ¹/₂ In. (13 mm) Through 3 In. (76 mm), for Water Service. ANSI/AWWA C901-96. 1996. Denver, Colo.: American Water Works Association.

AWWA Standard for Underground Service Line Valves and Fittings. ANSI/AWWA C800-89. 1989. Denver, Colo.: American Water Works Association.

Chapter 13

Water Meters

Water meters can be considered the cash registers of a public water system. It is important that meters be properly chosen, installed, maintained, and read to obtain the necessary revenue for water system operations.

Customer Service Meters

Almost all water systems in the United States meter water to all customers. A few utilities with relatively abundant water supplies still charge a flat rate to small customers. The advantage of the flat-rate practice is that there is a considerable saving in not having to furnish, read, and maintain meters for these customers. On the other hand, customers on a flat rate tend to waste water. They commonly water gardens excessively, let water run during the summer to keep it cool, and have no incentive to fix leaks in plumbing fixtures.

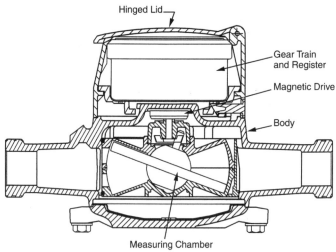

Hinged Lid

Gear Train
and Register

Magnetic Drive

Body

Measuring Chamber

Courtesy of Schlumberger Industries Water Division.

Figure 13-1 Nutating-disk meter with a plastic housing

140

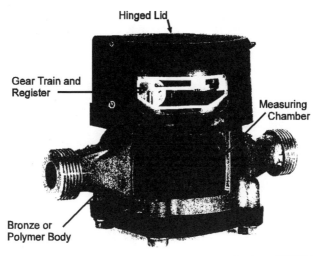

Figure 13-2 Piston meter

Courtesy of ABB Water Meters, Inc.

Positive-Displacement Meters

The meters used for measuring relatively low flow rates are called positive-displacement meters because they accurately measure all water that passes through them by means of a nutating disk or rotating piston. As illustrated in Figures 13-1 and 13-2, water passing past the disk or piston creates a rotary motion that is transmitted through gears to the register. The register then reads in gallons, cubic feet, or cubic metres.

Positive-displacement meters are usually used for residences and small to medium sized commercial establishments. The commonly used nominal sizes are from $\frac{5}{8}$ to 2 in. (16 to 50 mm) as listed in Table 13-1. Although maximum flow rates are shown,

Meter Size		Safe Max. Operating Capacity		Max. Pressure Loss at Safe Max. Operating Capacity		Recommended Max. Rate for Continuous Operations		Minimum Test Flow		Normal Test Flow Limits	
in.	(mm)	gpm	(m³/h)	psi	(kPa)	gpm	(m³/h)	gpm	(m³/h)	gpm	(m³/h)
½	(13)	15	(3.4)	15	(103)	7.5	(1.7)	¼	(0.06)	1–15	(0.2–3.4)
½ x ¾	(13 x19)	15	(3.4)	15	(103)	7.5	(1.7)	¼	(0.06)	1–15	(0.2–3.4)
⅝	(16)	20	(4.5)	15	(103)	10	(2.3)	¼	(0.06)	1–20	(0.2–4.5)
⅝ x ¾	(16 x19)	20	(4.5)	15	(103)	10	(2.3)	¼	(0.06)	1–20	(0.2–4.5)
¾	(19)	30	(6.8)	15	(103)	15	(3.4)	½	(0.11)	2–30	(0.5–6.8)
1	(25)	50	(11.4)	15	(103)	25	(5.7)	¾	(0.17)	3–50	(0.7–11.4)
1½	(38)	100	(22.7)	15	(103)	50	(11.3)	1 ½	(0.34)	5–100	(1.1–22.7)
2	(51)	160	(36.3)	15	(103)	80	(18.2)	2	(0.45)	8–160	(1.8–36.3)

Source: AWWA Standard C700-95.

Table 13-1 Characteristics of displacement-type meters

Courtesy of Schlumberger Industries Water Division.

Figure 13-3 A 1 ¹/₂-in. (40-mm) meter with flanged couplings

positive displacement meters are not intended to operate at full flow for extended periods of time. Continuous operation of a meter at full flow will quickly destroy it. A meter should ideally be sized so that the maximum flow rate will be one half of its maximum operating capacity. On the other hand, if a meter is greatly oversized, the customer will receive free water at flow rates that are too low to start the meter operating.

The threads on the ends of meters are the same spacing (pitch) as standard pipe thread, but there is no taper, in other words, they are the same diameter for the entire length of the thread. For this reason, they will not screw onto a regular threaded fitting, but are intended to be used with a special meter coupling designed to provide a seat against a gasket. The reason for using meter couplings is so that a meter can be simply replaced by loosening the nuts and sliding them out of the way. Meters that are 1¹/₂ and 2 in. (40 and 50 mm) are most commonly furnished with flanged meter couplings (Figure 13-3). Meter sizes and nominal dimensions are the same for all meters that conform to AWWA Standards (Figure 13-4).

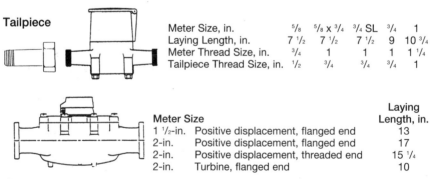

Meter Size, in.	⁵/₈	⁵/₈ x ³/₄	³/₄ SL	³/₄	1
Laying Length, in.	7 ¹/₂	7 ¹/₂	7 ¹/₂	9	10 ³/₄
Meter Thread Size, in.	³/₄	1	1	1	1 ¹/₄
Tailpiece Thread Size, in.	¹/₂	³/₄	³/₄	³/₄	1

Meter Size		Laying Length, in.
1 ¹/₂-in.	Positive displacement, flanged end	13
2-in.	Positive displacement, flanged end	17
2-in.	Positive displacement, threaded end	15 ¹/₄
2-in.	Turbine, flanged end	10

Figure 13-4 Small meter dimensions

Customers with high water bills often think their meter must be overregistering, but this is almost impossible for a positive-displacement meter. On the contrary, an old, worn meter will usually underregister and may not even start operating at nominal flow rates. Customers who insist on having their meter changed because they think it is running fast usually end up having even larger bills with the new meter. Almost all complaints of higher-than-normal water use can be traced to leaking toilets or other fixtures.

Small Meter Installation

As discussed in chapter 12, meters located in shallow meter boxes are usually installed with a curb stop directly ahead of them. Meter replacement is also greatly facilitated if a valve is installed past the meter. Without the second valve, the installer must enter the building to shut off water at the service entrance before the meter can be removed. Meters in deep pits are usually raised to within about 18 in. (46 cm) of the surface to facilitate reading.

Meters located in basements should ideally be located as close as possible to where the service enters through the floor or wall to discourage customers from installing a connection ahead of the meter. The meter should also be placed where it is relatively accessible for reading and repair. Even if the meter will have a remote reading device installed, it must be accessible for an inspector to periodically make a check reading and determine whether the meter should be repaired or replaced.

Several companies manufacture various styles of meter yokes to facilitate setting meters; examples are shown in Figure 13-5. Some of these devices have valves incorporated with them, and they automatically maintain the correct spacing for easy meter installation and replacement.

Although an AWWA policy statement discourages use of a water system as an electrical ground, many homes and buildings have the electric service grounded only to a water pipe. For this reason, many water utilities require an electrical jumper wire from the house piping to the service pipe so any electrical current will bypass the meter. If such jumpers are not installed, it is good practice for personnel replacing meters to carry jumper cables with alligator clips to install temporarily while the meters are changed.

The meter should always be mounted in a vertical position. Installing a meter in any other position will cause premature wear, and in some cases inaccurate readings.

Water Pilferage

Most water utilities find that there are some customers who, given an opportunity, will attempt to reduce their water bills by altering the meter readings. The common methods are to remove a register for part of the reading period or turn it backward, remove a meter and substitute a pipe nipple, or turn a meter around so it will run backward for part of the billing period.

To prevent this, meter seals should be installed on all meters. Although they will not prevent pilferage, they will show that some unauthorized tampering has taken place, and further action can be taken. Meter registers are generally sealed at the factory with a copper wire and an acrylic seal that cannot be removed without breaking the wire.

A meter coupling has a small hole that can be used for installing a copper wire

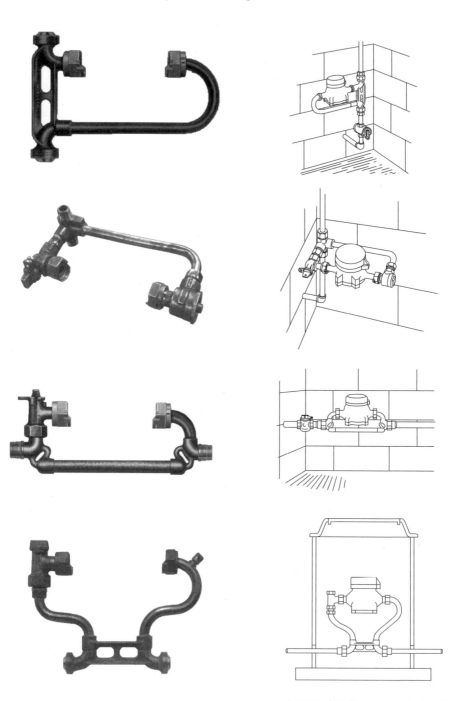

Courtesy of Mueller Company, Decatur, Ill.

Figure 13-5 Various styles of meter yokes

and seal to prevent unscrewing the coupling nuts without detection. Another device commonly used is a plastic shield that is clipped over the meter nuts and cannot be removed without breaking it.

Large Water Meters

For most large water services, the choice of meters usually lies among types of meters other than positive-displacement type.

Current Meters

Current meters are commonly called *velocity meters*. The principal types are turbine, multijet, and propeller meters.

A turbine meter has rotors turned by the flow of water (Figure 13-6). The volume of water passing through the meter is directly proportional to the revolutions of the rotor.

A multijet meter is similar, but has a multiblade rotor mounted on a vertical spindle within the measuring chamber. Water enters the chamber through several tangential orifices around the circumference and leaves the chamber through another set of orifices placed at a different level.

A propeller meter has a propeller turned by the flow of water, and the movement is transmitted to the register (Figure 13-7). On larger sizes, the propeller may be small in relation to the diameter of the pipe. Propeller meters are primarily used for main-line measurement where the flow rates do not change abruptly.

Turbine meters will underregister if the blades become clogged or coated with sediment, and multijet meters will underregister if the orifices become partially clogged. Such a meter can also be severely damaged by a hard object no larger than a pea. If there is a possibility of particles being in the water, a strainer should be installed ahead of the meter.

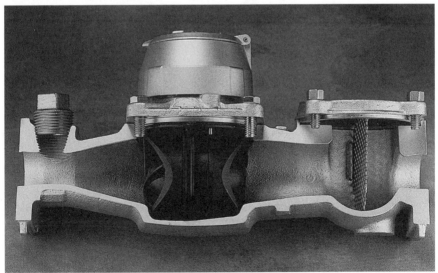

Courtesy of Badger Meter Inc., Milwaukee, Wis.

Figure 13-6 Turbine meter

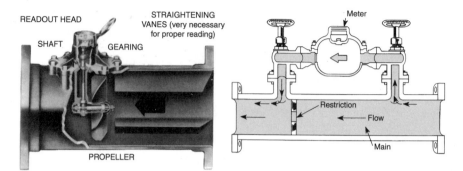

Figure 13-7 Propeller flowmeter   **Figure 13-8** Proportional flowmeter

Proportional Meters

A proportional meter has a restriction in the pipeline that forces a portion of the flow to pass through a small meter, as illustrated in Figure 13-8. The total flow is determined by reading the flow through the small meter and multiplying it by a factor.

Venturi Meters

In the venturi meter, there is a defined throat (constriction) within the meter body. As the flow is constricted by a decrease in the diameter, there is a proportional increase in flow velocity. The difference in pressure before the constriction and at the throat can be measured, as illustrated in Figure 13-9, and the change in pressure is proportional to the square of the velocity. The quantity of flow can be determined from the flow velocity, using electronic or mechanical instruments.

Venturi meters have the advantages of creating very little friction loss, requiring almost no maintenance, and being particularly useful on large pipelines. Their primary disadvantage is that they are accurate only for a specific flow range.

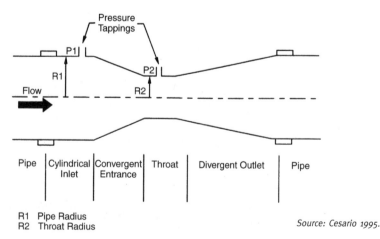

Source: Cesario 1995.

Figure 13-9 Schematic of a venturi meter

Orifice Meters

An orifice meter consists of a thin plate with a circular hole that is installed between a set of flanges (Figure 13-10). The flow rate is determined by a comparison between the pressure at taps on each side of the orifice plate in a fashion similar to that used for a venturi meter. An orifice is inexpensive and maintenance-free, but creates a relatively high head loss.

Magnetic Meters

A magnetic ("mag") meter measures flow by generating a magnetic field around an insulated section of pipe. Water passing through the field induces a small flow of electrical current that is proportional to velocity, and this is electronically converted to a registration of flow rate. Mag meters are most often used for measuring the flow of dirty or corrosive water that would damage other types of meters.

Ultrasonic Meters

An ultrasonic flow meter uses transducers to generate and receive sound pulses that are alternately sent in opposite diagonal directions across the flow of water. Because of the Doppler effect, the sound changes with the velocity of water flow, and this can be electronically converted to indicate flow rate.

Insertion Meters

An insertion meter provides a relatively inexpensive way of adding metering to an existing pipeline. The unit consists of a probe having a small rotor at the bottom that is inserted into the pipeline through a mounting on a saddle as shown in Figure 13-11. Units will mount in pipelines from $1\frac{1}{2}$ in. (40 mm) to 36 in. (0.9 m) or larger and have relatively good accuracy.

The electronic readout can either be mounted directly on the probe or at a remote location, and indicates both flow rate and total flow. Units are also available to provide either a 4-20 mA or pulse signal for use in operating a chart recorder or for pacing chemical feed equipment.

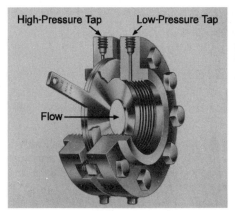

Courtesy of Bristol-Babcock Division, Acco Industries, Inc., Waterbury, Conn.

Figure 13-10 Orifice meter

Courtesy of Polysonics, Inc.

Figure 13-11 Insertion-type meter

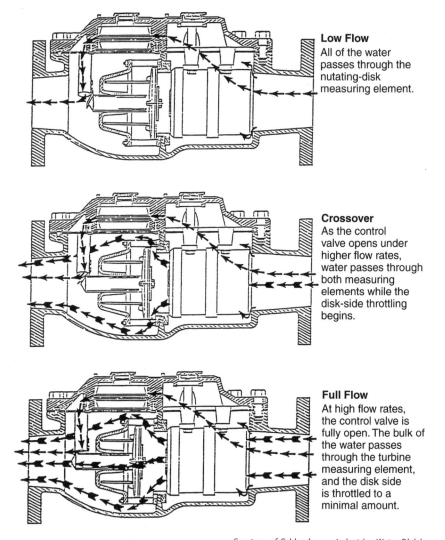

Low Flow
All of the water passes through the nutating-disk measuring element.

Crossover
As the control valve opens under higher flow rates, water passes through both measuring elements while the disk-side throttling begins.

Full Flow
At high flow rates, the control valve is fully open. The bulk of the water passes through the turbine measuring element, and the disk side is throttled to a minimal amount.

Courtesy of Schlumberger Industries Water Division.

Figure 13-12 Compound meter

Compound Meters

All meters have specified ranges over which they are acceptably accurate. Positive-displacement meters and propeller meters, for example, will not start to rotate until a certain velocity is reached. Other meters may register at flows below the suggested minimum accuracy point, but the reading may be only a fraction of actual flow.

Occasionally there are situations in which a customer has a wide variation in use and it is desired to meter all of the water accurately. An example would be a factory that uses only small amounts of water during the night but very large quantities during the day shifts. The best method of metering this type of customer is to use a compound meter.

A compound meter consists of both a large turbine meter and a small bypass meter. As illustrated in Figure 13-12, the water flows through the small meter until it reaches a certain velocity, then a valve actuates to divert flow through the turbine. Some compound meters have separate registers for each meter and others combine the readings onto one register. Another compound metering arrangement using two standard meters is shown in Figure 13-13.

Meter Accuracy

All meters that operate on the principle of determining flow velocity are designed with the assumption of laminar flow through the meter. Any disturbance, such as pipe bends or valves that might create eddies in the water, either before or after the meter, can cause the meter to be inaccurate. Every meter manufacturer has a recommendation for the minimum straight-pipe distance that should be maintained on either side of a meter. This is usually expressed as pipe diameters because it is dependent on the pipe size. In addition, some flowmeters have vanes ahead of the meter to help ensure straight-line flow as the water enters the meter.

Meter Reading

Early water meters were furnished with a *circular* or *round reading register* (Figure 13-14). These were difficult to read and it was easy for meter readers to make mistakes. It was also difficult for customers to read their own meters. This type of register has gradually been replaced by "straight reading" registers that are like the odometer on a car. Most registers have one or more fixed zeros as shown in black in Figure 13-14. Some larger meters also have a note on the register that a multiplier is to be used, such as "10X" or "100X."

Meters used in the United States are generally furnished with registers reading in either gallons or cubic feet, but meters are also available with registers for Imperial gallons or cubic metres.

Courtesy of ABB Water Meters, Inc.

Figure 13-13 Compound meter arrangement that uses two standard meters

Direct Meter Reading

Traditional meter reading involves a meter reader visiting each building and directly reading the meter. One of the few advantages of this system is that the meter reader can make a quick calculation as the meter is read and immediately alert the customer that there may be a leak if use has been greatly in excess of previous billing periods. However, water in the pits or snow cover may make direct reading of meters in pits difficult. If most meters are located inside buildings, however, there is a long list of problems.

Customers are increasingly reluctant to allow utility workers in their homes because of publicized reports of robbers or attackers gaining access by posing as utility representatives. The best way to combat this is to provide meter readers with identification and distinctive uniforms, and to try to keep the same people on each route so that customers get to know them.

Other reasons customers do not want meter readers entering their homes include dirty boots, they are embarrassed about the condition of themselves or their homes at the time, and they do not want to be bothered.

With increasing numbers of homes where everyone is working during weekdays, the only way of obtaining direct readings at these homes is to have a meter reader work on Saturday. There are also areas in some communities where, for a variety or reasons, the meter reader is reluctant to enter to make the reading.

To reduce some of these problems, many water systems are now using a doorknob card that asks the customer to read the meter and drop the postage-free card in the mail (Figure 13-15). Many customers who do not want to be bothered by the meter reader have standing orders to leave the cards. As long as customers promptly make the readings the system works well. If one reading is missed, the utility will usually send an estimated bill. If a second self-reading is missed, the meter should be read by the meter reader to verify that water use has been normal.

Because of the difficulty and time required to obtain direct meter readings, many water systems read and bill every three months (quarterly).

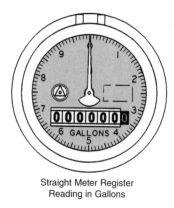

Straight Meter Register
Reading in Gallons

Circular Meter Register
Reading in Cubic Feet

Courtesy of Schlumberger Industries Water Division.

Figure 13-14 Meter registers

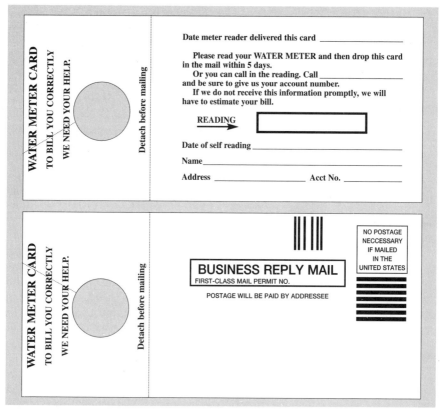

Figure 13-15 Water meter self-reading doorknob card

Remote Reading Devices

Remote reading devices have been developed to eliminate most of the problems associated with making direct readings inside buildings. The basic type uses a meter with a special register that creates a small electrical impulse at each 10 ft^3 or 100 gal. The register is connected with a pair of wires to the remote register that can be mounted at any convenient location on the outside of the building. The register advances one digit for each pulse it receives (Figure 13-16). The meter reader still carries a meter-reading book and records the numbers by hand.

The next advancement in remote meter reading uses a similar signal from the meter, but all that is mounted on the outside of the building is a special plug receptacle. The meter reader carries a special electronic unit that is plugged into the receptacle to obtain the reading. The reading may be displayed on a screen and electronically recorded for later direct entry into a computer.

A further refinement to this system is called *electronic meter reading*. It uses an inductive coil on the exterior of the building in place of the receptacle. The meter reader carries an electronic unit (interrogator) with a probe that only needs to be held in the proximity of the coil to obtain a reading. Power from the interrogator is

Courtesy of Schlumberger Industries Water Division.

Figure 13-16 Meter with remote register

Courtesy of Badger Meter Inc., Milwaukee, Wis.

Figure 13-17 Wall mount and pit receptacles and hand-held computer for reading meters with a radio signal

transmitted through the coil to a microprocessor in the meter, and the meter reading is transmitted back to the meter reader. The advantage of this system is that the same unit can be installed on meters in pits with the induction coil mounted under the lid so the meter reader does not have to open the pit to obtain a reading.

Automatic Meter Reading

The most recent advancement used by increasing numbers of utilities is called *automatic meter reading*. With this system, each meter has a small transmitter that will send the meter reading electronically on command. The methods used to send the interrogating signal and to receive the reading data include telephone lines, the electric power distribution system, sound transmission through the water mains, and the cable television system. Some trials with these systems have been in conjunction with other utilities so that electric and gas meter readings may also be transmitted back to a central location using the same system.

The other alternative that seems to be gaining increasing acceptance is to send the signal by radio. With one system, the meter reader only needs to walk down the street with a hand-held computer and enter the codes of adjacent meters to interrogate them. The meter readings are transmitted back and stored in the computer. Examples of interior and pit-mount meters and a hand-held computer are shown in Figure 13-17.

Another system has the computer mounted in a truck and obtains readings from adjacent buildings as it is driven. If a community is not too large, it may also be possible to mount an antenna on a high mast at a central location and obtain all meter readings from that location.

Besides the obvious advantage of saving labor, this system makes it practical to bill monthly, which has some financial advantages and presents the customers with regular, smaller bills. It also provides a means of easily performing water use studies, such as determining how much water is used by certain customers on high-use days.

The one caution about all remote or automatic reading systems is that the utility must not forget to occasionally inspect the meter. The general condition of the meter should be checked, the seals inspected for any sign of damage, and the register reading checked to be sure it matches the remote reading.

Meter Maintenance

Manufacturers usually test new meters before they are shipped, so many small communities do not retest them before installation. Some state public utility regulatory commissions require that a certain percentage of all new meters be tested. The limits of acceptable accuracy are dictated by AWWA standards.

Customer water meters gradually decrease in efficiency and underregister as a function of both wear from use and water quality. Because of the many variables, it is hard to set specific limits, but AWWA recommends that $5/8$-in. (17-mm) meters be tested every 10 years. Larger meters should be tested more often because of the greater loss of revenue if they are not registering correctly. Recommended testing intervals are provided in AWWA meter standards.

When meters are to be periodically tested, there are two procedures in common use. One is to remove the meter and replace it with a space pipe for a few days while the meter is tested and repaired if necessary, and then return to reinstall the same meter. This requires two trips and bothering the customer twice to gain entrance, but simplifies meter record keeping because the same meter is used at the address. The other method is to immediately replace the removed meter with a new or reconditioned meter, but this requires that both the meter records and the billing records be changed to show the new meter serial number and initial reading of the new meter.

Testing meters is not very complicated and requires a meter test bench with the components shown in Figure 13-18. Most test benches will test several meters at the same time. Meters are usually tested at high, medium, and low flow rates and checked to be in conformance with AWWA standards. Meters in need of repair must be disassembled, cleaned, and worn parts replaced as necessary. Specific instructions on meter repair should be obtained from the meter manufacturer. General information on meter repair is available in AWWA Manual M6, *Water Meters— Selection, Installation, Testing, and Maintenance.*

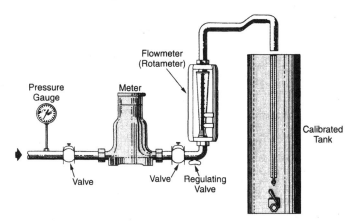

Figure 13-18 Meter-testing equipment

Another alternative to testing meters in-house is to send them to a local firm that specializes in this work. Because of the weight involved, it is not usually practical to ship meters a great distance for repair.

The third alternative that is used by many small water systems is simply to dispose of worn meters and replace them with new ones. This is particularly practical if it is also desired to change the style of meter or to start installing meters with new features, such as remote readout accessories. Some of the replacement cost can sometimes be recovered by selling removed meters to firms that specialize in reconditioning old meters.

It is essential that a water utility maintain good records of each meter installed on the system. Meter record keeping is discussed in chapter 20.

Bibliography

AWWA Manual M6, Water Meters—Selection, Installation, Testing, and Maintenance. 1986. Denver, Colo.: American Water Works Association.

AWWA Manual M22, Sizing Water Service Lines and Meters. 1975. Denver, Colo.: American Water Works Association.

AWWA Manual M33, Flowmeters in Water Supply. 1989. Denver, Colo.: American Water Works Association.

AWWA Standard for Cold-Water Meters—Displacement Type, Bronze Main Case. ANSI/AWWA C700-95. 1995. Denver, Colo.: American Water Works Association.

Cesario, L. 1995. *Modeling, Analysis, and Design of Water Distribution Systems.* Denver, Colo.: American Water Works Association.

Schlenger, D.L., and F. Gradilone III. 1992. *Automatic Meter Reading for the Water Industry.* Denver, Colo.: AWWA Research Foundation and American Water Works Association.

Chapter 14

Cross-Connection Control

Cross-Connection Terminology

Some of the terminology used in describing the problems and conditions relating to cross-connections follows.

Backflow is the flow of any water, foreign liquids, gases, or other substances back into a potable water system. There are two conditions that can cause backflow: backpressure and backsiphonage.

Backpressure is a condition in which the foreign substance is forced into a water system because it is under a higher pressure than the system pressure.

Backsiphonage is the condition under which the water system pressure is less than atmospheric (i.e., it is under vacuum), and the foreign substance is essentially sucked into the potable water system.

Cross-connection is any connection between a potable water system and any source of contamination through which contaminated water *could* enter the potable water system.

Public Health Significance

Water utilities go to great lengths to ensure that the water entering the system is properly treated and the distribution system is operated with care to prevent contamination. In spite of these efforts, many systems have some unknown cross-connections that could cause a disease outbreak, poisoning, or degraded water quality if certain conditions should occur.

Diseases and Poisonings Attributable to Cross-Connections

One of the most catastrophic results of a cross-connection occurred in two Chicago, Ill., hotels during the 1933 World's Fair. As a result of backsiphonage during a pressure loss in the system, drinking water was contaminated with amoebic dysentery germs and infected over 1,400 people. Of this number, at least 98 are known to have died directly from the disease.

Other diseases that have caused the deaths and illnesses of many people as a result of cross-connections are gastroenteritis, hepatitis, and salmonellosis. Many people have also become ill as a result of fertilizer, pesticides, herbicides, and boiler chemicals introduced into a water supply through a cross-connection.

Courtesy of USEPA, Region VIII, Water Supply Division.

Figure 14-1 Water tank cross-connection

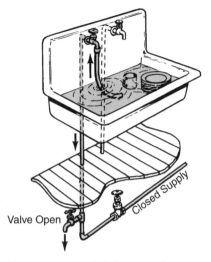

Figure 14-2 Backsiphonage (hose forms cross-connection)

Potential Cross-Connections

Situations in which some of the conditions for a cross-connection exist, but require something else to be done to complete the connection, are called *potential cross-connections*. In the examples shown in Figures 14-1 and 14-2, the end of the hose must be immersed in liquid for there to be a cross-connection. Although the likelihood is remote that there will be a vacuum on the water system just at the time the hose is submerged in liquid, the tank truck or sink could hold a toxic substance, and consequences of backsiphonage could be very serious.

One common cross-connection that almost everyone has seen is a chemical dispenser connected to a garden hose (Figure 14-3). If a vacuum should occur while the unit is in use, the chemical solution would be sucked back into the house plumbing.

Many potential locations for cross-connections exist in factories, restaurants, canneries, mortuaries, and hospitals. Any place where a water fill line is below the rim of a container, a cross-connection can exist. A summary of common cross-connections and potential hazards is presented in Table 14-1.

Figure 14-4 illustrates how heavy use by the fire department in fighting a fire can reduce the pressure on the upper floors of a building, and water could be siphoned from an old-style bathtub with a submerged inlet. Because of this contamination potential, all new bathtubs must have the fill spout located above the tub rim.

Backflow Control Devices

When a cross-connection situation is identified, one of two actions must be taken. Either the cross-connection must be removed, or some means must be installed to protect the public water supply from possible contamination.

Figure 14-3
Garden hose
cross-connection

Connected System	Hazard Level
Sewage pumps	High
Boilers	High
Cooling towers	High
Flush valve toilets	High
Garden hose (sil cocks)	Low to high
Auxiliary water supply	Low to high
Aspirators	High
Dishwashers	Moderate
Car wash	Moderate to high
Photographic developers	Moderate to high
Commercial food processors	Low to moderate
Sinks	High
Chlorinators	High
Solar energy systems	Low to high
Sterilizers	High
Sprinkler systems	High
Water systems	Low to high
Swimming pools	Moderate
Plating vats	High
Laboratory glassware or washing equipment	High
Pump primers	Moderate to high
Baptismal founts	Moderate
Access hole flush	High
Agricultural pesticide mixing tanks	High
Irrigation systems	Low to high
Watering troughs	Moderate
Autopsy tables	High

Table 14-1 Some cross-connections and potential hazards

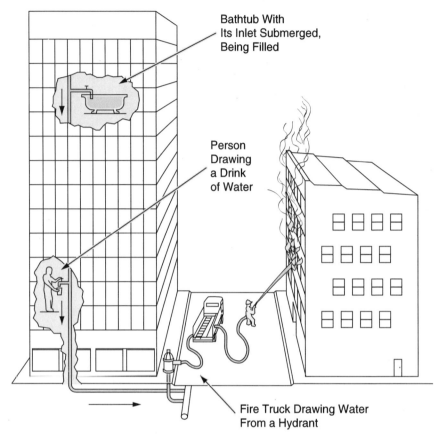

Figure 14-4 Backsiphonage due to pressure loss

Air Gaps

The least expensive and most positive method of protecting against backflow is to install an air gap. There are no moving parts to maintain or break, and surveillance is necessary only to ensure that it is not altered. The only requirement for an air gap between the supply outlet and the maximum water surface of a nonpotable substance is that it must be at least twice the internal diameter of the supply pipe, but no less than 1 in. (25 mm) in any situation.

Typical uses of an air gap are for supplying water to tank trucks, to a nonpotable supply, or a surge tank in a factory as illustrated in Figure 14-5.

Reduced-Pressure-Zone Backflow Preventers

A device that can be used in every cross-connection situation is the reduced-pressure-zone backflow preventer, usually abbreviated RPZ, RPBP, or RPZBP. It consists of two spring-loaded check valves with a pressure-regulated relief valve located between them. As illustrated in Figure 14-6, if there is a potential back-

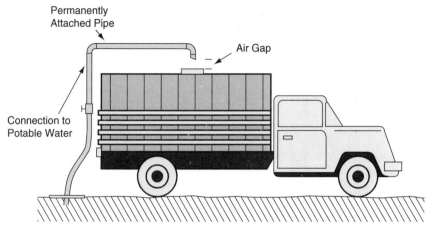

Figure 14-5 Water truck cross-connection prevented by air gap

siphonage situation, both check valves will close, and the space between them is opened to atmospheric pressure. If there is backpressure in excess of the water main pressure, both check valves will close, and if there is any leakage in the second valve, it will be allowed to escape through the center relief valve.

An RPZ is much safer than one or two check valves because there is always the potential of a check valve leaking. Even though RPZs are designed to be depend-

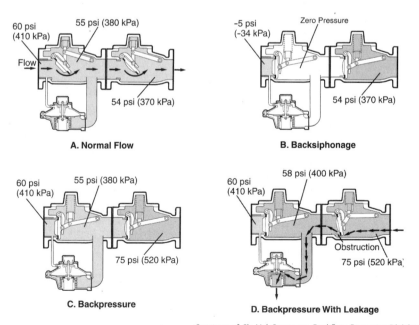

Courtesy of Cla-Val Company, Backflow Preventer Division.

Figure 14-6 Valve position and flow direction in an RPZ

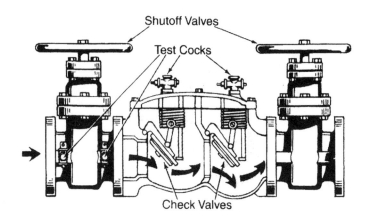

Figure 14-7 Double-check-valve assembly

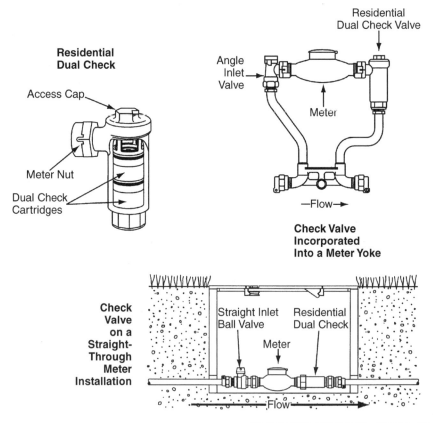

Courtesy of The Ford Meter Box Company, Inc.

Figure 14-8 Examples of residential dual check valves

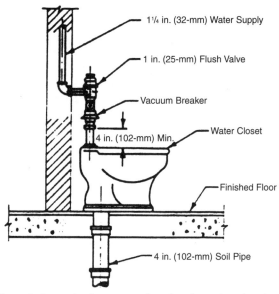

1¼ in. (32-mm) Water Supply

1 in. (25-mm) Flush Valve

Vacuum Breaker

Water Closet

4 in. (102-mm) Min.

Finished Floor

4 in. (102-mm) Soil Pipe

Figure 14-9 Position of atmospheric vacuum breaker in water closet arrangement

able, they are mechanical devices that must be tested and maintained regularly in accordance with the manufacturer's recommendations. They must be installed in locations where the relief port cannot be submerged, and where they are protected from freezing and vandalism.

Double Check Valves

A double-check-valve backflow preventer is designed similarly to an RPZ except there is no relief valve between the two checks (Figure 14-7). The protection is not as positive as an RPZ because of the possibility of the check valves leaking, so they are not recommended for use in situations where a health hazard may result from valve failure. Local and state officials should be contacted for approval before a double check valve is installed for cross-connection protection in a potable water line.

Some water utilities install check valves on some or all customer water services. This is particularly desirable for customers with operable private wells because of the potential of well water being forced backward into the utility's system if there is some piping change by the customer. Several manufacturers have developed double-check-valve assemblies for this use as illustrated in Figure 14-8.

Vacuum Breakers

There are two general types of vacuum breakers: atmospheric and pressure. Atmospheric vacuum breakers are often called antisiphon valves, backsiphonage preventers, or antisiphon vacuum breakers. They are designed for intermittent use on piping connections where there will be no backpressure. Common uses are on toilet flush valves (Figure 14-9), on faucets with hose threads such as janitors' sinks,

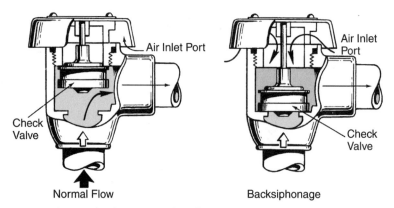

Normal Flow   Backsiphonage

Figure 14-10 Atmospheric vacuum breaker

and on lawn sprinkler systems. Atmospheric vacuum breakers must be installed beyond the last valve in the piping system.

As illustrated in Figure 14-10, when the supply pipe is under pressure, the check valve closes against an upper seat to prevent leakage from the valve. When there is no pressure in the supply, the valve drops and allows air to enter the discharge pipe, thus preventing possible backsiphonage. If this device is installed in a situation where it is under continuous pressure, the check valve may stick shut permanently or become unreliable in operation.

The pressure-type vacuum valve is similar, but is designed for use under pressure over long periods of time (Figure 14-11). This type of valve, too, should never be used where there is any possibility of backpressure on the discharge pipe. They must, therefore, be installed above the highest fixture on the discharge piping. A typical use is on water lines in industrial plants that should be separated from the potable water supply.

Complete Isolation

The most positive method of preventing connection between piping systems from two different sources is complete separation. When piping systems from two sources are located in the same building, they can be identified by signs and color coding. The need for monitoring continues, however, to ensure that the systems are not inadvertently connected.

Someone who does not realize the potential consequences may install a temporary connection between two systems using a spool piece or a swing connection. Such connections are not recommended for use regardless of the degree of risk involved, and they should be completely removed to eliminate any possibility of a cross-connection.

Cross-Connection Control Programs

The Safe Drinking Water Act of 1974 makes each public water supply utility responsible for the quality of water at the consumer's tap. Legal proceedings have also established that the utility is primarily responsible for cross-connection control,

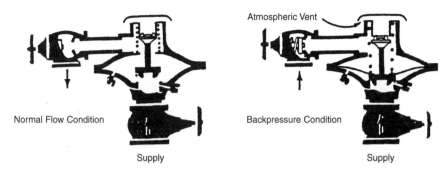

Atmospheric Vent

Normal Flow Condition

Backpressure Condition

Supply

Supply

Figure 14-11 Pressure-type vacuum breaker

and many state regulatory agencies have specifically assigned the responsibility directly to the water supplier.

The problem in administering a cross-connection control program is that the two primary sources of cross-connection problems are usually not directly under the jurisdiction of the water utility. The cross-connections are usually within the customer's premises, which is under the supervision of the local building or health department, or the state health department. Cross-connections between the municipal water system and auxiliary water sources may be under the jurisdiction of a health department or environmental protection agency or its equivalent. When different agencies have an interest, the program must be administered as a cooperative effort.

Most states have established recommended procedures for establishing a cross-connection control program. These recommendations should be reviewed for specific guidance, but the general elements of an effective cross-connection control program are:

- designation of an organization or agency with overall responsibility and authority for administering the program, with adequate staff
- an adequate plumbing and cross-connection control program
- a program of systematic inspection of new and existing installations
- follow-up procedures to ensure compliance
- backflow-prevention device standards, as well as standards for inspection and maintenance of the devices
- cross-connection control training
- a public awareness and information program

Guidelines for establishing and operating a cross-connection control program are detailed in publications listed in the bibliography.

Bibliography

Angele, G.J., Sr. 1974. *Cross-Connection and Backflow Prevention.* Denver, Colo.: American Water Works Association.

AWWA Manual M14, Recommended Practice for Backflow Prevention and Cross-Connection Control. 1990. Denver, Colo.: American Water Works Association.

Chapter 15

Water Storage

Purposes of Water Storage

To the casual observer, the only purpose of water storage tanks may be to supply large quantities of water during a fire or in the event of failure of the water source. In actuality, there are many other functions of a properly designed storage system.

Equalizing Supply and Demand

Domestic water use usually changes throughout the day and night as illustrated in Figure 15-1. There is usually relatively heavy use in the morning as customers prepare breakfast and begin other household duties, then use slacks off at midday. Near supper time there is greatly increased use because almost everyone is at home and customers water their gardens, wash cars, and perform other duties that require water. Then about 10:00 p.m., when most people go to bed, use falls off very sharply. The size of the peaks vary with the season, and water systems with large industrial customers may have unusual use patterns as shifts change or process water is used.

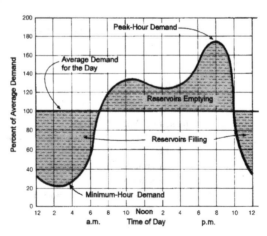

Figure 15-1 Daily variation of system demand

In Figure 15-1, the peak-hour demand is about 175 percent of the average demand for the day. So if this water system had no storage at all, it would need a plant capacity almost double the average requirement to meet the peak-hour use requirement. It would also mean that the system would need a number of pumps of various sizes that could be switched on and off to match the demand. If the water system has a treatment plant, operation would become increasingly difficult because filters and other equipment would have to be operated at highly variable rates.

With adequate storage, water can be treated and pumped at a more uniform rate and does not have to directly follow customer use. During the day, water is taken from storage, and during the night, the storage reservoirs are refilled.

A water system that purchases water from another water system has a somewhat different situation. It is usually offered the following three choices:

- It can draw directly from the selling water utility and have no storage of its own. In this case it will have to purchase the water at a very high rate because the selling utility must furnish either additional storage or pumping capacity to meet the maximum demand.
- It can furnish enough storage to meet its entire daytime use, and draw water to fill the reservoirs only at night when the selling utility is in its low-use mode. The rate for this water is often called a dump rate and may be quite low because the cost to the selling utility is minimal.
- A third option is somewhere in between. One arrangement is that the purchasing system can draw water 24 hours a day, but only at a set rate through a throttling valve. It must then have enough storage to cover the additional water required during the high-use periods.

Increased Operating Convenience

Some small water systems with their own treatment plants have found it most convenient to operate the plants only one or two shifts during the day, and then let the systems "coast" at night, using water from storage. The cost of the additional storage required must be balanced against reduced personnel costs. There must also be an arrangement to quickly start up the plant in the event of unusual use, such as a main break or fire.

Balancing Pumping Requirements

Water use is continually changing, depending on the time of day, day of the week, weather conditions, and even such factors as which shows are on television. If it is necessary to frequently turn pumps on and off to meet the demand, it adds to the wear on the pumps and significantly increases electrical costs.

By having some elevated storage in the distribution system, the cycling of pumps can be minimized. For example, if the pump in use is larger than required to meet demand, water in the elevated tank will rise. So, just before the tank would overflow, the pumps are switched to use a smaller unit. The tank level will then probably slowly fall, and at some preset point, such as when the tank is down to half-full, the pumps are switched again. In this way, it is often possible to operate on one pump size or combination of pumps for several hours without changing.

Decreasing Power Costs

If the local electric utility has special power rates for off-peak use (usually at night), it may be possible to make a significant saving in power cost by providing additional storage and operating the larger pumps only during the off-peak period to fill the tanks. This plan would be particularly applicable to a water system that can construct a large ground-level storage tank on a high point of ground so it will gravity-feed the system during the daytime.

Emergency and Fire Requirements

One of the principal reasons for distribution system storage is to meet the very high demands for water during a fire. Other unusual demands that must also be considered are unusually high use during large main breaks, temporary loss of power, or problems that might disrupt the water source. In all of these cases, the objective is to try to supply as much water as is required, without loss of pressure.

If a water utility has a sizable quantity of elevated storage, the quantity of water available may be sufficient to meet the emergency demands through gravity feed. If most of the system storage is in ground-level reservoirs, pumps must be activated quickly to maintain system pressure. Fire demand can account for as much as 50 percent of the total required distribution system storage.

It is not advisable to rely on storage to make up any shortfall between the quantity of water available from the water source and quantity needed to meet maximum day demand. Maximum day demand can, on occasion, last for several days.

Surge Relief

As large pumps are stopped and started and when valves or hydrants are closed quickly, extremely high pressure surge or water hammer can damage the system piping and customer services. Elevated tanks that are directly connected to the system help to absorb any surges by allowing the shock wave in the water to travel up the riser and into the upper tank section.

Increasing Chlorine Detention Time

Requirements under the federal Surface Water Treatment Rule specify the length of time that chlorine must be in contact with water before the water reaches the first customer. In cases where there is not sufficient detention time in the water treatment process, additional detention can be provided by directing the water into a storage reservoir before it enters the distribution system. The reservoir is then serving two functions. The only special provision for this type of reservoir is that it must have baffles to channel the water in a long path so that the required contact time between the chlorine and water is maintained.

Blending Water From Different Sources

Occasionally a water system will draw water from two or more sources having different qualities, such as hardness and temperature. A relatively common example is a system that primarily uses groundwater, but because the supply is inadequate, it is supplemented with water from a surface water source.

Residential customers generally dislike having the quality vary and will complain if the changes are significant. Industrial customers are also often disturbed by changes in water quality. If water is used for cooling, they will be bothered by quick changes in water temperature. If water is incorporated into their products, such as soft drinks, consistent water quality is essential.

Another reason for wanting to blend water from different sources would be that a utility has one source with a fluoride concentration exceeding the maximum contaminant level, and another source with low fluoride. When water from sources with dissimilar quality is properly blended in a reservoir before distribution, the quality furnished to customers can be maintained relatively uniform.

Types of Storage Facilities

Facilities for storing water in the distribution system may be either elevated or at ground level. Storage facilities fall into the general classifications of elevated tanks, standpipes, reservoirs, and hydropneumatic systems.

Elevated Tanks

An elevated tank consists of a tank supported by a steel or concrete tower (Figure 15-2). Most elevated tanks are designed to float on the system—in other words, they are directly connected to a system main, and the overflow point of the tank is the

Courtesy of Chicago Bridge & Iron Company.

Figure 15-2 Old and new elevated tanks

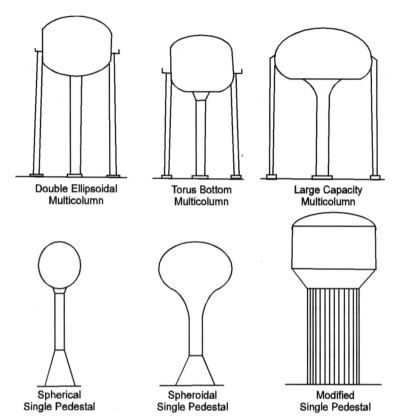

Figure 15-3 Cross-sectional views of some common elevated tank designs

maximum system pressure. Occasionally, for some reason, a tank is not high enough and the maximum system pressure would cause it to overflow. In this case, the tank must be connected to the main through an altitude valve as described in chapter 7, Distribution System Valves.

Most elevated tanks are constructed of steel. Early steel tanks were assembled with rivets, but tanks are now welded to provide a smooth appearance and to make them easier to maintain. Welding also allows tanks to be designed in new, more pleasing designs. Figure 15-3 illustrates several designs currently in use. The spherical and spheroidal tanks are very popular for small- to medium-sized tanks, both because they are visually more pleasing and because they are easier to maintain than tanks with individual legs. The single-pedestal tank is applicable to large tanks and offers the added advantage of providing space for water system storage in the pedestal.

Standpipes

A tank that has a height greater than its diameter is referred to as a *standpipe* (Figure 15-4). Standpipes have the advantage of providing storage for a great

Courtesy of Chicago Bridge & Iron Company.

Figure 15-4 Twin standpipes holding 5 mil gal (19 ML) each

Courtesy of A.O. Smith Engineered Storage Products Company.

Figure 15-5 Aquastore® bolted steel tank

quantity of water at a cost proportionally not much greater than the cost of a pedestal tank. The disadvantages are that their great bulk may make them visually objectionable to residents, and the tremendous weight of the stored water means that they can only be constructed where foundation conditions are exactly right.

In most cases, only a portion of the water in the top of the standpipe will provide usable system pressure. When the water level falls to less than 70 ft (21 m) from the ground surface, there will be less than 30 psi (207 kPa) of pressure, which is generally the minimum that should be maintained in the distribution system. For this reason, most standpipes are constructed with an adjacent pumping station that can be used to boost the pressure of water from the lower section of the standpipe if it should be needed.

Standpipes may be constructed of welded steel or concrete. Standards for the construction of welded steel tanks are covered in AWWA Standard D100-96, *Welded Steel Tanks for Water Storage.*

Standpipes are also available that are field-assembled by bolting together uniformly sized steel panels (Figure 15-5). The panels are factory coated by hot-dipped galvanizing, coating with fused glass, or epoxy coated to provide long-term corrosion protection. A watertight seal is achieved by using a gasket or sealant between the panels. Guidelines for the design of bolted steel tanks may be found in AWWA Standard D103-97, *Factory-Coated Bolted Steel Tanks for Water Storage.*

Reservoirs

The term *reservoir* has a wide range of meanings in the water supply industry. A raw water reservoir is typically a pond, lake, or basin that is either naturally occurring or constructed. For the storage of finished water, the term is generally applied to a large storage tank that is larger in diameter than its height, and is set on the ground surface or buried. A typical ground-level reservoir is shown in Figure 15-6.

For equal-sized facilities, the reservoir will have a lower initial cost but must have a pumping station to transfer the water to the distribution system. After the

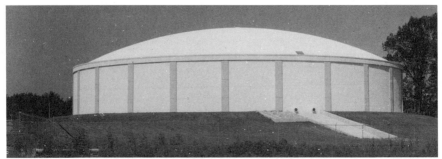

Courtesy of Preload Inc.

Figure 15-6 Ground-level reservoir

maintenance and operation of the reservoir facilities are taken into account, the long-range costs will be approximately equal.

Reservoirs are usually selected for storage either because a larger quantity of water must be stored than is practical for an elevated tank, or because elevated storage would be visually objectionable to residents. Where a ground-level reservoir would be objectionable, the installation may be made partially or completely underground. Some buried installations have been made into parks with baseball or tennis facilities installed over the reservoirs.

One of the problems with reservoirs is that some water must be removed and replaced daily so that the water does not become stagnant. Most water systems pump out some water every day during peak use periods and refill at night. A reservoir is usually filled through an altitude valve that can be remotely operated and is hydraulically connected to sense the reservoir water level and to automatically close when the reservoir is full. Careful monitoring of water in reservoirs is needed to ensure constant quality.

Early reservoirs were constructed with part excavation and part embankment and paved with riprap, brick, or concrete, and were usually not covered. Among the problems were leakage, freezing, contamination by birds and other animals, algae growth, and potential vandalism. The availability of better construction methods, and state and federal pressure because of the potential health hazards, gradually caused these facilities to be replaced with new reservoirs.

Some ground-level reservoirs are constructed of bolted or welded steel set on a concrete foundation and floor. Although interior and exterior corrosion coatings must be maintained and occasionally replaced, new coating systems currently available last quite a long time.

Concrete reservoirs may be constructed by several different methods.

Cast-in-place tanks are constructed about the same as a basement for a building, except that much more reinforcing steel is required to resist the outward pressure of the water. They are generally square or rectangular in shape and special provisions must be made to prevent leakage at the construction joints. It is difficult to prevent some cracking of cast-in-place concrete tanks, but they can be filled with new types of flexible caulking compound.

Circular prestressed concrete tanks are constructed by beginning with an inner

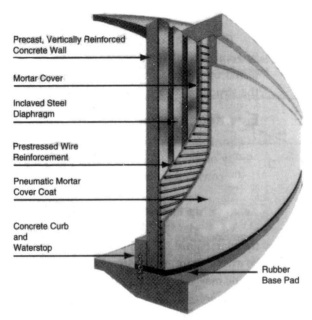

Precast, Vertically Reinforced
Concrete Wall

Mortar Cover

Inclaved Steel
Diaphragm

Prestressed Wire
Reinforcement

Pneumatic Mortar
Cover Coat

Concrete Curb
and
Waterstop

Rubber
Base Pad

Courtesy of Preload Inc.

Figure 15-7 Sectional view of a prestressed concrete tank

concrete core wall set on a ring foundation. Steel wire is then wrapped around the core under tension, and the wire is protected by a layer of gunite (hydraulically applied concrete) as illustrated in Figure 15-7. Because of the strength of the prestressed concrete, the walls can be made thinner than on a cast-in-place reservoir. The applicable AWWA standards are D110-95, *Wire- and Strand-Wound Circular, Prestressed Concrete Water Tanks* and D115-95, *Circular Prestressed Concrete Water Tanks With Circumferential Tendons*.

Hydraulically applied concrete-lined reservoirs are constructed much the same as some swimming pools. An earth excavation or embankment is first covered with reinforcing rods, and then covered with gunite. A reservoir of this type is typically relatively small and requires special provisions for installing a tight cover.

Hydropneumatic Storage Systems

Hydropneumatic storage tanks are used by very small systems that cannot justify an elevated or ground-level tank. As illustrated in Figure 15-8, a steel pressure tank is kept partially filled with compressed air to provide quantities of water in excess of the pump capacity when required. It also keeps the pump from cycling too often, and will provide water for a limited time in the event of pump failure.

The system provides relatively little fire protection, but is a fairly reliable source for domestic water for a few customers. State regulatory agencies usually specify the minimum size tank size that must be used, based on the number of persons or houses served.

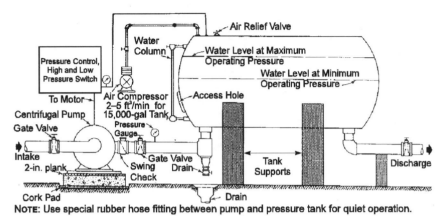

NOTE: Use special rubber hose fitting between pump and pressure tank for quiet operation.

Joseph A. Salvato, Environmental Engineering and Sanitation, 4th ed. Copyright © John Wiley & Sons, Inc. Reprinted by permission of John Wiley & Sons, Inc.

Figure 15-8 Hydropneumatic water pressure system

Location of Distribution Storage

The locations of distribution system elevated tanks or ground-level reservoirs are governed by two principal factors: the hydraulics of the system and the availability of appropriate land that is acceptable to the public for construction of the facility.

Hydraulic Considerations

As illustrated in Figure 15-9, there are three primary alternatives in locating storage facilities. It is often most convenient to locate storage at the water source, but as the water system grows, the head loss to the far ends of the system can become excessive. If the only storage for a large system is located at the source, large-diameter transmission mains must be installed to provide adequate flow to all areas. Installing these mains is usually quite expensive if they must be constructed through built-up neighborhoods.

To avoid the cost of adding transmission mains, storage can be located at the far ends of the distribution system. During high-use periods, water will flow from the tanks to improve the pressure in remote areas. The only problem that must be carefully studied is that there must be adequate main capacity between the source and the remote tanks to refill the tanks at night. If they cannot be completely filled, additional transmission mains may have to be installed just to transport water to the tanks.

Quite often, the best alternative is to install the storage tanks at an intermediate location where the existing distribution system is more likely to support them, but they will still reinforce the far ends of the system.

Installation of one large storage tank will usually require main reinforcement to support it, whereas several smaller tanks at different locations may be able to individually work acceptably on the existing system. The economic factors of the alternatives must be carefully considered during planning.

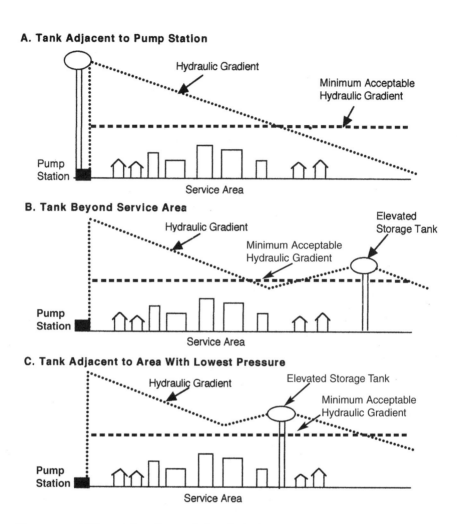

A. Tank Adjacent to Pump Station

Hydraulic Gradient

Minimum Acceptable
Hydraulic Gradient

Pump
Station

Service Area

B. Tank Beyond Service Area

Elevated
Storage Tank

Hydraulic Gradient

Minimum Acceptable
Hydraulic Gradient

Pump
Station

Service Area

C. Tank Adjacent to Area With Lowest Pressure

Hydraulic Gradient

Elevated Storage Tank

Minimum Acceptable
Hydraulic Gradient

Pump
Station

Service Area

Figure 15-9 Different locations of elevated storage

Aesthetic Considerations

It his been found that people who live next to an existing elevated water tank rarely notice or are bothered by it. But if a new tank is proposed for an urban area, the residents will usually find it unacceptable. Many new designs and colors are now available that are quite pleasing, but the public reaction is still generally negative. An additional complaint is that the tank might affect television reception in the area.

As a result of these concerns, an ideal piece of land meeting the requirements of a reasonable price, a high elevation, and a good location hydraulically on the distribution system may not be acceptable for the location an elevated tank. If the tank must be elevated, one of the few alternatives in most communities is to place it in an industrial park, public park, or other area away from homes. In many cases, an acceptable site may not be a very good location for hydraulic flow, elevation, or other reasons, so the installation may cost considerably more than it would at the optimum location.

Another alternative is to install an underground reservoir in the urban area. Many concessions may have to be made with residents, but the installation can usually be designed to gain their acceptance.

Elevated Tank Equipment

The principal accessories to an elevated storage tank are illustrated in Figure 15-10.

Riser Pipe

There is usually only one pipe that serves as both water inlet and outlet to a tank, and it is called the *riser*. In cold climates the riser must either be protected from freezing, or be large enough in diameter so that it can partially freeze around the outside, but still allow flow through the center. The riser of a multi-column tank is often 6 ft (1.8 m) or larger. An advantage of the single-pedestal tank design is that some heat can be provided inside the column to protect the small-diameter riser from freezing.

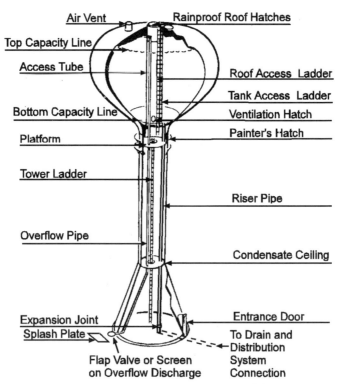

Courtesy of Chicago Bridge & Iron Company.

Figure 15-10 Principal accessories for an elevated storage tank

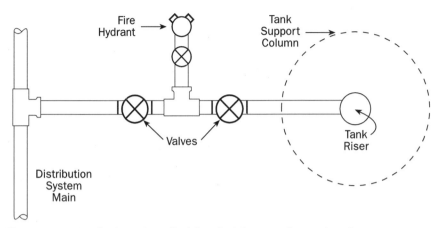

Figure 15-11 Fire hydrant installed for draining an elevated tank

Overflow Pipe

An important accessory for all tanks is the overflow pipe, which relieves excess water in the event of excessive system pressure. Proper functioning of the overflow is particularly important in freezing weather. If excess water flows out of the vent at the top of the tank, it will freeze and the excess weight can be sufficient to cause the tank to collapse. The overflow pipe begins at the maximum tank water level and is brought down to within a foot or so of the ground. The end of the pipe is usually closed by a weighted flap to exclude insects and animals, but it must positively break open if overflow takes place. The overflow discharge should empty onto a splash plate to prevent erosion, but should never be directly connected to a sewer or storm drain.

Drain Connection

An elevated tank must be furnished with a drain connection that can be used to empty it for maintenance and repair. Figure 15-11 shows a common method of draining through a hydrant located on the pipe at the base of the tank. Provisions must be made for discharging the flow from the hydrant without causing erosion or creating a cross-connection. If chlorinated water is to be discharged following disinfection of the tank, environmental officials should be consulted about which method of disposal is acceptable.

Air Vent

A tank must be provided with a vent that will allow air to enter and exit as the water level rises and falls. If the vent should become blocked as water is draining from the tank, the vacuum formed could be sufficient to collapse the tank walls.

The vent must be screened to keep out birds, but the mesh cannot be so fine that it might become blocked by freezing moisture. Insects are not usually a problem because of the height of the tank. Most state regulations require a screen with $1/4$-in. (6-mm) mesh.

Worker using the device.   Detail of the locking pawl that
slides on the notched rail.

Photos courtesy of North Safety Products, Brea, Calif.

Figure 15-12 Use of a rail-type fall prevention device mounted on a water tank ladder

Access Hatches

Storage tanks must have hatches installed both for workers to enter and for top and bottom ventilation during maintenance and inspection. Roof vents are designed with a rim under the cover to prevent surface runoff from entering the tank.

A tank having a large-diameter wet riser has a heavy access hatch near ground level that is constructed of steel to withstand the high pressure. This hatch is used for cleaning the riser and to provide ventilation to the tank during repair.

Ladders

A multicolumn tank (such as the old tank shown in Figure 15-2) will usually have three ladders. The tower ladder runs up one leg to the balcony, another ladder goes from the balcony to the roof, and the roof ladder reaches from the balcony ladder to the roof hatch. The tower ladder usually starts at a point about 8 ft (2.5 m) above ground level to deter unauthorized persons from climbing it. A pedestal tank has similar ladders located inside the pedestal.

All ladders must have safety devices in compliance with the federal Occupational Safety and Health Administration requirements. One method is to have a safety cage around the ladder. One type of ladder safety rail system is shown in Figure 15-12. The device is fastened to the worker's safety belt and easily rides on the rail while the worker climbs up or down, but if there is a quick downward movement, a locking pawl engages with notches in the rail.

Obstruction Lighting

Depending on the height of a tank and the proximity to an airport, the Federal Aviation Administration (FAA) may require the installation of a red light or a strobe light on top of the tank. In locations considered particularly hazardous to aviation, orange and white obstruction painting on the tank may also be required. The FAA should be contacted before construction of any elevated tank to make sure it has no objection and to identify any special requirements.

Ground-Level Reservoir Equipment

The same general accessories are required for reservoirs as for elevated tanks, with the exception that increased caution must be exercised to prevent vandalism. Vents and hatches in particular are more accessible, so special care must be taken to keep them locked and guarded.

Inlet and Outlet Piping

Reservoirs may in some instances use a single inlet and outlet pipe. Other designs use separate pipelines for the purpose of increasing circulation to maintain uniform water quality and help reduce freezing.

The outlet to a reservoir is usually located a short distance above the floor to prevent any silt that accumulates on the floor from being drawn into the water leaving the tank.

Drains

It is often difficult to install a gravity drain for a reservoir without creating a potential cross-connection, unless the installation happens to be on the top of a hill. The usual practice is to dewater the reservoir for inspection and repair by pumping most of the water to the distribution system. But it is not wise to pump all the way to the outlet opening because, if there is any accumulated sediment on the bottom, it will be picked up and pumped out as cloudy water. The last couple of feet of water in the tank should be pumped out and wasted using portable pumps. Disposal of reservoir sediment and water may be subject to local regulations that may require dechlorination and/or removal to an approved site.

Operation and Maintenance of Storage Facilities

Cold-Weather Operation

Freezing of ground-level reservoirs is typically not a problem because the water picks up some heat from the ground. Some ice may form around the walls of the tank, but it does not harm anything. Some utilities in northern areas drain some of their reservoirs during the winter because they are not needed due to decreased water use. This simplifies winter operation, but creates a sizable job of having to disinfect the reservoir before returning it to service in the spring.

The problems of ice formation in elevated tanks in northern areas must be clearly understood by system operators. If a tank should be allowed to freeze solid, it not only might damage the structure, but it will be very costly to have it thawed by a professional firm.

It is normal for ice to form around the walls of the tank, and it usually will not damage the structure. What is important is to keep thick ice from forming on the water surface. This is done by keeping the surface of the water moving up and down by continually varying system pressure. Each time the tank level is raised, warmer water is

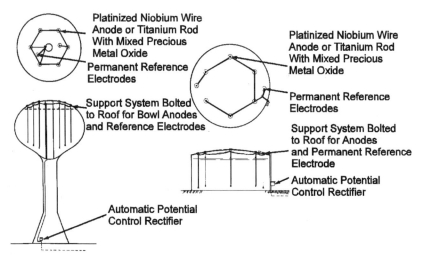

Source: Harco/CPS Waterworks, a Corrpro Company, 1055 West Smith Road, Medina, Ohio 44256.

Figure 15-13 Typical methods of suspending cathodic protection anodes in steel tanks where icing conditions do not exist

brought in. If system pressure is maintained by automatic controls, they must be set in the winter to purposely vary the pressure over a relatively wide range.

Coatings for Steel Tanks

When steel is exposed to oxygen and moisture, it corrodes, thus protection is required for both the interior and exterior of a steel tank. The exterior of a tank is exposed to a rather uniform environment, but the interior has more severe conditions, and parts of the interior walls may be severely scraped by ice.

New coatings now available are much more durable then those available just a few years ago, but they will still eventually need to be replaced. If an old tank was originally coated with lead-based paint, it is best removed by sand blasting. This must be done by special means to prevent environmental pollution. State officials should be consulted about the allowable levels of both lead and silica that can be released to the environment.

Care should be taken to ensure that the coatings to be used on the interior of a tank comply with NSF International standards for not imparting any taste or odor or releasing harmful chemicals to the water. When a tank is painted by contract, the work should be inspected to make sure the contractor is fully meeting the specifications. Inspecting the work is both dangerous and beyond the knowledge of most water system operators, so it is suggested that a qualified third party be employed to inspect the work. Competing contractors should not be used for inspection because of possible conflict of interest. Steel tank coating is covered in AWWA Standard D102-97, *Coating Steel Water-Storage Tanks.*

Cathodic Protection

Even if the interior of a tank is fully coated, there is still some chance for corrosion. If there are any small breaks in the coating (holidays), the corrosion will con-

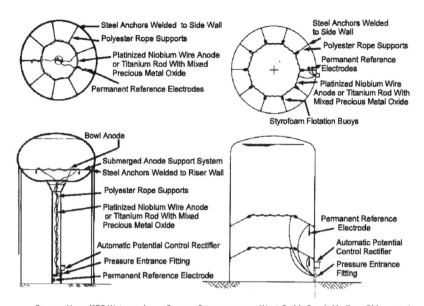

Source: Harco/CPS Waterworks, a Corrpro Company, 1055 West Smith Road, Medina, Ohio 44256.

Figure 15-14 Typical methods of suspending cathodic protection anodes in steel tanks where icing conditions exist

centrate in these areas and can do serious damage in a relatively short time. A cathodic protection system can greatly reduce corrosion of a tank interior.

A cathodic protection system consists of a series of anodes that are suspended in the tank with a direct current impressed on them. Instead of corrosion dissolving iron from the tank surface, the current causes the anodes to corrode (or be sacrificed). In warm climates, the anodes can be suspended from the tank roof and left in place until they require replacement (Figure 15-13). In climates where ice will form in the tank, ice will pull down suspended anodes so a submerged anode system is used that resists icing damage (Figure 15-14).

Anodes will usually last as long as 10 years, but it is recommended that the system be inspected annually to ensure they are operating properly. A cathodic protection system can be successfully operated on a tank with no interior coating, but the anodes will disintegrate rather quickly, so it is usually recommended that the system be used in conjunction with a good interior coating. Details of cathodic protection systems are covered in AWWA Standard D104-97, *Automatically Controlled, Impressed-Current Cathodic Protection for the Interior of Steel Water Tanks.*

Tank Inspection, Cleaning, and Disinfection

Inspection of elevated tanks is both dangerous and specialized, so it is best to employ a qualified firm to inspect the tank and submit a report on the condition with suggestions on any repairs that are necessary. It is generally best to have the inspection done annually or periodically by a firm other than the one that will be doing the repair work.

Annual or periodic inspection and minor repair of ground-level reservoirs is within the capability of most water system repair crews if safety measures are carefully followed. If the reservoir is emptied for interior inspection, special safety measures include provision of adequate ventilation, adequate lighting with special care to prevent electric shock, proper boots and other gear for workers, and security and fall protection on ladders. In most cases, a confined-space program must be instituted.

Tanks should be inspected for the condition of overflows and vents to make sure they are not blocked and that screens are clean and in place. Leaks in roofs may need to be investigated during wet weather to ensure against intrusion. Concrete tanks should particularly be inspected for cracks. After inspection and cleaning, tanks must be disinfected per AWWA Standard C652-92, *Disinfection of Water-Storage Facilities*.

Exterior inspection of all tanks and reservoirs should be made frequently. Among the items that should be checked are

- all hatches and locks to make sure they are secure
- general condition for any signs of vandalism
- proper operation of security lights and aircraft warning light
- leaks in roof where contaminants can enter

Records of Tank Maintenance

Because most water systems have only a few water tanks or reservoirs, record keeping does not have to be elaborate. Basic information that should be kept in a file includes the tank location and original construction information, copies of all inspection reports, and details of each inspection and repair that is made. A record should also be kept of the names and phone numbers of the tank manufacturer, repair contractors, and equipment suppliers so they are readily available in the event of an emergency.

Bibliography

AWWA Manual M42, Steel Water Storage Tanks. 1998. Denver, Colo.: American Water Works Association.

AWWA Standard for Automatically Controlled, Impressed-Current Cathodic Protection for the Interior of Steel Water Tanks. ANSI/AWWA D104-97. 1997. Denver, Colo.: American Water Works Association.

AWWA Standard for Circular Prestressed Concrete Water Tanks With Circumferential Tendons. ANSI/AWWA D115-95. 1995. Denver, Colo.: American Water Works Association.

AWWA Standard for Coating Steel Water-Storage Tanks. ANSI/AWWA D102-97. 1997. Denver, Colo.: American Water Works Association.

AWWA Standard for Disinfection of Water-Storage Facilities. ANSI/AWWA C652-92. 1992. Denver, Colo.: American Water Works Association.

AWWA Standard for Factory-Coated Bolted Steel Tanks for Water Storage. ANSI/AWWA D103-97. 1997. Denver, Colo.: American Water Works Association.

AWWA Standard for Flexible-Membrane-Lining and Floating-Cover Materials for Potable Water Storage. ANSI/AWWA D130-96. 1996. Denver, Colo.: American Water Works Association.

AWWA Standard for Welded Steel Tanks for Water Storage. ANSI/AWWA D100-96. 1996. Denver, Colo.: American Water Works Association.

AWWA Standard for Wire- and Strand-Wound, Circular, Prestressed Concrete Water Tanks. ANSI/AWWA D110-95. 1995. Denver, Colo.: American Water Works Association.

Chapter 16

Water Wells

Groundwater sources are usually relatively simple to develop and often require little or no treatment. About 95 percent of the rural population in the United States is served by wells.

Aquifers and Confining Beds

Groundwater is the result of the infiltration and percolation of water down to the water table through the soil and cracks in consolidated rocks. Referring to Figure 16-1, the water table that is immediately below the surface is not confined and often rises and falls due to variations in rainfall. When a well is drilled into the water table, water rises in the well just to the level of the top of the water table.

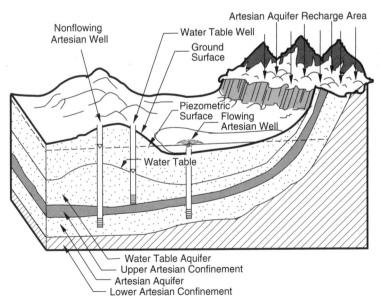

Figure 16-1 Cross-section of an artesian aquifer

A confined aquifer is a permeable layer of rock that is confined by upper and lower layers that are relatively impermeable. As illustrated in Figure 16-1, if the recharge area for the confined aquifer is elevated, the water in the aquifer will be under pressure. If there is sufficient pressure for the water to flow from a well that taps the aquifer, it is called a *flowing artesian well*. More often, there is pressure in the aquifer so that water will rise in the well, but not sufficiently to flow out of the well. In this case, it is called a *nonflowing artesian well*. The height to which water will rise in wells located in an artesian aquifer is called the *piezometric surface*.

On occasion, there are several aquifers available, each with different water quality. In this case, the well is drilled and cased through the aquifers of poor quality so as to tap only the best aquifer.

The mineral content of water from shallow wells will vary with the mineral content of the soil in the area. Water from deep wells almost always contains concentrations of dissolved minerals and may have considerable hardness, but it is usually clear and colorless.

Groundwater Sources

Groundwater used for supplying public water systems is obtained principally from either springs and infiltration galleries or from drilled wells.

Springs and Infiltration Galleries

It is rare for springs to have adequate capacity to serve a public water system, but if a spring is to be used, the collection point must be enclosed in a concrete box constructed around the spring to prevent insects, animals, and surface drainage from entering the water. It is usually difficult to tell where spring water originates. It may come from a distant point and travel through the ground for many years, or it could come from a nearby septic tank. A thorough analysis of the water should be conducted before a spring is used for a public water supply source.

Infiltration galleries are often constructed by burying a perforated pipe under or along the edge of a lake or stream and conducting the water to a central collection box. The intent is to obtain surface water that is partially filtered, thus eliminating the problems of a surface water intake. If the proper soil conditions are present, infiltration galleries work quite well. But remember that the water collected by the perforated pipe may actually be surface water from the adjacent river banks that is migrating toward the stream. If this is the case, care must be taken that there are no sources of surface or buried contamination in the surrounding area.

Under provisions of the federal Surface Water Treatment Rule (SWTR), state regulatory agencies must require that treatment of water from springs and infiltration galleries be the same as for a surface water source.

Drilled Wells

Drilled wells are the most common type of well installed for public water supply use. They may be up to 4 ft (1.5 m) in diameter and anywhere from relatively shallow to several thousand feet (metres) deep. Common drilling methods include the cable tool, rotary hydraulic, rotary air, and down-the-hole hammer methods. All methods use some means of breaking through the soil or rock and bringing the removed material to the surface.

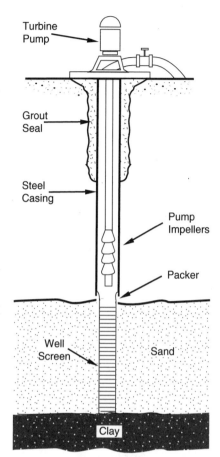

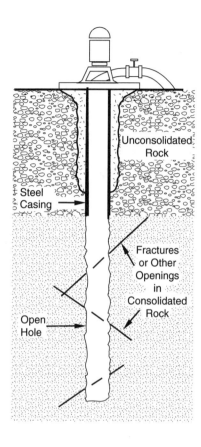

Figure 16-2 Exposed well screen

Figure 16-3 Casing seated at top of rock layer with an open hole underneath

If the water-bearing stratum is sand or gravel, the usual practice is to drill the well and install the casing to the bottom of the sand layer. The well screen is then lowered into the casing and the casing is withdrawn to expose the screen as illustrated in Figure 16-2. The seal between the top of the screen and the bottom of the casing is called a *packer.*

When the source of water is from fractures or openings in consolidated rock, the casing is usually seated firmly on top of the rock layer and the hole is then left open through the rock as illustrated in Figure 16-3.

If the water-bearing stratum is composed of very fine sand, it is usually difficult to hold back the sand with a well screen while still admitting an acceptable flow of water. In this situation, a gravel-wall (or gravel-packed) well may be installed. One common installation method is to first install a large-diameter construction casing into the sand layer. The working casing and screen is then dropped into place and selected coarse gravel is placed around it. As illustrated in Figure 16-4, the construction casing is then withdrawn and the gravel holds back the fine sand.

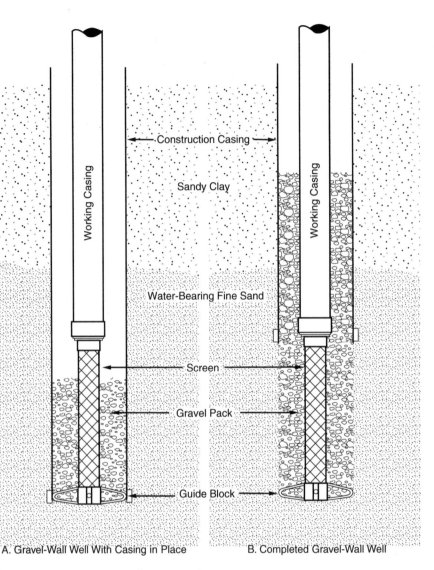

Figure 16-4 Gravel-wall well construction

Well Terms

Some important terms for the hydraulic characteristics of a well are illustrated in Figure 16-5 and/or defined as follows:

Static Water Level The natural water surface with the well not in operation. It is measured from the ground surface to the water surface. In some areas of the country, the water surface may be just below the ground surface; in other locations it may be near the level of a deep aquifer.

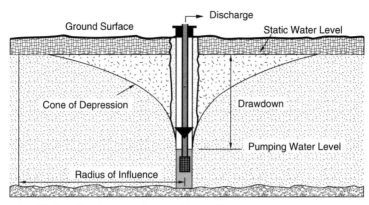

Figure 16-5 Hydraulic characteristics of a well

Pumping Water Level The level of the water in the well after the pump has been operating for a period of time. The intake of the well pump must be located below this level, otherwise it will begin to draw in air.

Drawdown The drop in water level from the static level to the pumping level. A well located in very porous gravel may have almost no drawdown because water flows to the well screen as fast as it is pumped. A well located in an aquifer with low porosity will have a very large drawdown.

Cone of Depression The depressed water surface surrounding the well when the well pump is in operation. The water surface takes the shape of an inverted cone.

Zone of Influence The distance that the cone of depression affects the normal (static) water level. It may be from a few feet (or metres) to hundreds of feet (or metres), depending on the porosity of the aquifer and other factors. In general, it is not good practice to install wells so that their zones of influence overlap. As illustrated in Figure 16-6, the cone of depression of closely situated wells will significantly lower the required pumping level of two adjacent wells.

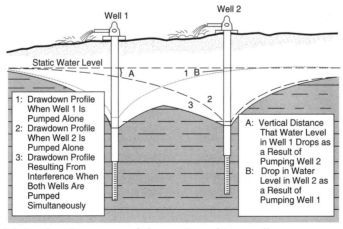

Figure 16-6 Overlapping cones of depression of two wells

Residual Drawdown A lowered water level, below the original static level that remains after pumping has been stopped for a period of time.

Well Yield The rate of water withdrawal that a well can supply over a long period of time. In other words, it is the recharge rate that the aquifer can continuously sustain to the well. The yield of small wells is usually expressed in gallons or litres per minute. For large wells, it may be expressed in cubic feet or cubic metres per second.

Recovery Time The time it takes after pumping has stopped for the water level to return to the static water level.

Specific Capacity The well yield per unit of drawdown, or

$$\text{specific capacity} = \frac{\text{well yield}}{\text{drawdown}}$$

Example: A well has been tested by pumping at various rates, and it has been found that the maximum amount it can produce while operating for an extended period of time is 500 gpm. When operating at that rate, the drawdown is 10 ft. The specific yield is therefore

$$\frac{500 \text{ gal/min}}{10 \text{ ft}} = 50 \text{ gal/min per ft drawdown}$$

Well Protection

Until about two decades ago, all groundwater was considered pristine because the water was thought to be cleansed as it passed through the soil. Then, as new chemical analysis techniques were developed and more wells were tested, it was found that many aquifers were affected by both natural and human chemical contamination that could be a danger to health.

It has also been found that many shallow wells are at risk of contamination from surface water. Under provisions of the federal Surface Water Treatment Rule (SWTR), the state primacy agency must make a ruling on each well, and those that are considered vulnerable are labeled "groundwater under the direct influence of surface water." These wells must be treated as surface water sources. In general, wells less than 50 ft (15 m) deep are likely to be considered vulnerable.

Contamination Sources

Under federal and state regulations, all wells serving public water systems must be tested for a variety of contaminants that might pose a threat to public health. In some cases, contamination originates from sources that were not anticipated or known when the well was constructed. Potential sources of groundwater contamination include landfills, liquid-waste storage ponds, septic systems, agricultural activities, and illegal dumping activities.

Problems caused by groundwater contamination include disagreeable tastes and odors, the presence of disease-causing organisms, and chemical contamination above recommended health limits for drinking water. Unfortunately, there is no set limit on how far a well must be from a contamination source to be safe. It depends on groundwater flow, soil conditions, and many other factors. Some organic chemicals in

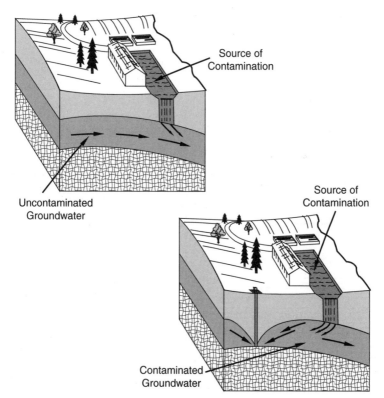

Figure 16-7 Reversal of flow in an aquifer due to well drawdown

aquifers have been tracked to sources more than 0.5 mi (0.8 km) away. As illustrated in Figure 16-7, when siting a new well it is necessary to consider the possibility that the groundwater flow may be reversed when the well is put into operation.

Well Grouting

An important installation procedure in well construction is that the space between the walls of the drilled hole and the well casing must be cemented or grouted as illustrated in Figure 16-8. The primary purpose is to prevent surface water pollution from traveling down along the outside of the casing and causing contamination of the water being drawn into the well. Secondary purposes of grouting are to protect the casing from corrosion, to restrain unstable soil and rock formations, and to seal off any aquifers with poor water quality. Also illustrated in Figure 16-8 is a well slab that is poured around the top of the well to pitch rain and surface water away from the well.

Sanitary Seal

The top of the well casing must always be sealed to prevent the entrance of water, insects, and animals. The seal has openings for the discharge pipe, pump controls, and a screened air vent that allows air to enter and leave the casing as the water level

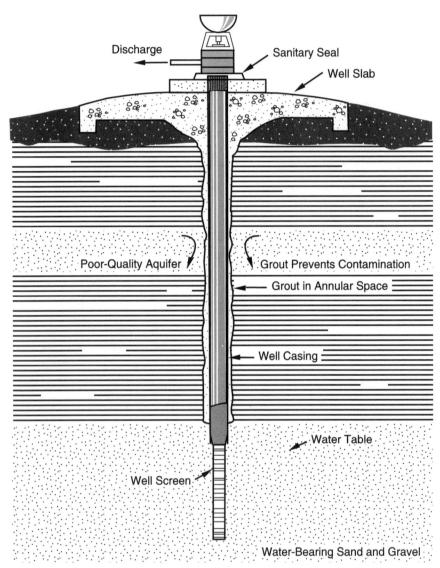

Figure 16-8 Sealed annular space that prevents contamination

rises and falls. Figure 16-9 illustrates a sanitary well seal for a small well having a submersible pump.

Measuring the Water Level in a Well

There are three common methods used for measuring the depth of the water in a well: chalked steel tape, electronic, and air-pressure tube. The methods are illustrated in Figure 16-10.

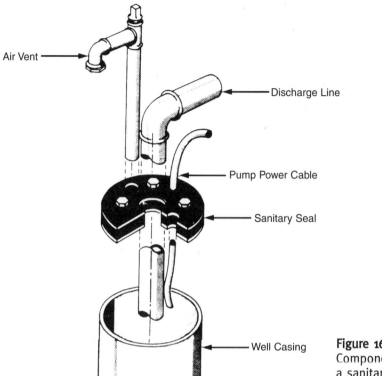

Air Vent

Discharge Line

Pump Power Cable

Sanitary Seal

Well Casing

Figure 16-9
Components of
a sanitary seal

Chalked Steel Tape Method

With the chalked steel tape method, a weight is attached to the end of a steel tape and chalk is applied for a distance of several feet (metres) at the end of the tape. The tape is lowered into the well until the end is sure to be below the water level, and the tape reading is recorded at ground level. When the tape is withdrawn, the wetted portion shows up because of the chalk, and the wetted length can be deducted from the reading at ground level to arrive at the water depth.

Electronic Method

Electronic depth-measuring devices are the quickest and easiest to use. A probe on the end of a wire or tape is lowered into the well, and a light or sound signal is activated when the probe touches the water. The depth is then read from markings on the wire or tape.

Air-Pressure Tube Method

The method of measuring well water level used by most water systems before the electronic units became available, included a small-diameter air tube permanently installed in the well. The end of the tube was suspended so that it would always be below the lowest drawdown of the water, and the exact distance from the end of the tube to the surface was measured before installation.

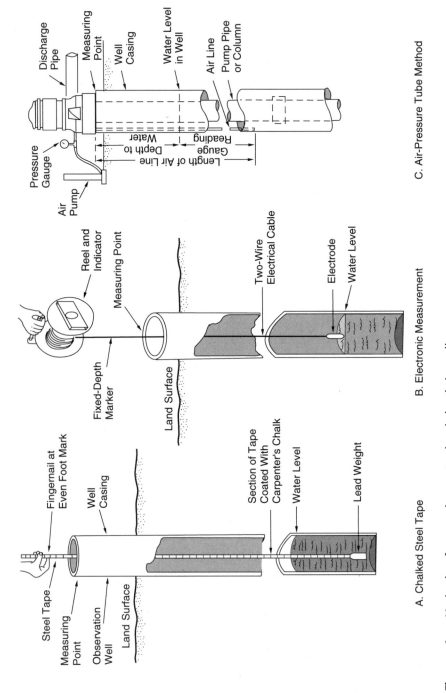

Figure 16-10 Methods of measuring water level depth in wells

The top of the tube was fitted with a pressure gauge and a source of air, such as a tire pump. The water depth was determined by forcing air down the tube until air bubbles formed at the end of the tube, and at that point, the gauge pressure was read. For each pound of pressure shown on the gauge, it is known that 2.31 ft (0.70 m) of water has been forced from the end of the tube, so the length of tube below the water surface could be computed. This amount could then be subtracted from the length of the tube to arrive at the water depth. This is illustrated in the following example:

Example: The air tube in a well is 90 ft long. When the tube is pumped with air, the gauge reading stabilizes at a reading of 20 psi. What is the water level in the well?

20 psi × 2.31 ft/psi = 46.2 ft (the water level is 46 ft above the end of the tube)

90 ft (the length of the tube) − 46.2 ft = 43.8 ft (distance from surface to water level)

Well Records

It is important that the water system operator maintain good records of the performance of each well. When properly analyzed, the records can indicate problems such as blocking of the well screen, decreasing capacity of the well pump, and drop in water level in the aquifer. Many well problems occur slowly, so by anticipating the problem, arrangements can be made to take corrective action before complete failure occurs.

It is suggested that the following data be recorded at regular intervals:

- static water level
- drawdown
- well yield
- specific capacity
- pumping water level
- well production
- recovery time
- water quality analysis reports
- if the well is relatively shallow, the correlation between water level and rainfall

Analysis of these data over a period of time can provide information about the aquifer, pump, and well. For example, if the static level drops but the drawdown remains the same, the operator knows that the water table is falling. This could mean that the aquifer is being pumped in excess of the recharge, so the well could eventually become useless if use of the aquifer is not reduced.

If the static level is unchanged but the drawdown is decreasing, it usually indicates that the pump is losing efficiency. If the static level is unchanged but the drawdown is increasing, it may indicate that the screen is clogged and water is not flowing freely into the well.

Bibliography

AWWA Manual M21, Groundwater. 1989. Denver, Colo.: American Water Works Association.

AWWA Standard for Water Wells. ANSI/AWWA A100-97. 1997. Denver, Colo.: American Water Works Association.

Water Sources. 1995. Denver, Colo.: American Water Works Association.

Chapter 17

Pumps and Motors

Types of Pumps

Most pumps used on a public water system are of a type called *velocity pumps*. The pumps move water by a spinning impeller or propeller operating at high velocity. Another type of pump is the positive-displacement pump. Early water systems used piston pumps powered by steam engines to pump water, but these were replaced with centrifugal pumps as higher speed electric motors became available. About the only positive-displacement pumps used by a modern water utility are some types of portable dewatering pumps (mud pumps) and chemical feed pumps.

Centrifugal Pumps

A centrifugal pump has a rotating impeller within a pump case. Water is drawn in at the center of the impeller and is thrown outward where the high velocity (centrifugal force) is converted to pressure. The most commonly used centrifugal pump is the volute design, in which the impeller discharges into a progressively expanding spiral casing. With this design, the velocity of the liquid is gradually reduced as it flows around the casing, changing velocity into pressure. Volute and diffuser styles of pump casings are illustrated in Figure 17-1.

A diffuser pump operates similarly to the volute type, but instead of having the case designed to convert the energy from velocity to static pressure, the diffuser type has specially designed vanes on the impeller that perform the same task.

Smaller centrifugal pumps are usually manufactured with a single suction, as pictured in Figure 17-2. The suction opening is at one end of the pump and the discharge is at a right angle on one side of the casing. A close-coupled pump has the impeller mounted directly on the motor shaft, whereas a frame-mounted unit has a pump with separate motor bearings and is connected to the motor by a coupling.

Larger pumps are usually manufactured in a style called *double suction* because the inlet water enters on both sides of the impeller (Figure 17-3). A double-suction pump is also commonly referred to as a *horizontal split-case pump* because the casing is split into two halves along the centerline of the pump shaft, which is normally set in a horizontal position. However, some pumps of this type are designed to be mounted with the shaft vertical.

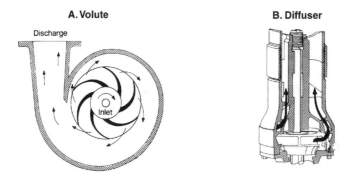

A. Volute

Discharge

Inlet

B. Diffuser

Reproduced by permission of US Filter/Johnson Screens from Groundwater and Wells, Second edition (1986).

Figure 17-1 Centrifugal pump casings

A. Close-Coupled Pump

B. Frame-Mounted Pump

Source: Centrifugal Pumps and Motors: Operation and Maintenance *(1992).*

Figure 17-2 Single-suction pumps

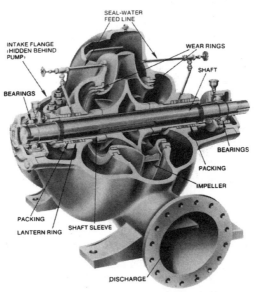

Figure 17-3 Double-suction pump

Courtesy of Ingersoll-Dresser Pump Company.

Figure 17-4 Section of a two-stage pump

Courtesy of Aurora Pump.

Centrifugal pumps can be manufactured in a wide range of flow rates and pressures by varying the width, shape, and size of the impeller as well as varying the clearance between the impeller and the casing. Although maximum theoretical suction lift is 34 ft (10 m) at sea level, the maximum practical lift is generally between 15 and 25 ft (4.6 and 7.6 m). Pumps can develop heads up to 250 ft (76 m) for a single stage, and higher heads can be achieved by using multiple stages as illustrated in Figure 17-4. Pump efficiencies can be as high as 75 to 85 percent.

The advantages of centrifugal pumps include simple construction, moderate initial cost, small space requirements, low maintenance, and ability to operate against a closed discharge head for short periods of time. One disadvantage is that maximum efficiency is achieved only over a rather limited pressure range. If a pump is operating under conditions somewhat different than the design conditions, efficiency may be considerably decreased.

Axial-Flow Pumps

Axial flow pumps are often called *propeller pumps*. As illustrated in Figure 17-5, they have neither volute or diffuser vanes and achieve flow by the lifting action of a propeller-shaped impeller. These pumps handle very high volumes of water but can achieve only limited head. They must be installed so that the impeller is submerged at all times.

Mixed-Flow Pumps

The mixed-flow pump illustrated in Figure 17-6 is a compromise between centrifugal and axial-flow pump designs. The impeller is shaped so that centrifugal force will impart some radial component to the flow. This type of pump is particularly useful for moving large quantities of water containing some solids, such as in raw water intakes.

Vertical Turbine Pumps

Vertical turbine pumps are really a type of centrifugal pump. They are usually furnished in multiple stages to obtain very high pressure at efficiencies as high as 90 to 95 percent. However, to achieve these efficiencies, the impellers are very close fitting, so sand, silt, or other grit in the water will quickly wear them and decrease the efficiency. Turbine pumps have a higher initial cost and are considerably more expensive to maintain than regular centrifugal pumps of equal capacity.

A deep-well pump has a turbine pump suspended below water level in a well, and the pump is driven through a long shaft from the motor located at the ground surface (Figure 17-7). Deep-well turbines have been installed with lifts of over 2,000 ft (610 m).

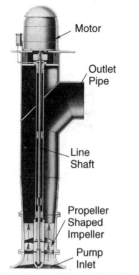

Courtesy of Ingersoll-Dresser Pump Company.

Figure 17-5 Axial-flow pump

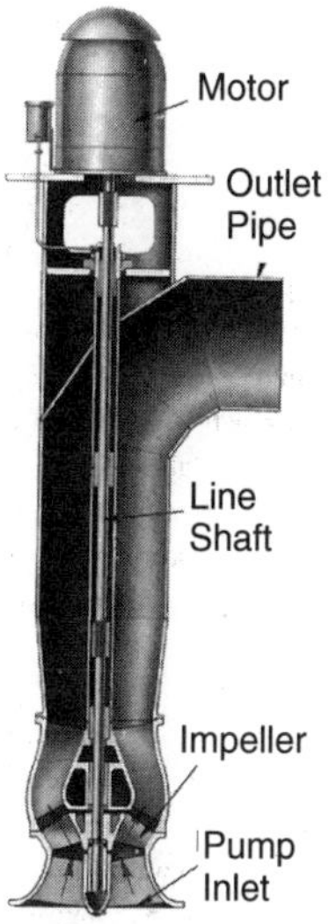

Figure 17-6 Mixed-flow pump

Courtesy of Ingersoll-Dresser Pump Company.

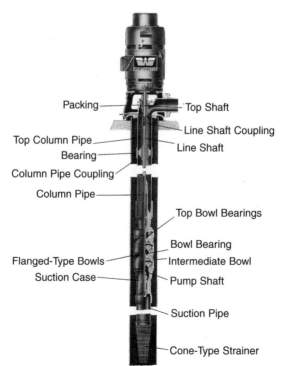

Courtesy of Ingersoll-Dresser Pump Company.

Figure 17-7 Deep-well pump

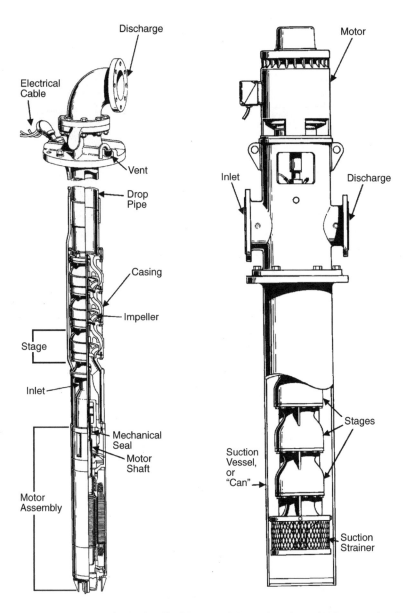

Source: Centrifugal Pumps and Motors: Operation and Maintenance *(1992).*

Figure 17-8 Submersible pump   **Figure 17-9** Turbine booster pump

A submersible pump combines a turbine pump with a submersible motor that is close-connected in a single unit (Figure 17-8). Submersible pumps are generally replacing deep-well pumps for deeper installations because they eliminate the maintenance and problems associated with the long drive shafts of the deep-well pumps.

Turbine pumps are also used as in-line booster pumps. An example of this use is in a distribution system where pressure must be raised for a service area that is at a higher elevation than rest of the system. The pump is essentially a turbine pump mounted in a container (Figure 17-9), thus it is commonly called a *can pump*.

Jet Pumps

As shown in Figure 17-10, a jet pump uses a centrifugal pump at the ground surface to generate high-velocity water that is directed down the well to an ejector. The partial vacuum created by the ejector then raises additional water to the surface. The discharge of the pump is split, with part of the water going to the distribution system and part being returned to the ejector.

Jet pumps are widely used for private wells because of their low initial cost and low maintenance. The pumps have relatively low efficiency, however, and are seldom used for public water systems.

Pump Operation and Maintenance

Reading Pump Curves

A pump curve is a graph showing the four characteristics of a particular pump. The four characteristics of capacity, head, required power, and efficiency are interrelated.

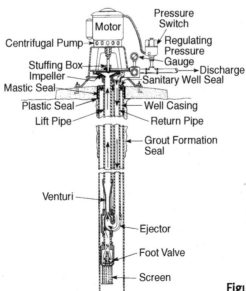

Figure 17-10 Jet pump

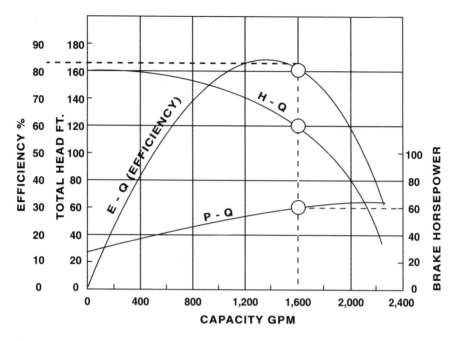

Figure 17-11 Example pump performance curve

The graph furnished by the manufacturer for each type and style of pump generally has the following three curves:

- The H-Q curve is the relationship between the head (H), usually expressed in feet of water, and the capacity (Q, for quantity) in gallons per minute (gpm). The highest possible head that the pump can attain is when it is not pumping at all, and head drops at an ever-increasing rate as the quantity increases.
- The P-Q curve shows the relationship between power required (P) and capacity (Q). Power is in brake horsepower, so motor efficiency must be known to determine the exact motor horsepower required.
- The E-Q curve provides the relationship between pump efficiency (E) in percent and capacity (Q). In sizing a pump, a model should be selected that provides the desired flow rate at or near the peak pump efficiency. The more efficient a pump is, the less costly it will be to operate.

Use of a typical set of curves is illustrated in Figure 17-11. In this case, suppose one wanted to determine the pump head, power, and efficiency when the pump is operating at 1,600 gpm. A line is first drawn upward from 1,600 gpm and the three graphs marked at the intersections. A line drawn to the left of the intersection with the E-Q curve indicates that the pump efficiency is about 83 percent. A line drawn to the left of the H-Q curve shows that the pump will be operating at a head of about 122 ft under these conditions. And a line to the right of the P-Q curve shows the brake horsepower required is about 60.

Another factor that must be figured into pump efficiency is the efficiency of the electric motor. Motors are available with various degrees of efficiency, with the more efficient ones being more expensive. Consultants often specify the overall efficiency of the pump and motor, usually called the *wire-to-water efficiency*. In this way, a manufacturer whose pump does not operate at maximum efficiency at the specified head and capacity may still meet the overall specified efficiency by supplying it with a very high-efficiency motor.

Pump Starting and Stopping

If the suction side of a pump is supplied with water under some pressure (flooded suction), the pump will always be primed and ready for immediate use. The only thing that is necessary is to provide a means of releasing any air that may accumulate at the top of the pump casing.

Priming Systems

Most pump installations have the pump located above the water source, so some provision must be made for priming the pump before use. One method of maintaining prime is to install a foot valve at the bottom of the suction pipe. This will usually hold enough water in the pump after each use to allow it to be started again. There must also be an emergency method of filling the pump with water in the event the foot valve does not hold or the pump must be drained for repairs, so a priming pump must be available to create a vacuum on the highest point on the pump casing to draw water up into the pump (Figure 17-12).

The method of maintaining prime used by most pumping stations today is to have a central priming system connected to all pumps. As illustrated in Figure 17-13, each pump is fitted with a priming valve. This valve has a float that raises and closes a small valve to the priming vacuum line as long as there is water in the pump. If there should be air in the pump, the float drops and opens the valve, which will apply a vacuum to pull water into the pump.

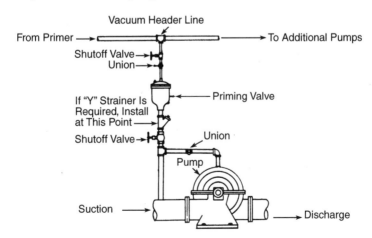

NOTE: Use pipe sizes recommended by the priming valve manufacturer.

Reprinted with permission of APCO/Valve & Primer Corp., 1420 So. Wright Blvd., Schaumberg, IL 60193 from APCO Valve Index by Ralph DiLorenzo, Exec. V.P., Copyrighted 1993.

Figure 17-12 Vacuum priming system

Courtesy of Henry Pratt Company.

Figure 17-13 Pump discharge valves

Start and Stop Operations

A small pump is usually provided with only a check valve on the discharge, which will automatically open when the pump is running and close when the pump is stopped. If there is some water hammer created by the stopping and starting, it can sometimes be relieved by installation of a pressure-relief valve or a surge chamber filled with air.

For a larger pump, the surge is so great that other means must be used to slowly bring the pump on line and slowly remove the flow as it is stopped. The general procedure requires special controls and a power-activated discharge valve that operate as follows:

1. When a pump is to be activated, power is first applied to the motor.
2. A pressure sensor on the pump discharge then determines that the pump is producing pressure before it will allow the discharge valve to open.
3. If pressure is detected, a contact closes that allows the power-operated discharge valve to open slowly. Hydraulically operated valves have a needle valve for adjusting operating speed, and should be set to give the motor plenty of time to come up to speed and to apply the additional supply of water slowly to the system.
4. On shutdown of the pump, the signal first goes to the discharge valve, which closes slowly while the motor continues to run.
5. As the valve reaches the end of travel and completely closes, a limit switch is activated that finally shuts off the motor.

Special provisions must also be made for closing the discharge valve in the event of power failure. If the motor suddenly stops with the valve open, the rush of water from the system will quickly begin to spin the motor backward with possibly disastrous results. Controls must therefore be provided to shut pump discharge valves quickly in the event of power failure.

Flow Control

Most pumps used in water system operations are constant speed, and varying demands are met by turning pumps on and off in different combinations. The discharge valve of a centrifugal pump can be partially closed to throttle flow without harm to the pump, but it should only be done in emergency situations. Throttling flow with a gate valve will eventually damage the valve because the gates are hung loose when the valve is in a partially open position. A butterfly valve can be used for throttling flow for short periods of time, but if used long-term, the gate will begin to flutter and eventually will be damaged.

If continual varying of pump discharge is required, several types of variable-speed drives are available, including stepped-speed and variable-speed motors, as well as hydraulic and mechanical variable-speed drives used with constant-speed motors. Pumps operated at variable speed may not have very good overall efficiency because all centrifugal pumps have a relatively narrow range at which they operate at maximum efficiency.

Monitoring Pump Operation

The following should be performed regularly to monitor pump operation and to determine whether a pump requires maintenance:

• Suction and discharge head should be monitored by reading gauges mounted on the suction and discharge sides of the pump. The initial readings for a new pump should be recorded so that comparisons can be made over the years.

• The bearing and motor temperatures should be regularly monitored on both pumps and motors. Many experienced operators make a habit of putting their hands on each surface as they make an inspection of operating pumps. A more accurate way is to use an infrared heat gun to record the exact temperatures periodically to determine whether there are changes (Figure 17-14). If there is a sudden increase in heat on any surface, the unit should be shut down until the cause is determined.

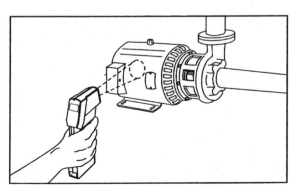

Figure 17-14 Infrared heat gun used to measure motor temperature

Courtesy of Raytek Corporation.

- As with temperature, experienced operators learn the normal sound and vibration levels of a pump. A sudden increase in vibration can be caused by misalignment of the motor coupling, imbalance of the pump impeller, or other problems that could become serious if the pump is allowed to continue operation. Automatic vibration sensors are also available that can be mounted on the pump unit and will alarm or shut down the motor if higher than normal vibration occurs.
- The pump output can be easily monitored if the discharge of individual pumps is metered. The pumpage rate at specific pressure conditions should be recorded for new pumps and then periodically compared. If the output is dropping, it is generally a sign of pump wear or damage that should be checked.
- Packing leakage should be observed. If the pump has mechanical seals, there should be no leakage, and if there is, it is a sign that repairs should be made relatively soon. If the pump has packing glands, water should be slowly dripping from them. If they are not dripping, the packing gland has been pulled too tight or there are other problems that should be investigated.
- The amperage drawn by the motor should be initially recorded and then periodically checked. If the amperage increases over a period of time with the pump running under the same operating conditions, the cause should be investigated.

Pump Maintenance

Every water system should have a regular program of major pump inspection and maintenance. It is better to take a pump out of service in winter and take all the time that is necessary to do a thorough maintenance job than to have it break down in summer and do a rush repair.

Besides a thorough cleaning of the pump and motor, other things that should be checked are the condition of the impeller, bearings, seals, and alignment of the coupling. The pump manufacturer should be consulted for a complete list of maintenance items and methods of repair.

Bearing Maintenance

Pump bearings may be either oil lubricated or grease lubricated. The bearing housing of oil-lubricated bearings should be kept filled with oil of the grade recommended by the equipment manufacturer. The oil should be changed in new pumps after the first month of operation. After the initial change, most manufacturers recommend that the oil be changed every 6 to 12 months, depending on the operating frequency and environmental condition.

For grease-lubricated bearings, bearing temperature on new pumps should be closely monitored for the first month. Bearings that are not operating properly can be touched with the bare hand. After the first month of service, the bearings should be regreased at the frequency recommended by the manufacturer.

It is important that bearings not be provided with too much grease. If the grease is packed too tightly, the bearing will run hot. Bearings should be regreased according to the following procedure:

1. Open the grease plug at the bottom of the bearing housing.
2. Fill the bearing with new grease until new grease flows from the drain plug.
3. Run the pump with the drain plug open until the grease is warm and no longer flows from the drain.
4. Replace the drain plug.

Motors

Electric motors are used to power 95 percent of the pumps used in water supply operations. Internal combustion engines are primarily used for standby service, although some utilities operate engines during peak demand periods to reduce electrical costs.

The alternating current (AC) electricity furnished by electric utilities for water utility use is generally in the form of three-phase current. This is then usually reduced to single-phase current within the plant for operating lights and small equipment. Principal motor components are labeled in Figure 17-15.

Single-Phase Motors

Single-phase motors are typically used only in fractional-horsepower sizes, but if there is a special requirement, they can be furnished with ratings up to 10 hp (7.5 kW) at 120 or 240 V. A single-phase motor has no power to bring it up to speed (starting torque), so it must be started by some outside device.

A starting winding is usually built into the motor to provide initial high torque, then as the motor comes up to speed, a centrifugal switch changes connections to the running winding. Single-phase motors are of the following three basic types:

- *Split-phase motors* use a rotor with no windings. They have a comparatively low starting torque so require a comparatively low starting current.
- *Repulsion-induction motors* are more complex and expensive than split-phase motors and also require higher starting current.
- *Capacitor-start motors* have high starting torque and high starting current. They are used in applications where the load can be brought up to speed very quickly and infrequent starting is required.

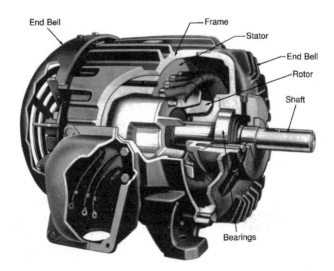

Source: Centrifugal Pumps and Motors: Operation and Maintenance *(1992).*

Figure 17-15 Motor components

Three-Phase Motors

Motors used in water treatment or distribution systems that are more powerful than $\frac{1}{2}$ hp (4 kW) are generally three phase, and may be operated at 230, 460, 2,300, or 4,000 V. The three main classes used are squirrel-cage induction, synchronous, and wound-rotor induction.

- *Squirrel-cage induction* motors are the simplest of all AC motors. The rotor windings consist of a series of bars placed in slots in the rotor and connected together at each end (which has the appearance of a squirrel cage). The stator windings located in the frame are connected to the power supply and the current flowing through them induces a rotating magnetic field. Simple starting controls are usually adequate for most of the normal- and high-starting-torque applications of these motors.
- *Synchronous* motors have power applied to the windings in such a way that a revolving magnetic field is established. The rotor is constructed to have the same number of poles as the stator and they are supplied with direct current so the rotor's magnetic field is constant. A slip-ring assembly (comutator) and graphite brushes are used to connect power to the rotor. Synchronous motors are used where the motor speed must be held constant and, because the motor has a power factor of 1.0, in areas where the power company has a penalty for low power factor conditions.
- A *wound-rotor induction* motor has a stator similar to a squirrel-cage motor, except that the resistance of the rotor circuit can be controlled while the motor is running, which varies the motor's speed and torque output. The starting current required for a wound-rotor motor is seldom greater than the full-load operating current. In contrast, squirrel-cage and synchronous motors generally have starting current requirements between 5 and 10 times their full-load current.

Motor Temperature

Motors convert electrical energy into mechanical energy and heat. About 5 percent of the energy is lost in heat and it must be removed quickly to prevent the motor temperature from rising too high. Motors are designed for an external (ambient) temperature of 104°F (40°C), so ventilation air should never have a higher temperature. The useful life of a motor is considerably shortened by being run at high temperatures. Care must be taken not to obstruct air flow around motors.

Mechanical Protection

The design of the motor housing must be considered in relation to where the motor will be located. A motor powering a pump inside a building can generally be of the simplest design because it will be in a clean environment. A motor to be installed outside must have protection from rain, dust, and wind-driven particles.

Motor housing designs commonly available include open, drip-proof, splash-proof, guarded, totally enclosed, totally enclosed with fan cooling, explosion-proof, and dust-proof.

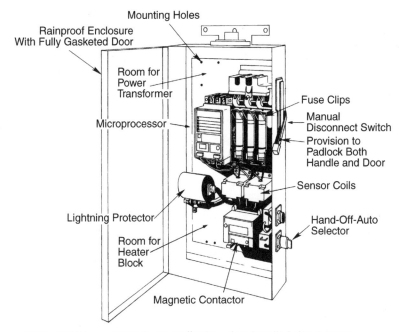

Mounting Holes

Rainproof Enclosure
With Fully Gasketed Door

Room for Power Transformer

Microprocessor

Lightning Protector

Room for Heater Block

Fuse Clips

Manual Disconnect Switch

Provision to Padlock Both Handle and Door

Sensor Coils

Hand-Off-Auto Selector

Magnetic Contactor

NOTE: Lightning protector is more effective when installed above power, in the area where transformer can be placed.

Source: Centrifugal Pumps and Motors: Operation and Maintenance *(1992).*

Figure 17-16 Combination motor starter

Motor Control Equipment

Motor Starters

Small motors are usually started by directly connecting line voltage to the motor. Motors larger than fractional horsepower are typically started and stopped using a motor starter. As illustrated in Figure 17-16, a typical motor starter includes a main disconnect switch, fuses or a circuit breaker, motor protection by temperature monitors on each of the phases, and provisions for remote operation.

Reduced-Voltage Controllers

When the starting current of a motor is so high that it may damage the electrical system or deprive other operating motors of sufficient current, a reduced-voltage controller is used. The controller supplies reduced voltage to start the motor, then applies full voltage when it is about up to speed.

Motor Control Systems

Remote and automatic controls eliminate the need for an operator to be near a pump to operate it. Manual remote controls for pumps are now usually located in a central control room.

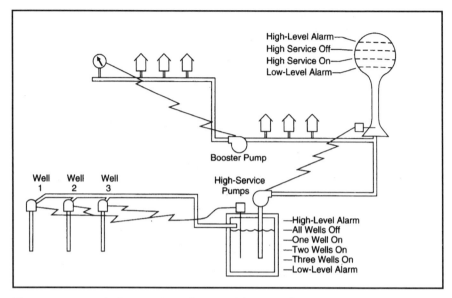

Figure 17-17 Typical pump installation with a number of controls

Figure 17-17 illustrates how controls can start and stop pumps on several levels to automatically meet customer demands. The system is also furnished with both high- and low-level alarms that will alert the operator of trouble if any of the preset limits are exceeded.

Pump, Motor, and Engine Records

Detailed records should be maintained on all equipment for use in scheduling maintenance, evaluating operation, and performing repairs. Most water systems maintain a quick-reference data card or notebook sheet for each piece of equipment, or a computer file with similar information. Typical information that should be recorded for each piece of equipment includes

- make, model, capacity, type, serial number, and warranty information

- date and location of installation and name of installer

- part numbers of special components likely to require replacement

- results of initial tests and of all subsequent tests of the equipment

- manufacturer's suggested inspection and maintenance schedules

- names, addresses, and phone numbers for the manufacturer and local representative

A file folder should also be maintained for each piece of equipment, containing the original manufacturer's literature, operating and repair manuals, and copies of correspondence, purchase orders, and other pertinent information.

Bibliography

Centrifugal Pumps and Motors: Operation and Maintenance. 1992. Denver, Colo.: American Water Works Association.

Prime Movers: Engines, Motors, Turbines, Pumps, Blowers & Generators— MOP OM-5. 1984. Alexandria, Va.: Water Environment Federation.

Rockis, G., and G. Mazur. 1997. *Electrical Motor Controls, Automated Industrial Systems*. Homewood, Ill.: American Technical Publishers.

Chapter 18

Maintaining Distribution System Water Quality

Poor quality water in the distribution system will result in customer complaints and may even present a threat to public health. Poor water quality may be caused by one or more of the following: poor quality water entering the distribution system, degeneration of the water quality after it enters the system, and contamination of the distribution system from outside sources.

Water Quality Entering the Distribution System

Federal and state regulations require that the quality of water entering the distribution system directly from a surface water treatment plant or well be monitored to ensure that it is safe for consumption at that point. The one situation in which water is not automatically tested for quality as it enters the distribution system is when it is purchased from another water system. If purchased water passes rather directly through transmission mains in the supplying water system, the chances are that the water quality is relatively unchanged.

But many water systems purchase water that has passed through two or more intermediate systems before it is received. In this case, the water could be several days old and could pick up contamination or degenerate in quality while it passes through the intermediate water systems. Even though it may not be required by regulations, it is wise for purchasing systems that have this situation to periodically collect special samples for water quality analysis at the entry point to their distribution system. If there are indications that the water being received has noticeably deteriorated in quality, the state regulatory agency should be consulted for advice.

Changes in Water Quality in the Distribution System

Regulations under the federal Safe Drinking Water Act (SDWA) state that the water purveyor is responsible for the quality of water furnished at the customer's tap. This requirement has been particularly emphasized in the federal Lead and Copper Rule. This rule recognizes that many water distribution systems have aggressive water that will leach lead and copper from distribution system materials and customer plumbing equipment, and thus they may furnish water to customers with unacceptable concentrations of lead and copper. There are also other ways in which water quality can degrade in the system that may lead to a threat to public health or consumer complaints.

Factors That May Cause Changes in Water Quality

One thing that must always be kept in mind in water treatment is that water is *disinfected*, but not *sterilized*. To sterilize means that all living organisms are killed, such as when a doctor's tools are prepared for an operation. When we disinfect water, we are, to the best of our knowledge, killing or inactivating all of the organisms that are harmful to humans—but there may still be more resistant organisms present in concentrations that are apparently not harmful to human health.

What this means is that, under favorable conditions, the organisms that are still present in the water can flourish and cause problems in the distribution system. It is also possible for problem organisms to enter the distribution system during inconsistencies in treatment. Such events as a chlorinator being out of operation for a few minutes or improper operation of a sand filter could let problem organisms pass into the distribution system where they may cause no immediate problem, but under certain favorable conditions, might multiply.

Water Temperature

One of the most important factors affecting the growth of organisms in the distribution system is water temperature. The water operator obviously has no control over water temperature, but when it is about 60°F (15°C) or higher, the operator should be particularly diligent in watching for the growth of organisms.

Nutrients

A high concentration of nutrients in the water can also promote the growth of organisms. Naturally occurring organic matter is present to some extent in all surface water and some groundwater. In some cases, the concentration may be very high. The total concentration of organic carbon present in the water is measured as *total organic carbon* (TOC) and the portion that can be easily consumed by microorganisms is called *assimilable organic carbon* (AOC).

Ozone disinfection is increasingly used in the United States because it is a very powerful technology and does not create taste and odor in the water. But distribution system operators should be aware that the use of ozone can increase the level of AOC, which could increase microorganism growth in the system.

Chloramine disinfection can result in increased concentrations of ammonia. With the loss of residual, organisms can feed on the ammonia and flourish.

Direct Contamination of the Distribution System

One way in which the distribution system can be directly contaminated is from a cross-connection. As discussed in chapter 14, the best way to prevent cross-connection contamination is to have a good cross-connection control program.

Another way in which the distribution system can be directly contaminated is during construction and maintenance work. Disinfection of mains during new construction is discussed in chapter 9. Care to prevent contamination during maintenance is discussed in chapter 11.

Dealing With Distribution System Water Quality Problems

Prevention and early warning programs can be developed to avoid water quality problems before customers notice and costs mount. The first indicator of water quality problems is often customer complaints. Common complaints are unusual or objectionable taste, odor, and color, or sickness blamed on the water. Although a large percentage of such complaints are found to be from a source other than the water supply, every complaint should be carefully investigated with the thought that it could be an early indicator of a serious system problem. To investigate customer complaints, samples should be taken for taste, odor, turbidity, chlorine residual, and bacteriological analysis. If facilities are available, a heterotrophic plate count (HPC) analysis provides a good indication of the total bacterial population in the water.

Taste-and-odor complaints can indicate a problem in raw water treatment, or the growth of organisms in the system. A very low chlorine residual at remote points on the system can indicate biofilm growth in the distribution system or poor system circulation, causing the water reaching the sampling point to be unusually old. Color and turbidity in the water might be caused by sediment or by the growth of iron bacteria in the system.

There are a number of steps that can be taken in the operation, maintenance, and design of a water distribution system to reduce the possibility of degraded water quality.

Maintaining Chlorine Residual

Maintaining a substantial chlorine residual in all parts of the distribution system can go a long way in eliminating many of the quality problems discussed. If there are remote portions of the system where chlorine residuals are routinely minimal, consider installing chlorine booster stations.

A good place to locate booster chlorination is at a ground-level storage reservoir. The site will include a building to house the equipment, and boost in residual can easily be added to water pumped from the reservoir. Either chlorine gas or hypochlorite may be used. The simplest installation is to provide one chlorine feeder connected to operate with each of the pumps in the pump station. Each feeder is set to provide the desired chlorine concentration, determined by the pump size.

Low chlorine residuals may also be caused by holding water in storage for too long. If water pressure in the system is maintained with little fluctuation, water may not circulate in and out of the elevated storage tank, particularly during times of the year with low water use. Efforts should be made to purposely vary pressure in the system so that water will flow from elevated storage for a period of time and then be replaced with fresh water.

The water must also be kept fresh in ground-level reservoirs. It is generally good practice to pump out a portion of the water from a reservoir and then refill it with fresh water daily. It is also often necessary to rechlorinate the water from a reservoir because it loses most residual while it has been sitting idle.

System Design

One of the design features that can cause serious degeneration of water quality is poor circulation. Long dead-end mains can be particularly difficult problems. Because water mains are designed for fire flow, domestic use may be so low that the water may be weeks old before it reaches the end of the main. The best policy is to not allow dead-end mains. If they already exist and are causing problems, an attempt should be made to add end connections back into the distribution system. Some water systems have found that they must flush their dead-end mains as often as weekly in order to prevent customer complaints of poor water quality.

Poor circulation in a distribution system can also be caused by closed valves. It is not unusual for a closed valve to be forgotten after a main break, so system operators should always be aware of the possibility. Closed valves will usually be identified during routine valve exercising. They will also usually be identified when hydrant flow tests show unusually low flow from a nearby hydrant.

Bibliography

Maintaining Distribution-System Water Quality. 1985. Denver, Colo.: American Water Works Association.

Modeling Water Quality in Drinking Water Distribution Systems. 1998. Denver, Colo.: American Water Works Association.

Water Transmission and Distribution. 1996. Denver, Colo.: American Water Works Association.

Chapter 19

Distribution System Safety

Personal Safety Considerations

Everyone is responsible for maintaining safe working conditions, including water utility upper management, supervisors, and operations personnel.

Management is responsible both for maintaining safe working conditions and for supporting a policy that encourages safe performance of work duties. Supervisors at all levels are responsible for the direct control of work conditions. This means that each crew chief has a responsibility to see that all work is done in compliance with safety practices and regulations.

The employees have a special position with regard to safety. Safety practices and safe equipment must be used or the safety program will not be successful. The employees must help guard against unsafe acts and conditions.

Regulatory Requirements

The obvious reason for exercising safe practices is to eliminate suffering, injury, and possible death of individuals. Beyond that is the cost to the utility from lost time, medical costs, and possibly even legal judgments. Other considerations are damage to equipment and property with their resulting repair costs.

Another reason for safe practices is the federal Occupational Safety and Health Act (OSHA). Under this act, the federal government has established minimum health and safety standards that are applicable to every industry. The act mandates that every employer must furnish employees with a workplace that is free from recognized hazards that are likely to cause death or serious physical harm. The act provides for six months in prison and/or a $10,000 penalty on conviction for violations.

Causes of Accidents

An accident can almost always be traced to either an unsafe act or to an unsafe condition. All supervisors and workers should learn to recognize unsafe conditions and unsafe acts.

212

Personal Protection Equipment

Most water utilities now provide basic personal protection equipment for workers. The equipment should be issued to all workers who will need it, thus they will have no excuse for not using it. Each person must be responsible for maintaining his or her equipment in good condition and having it available when it is needed.

A hard hat should be worn whenever a worker is in a trench or has someone working above him or her, or when he or she is near electrical equipment. Metal hard hats should never be used near an electrical hazard.

Gloves are necessary for protection from rough, sharp, hot materials and cold weather. Special long gloves are available to provide wrist and forearm protection. Workers should also wear gloves when handling oils, solvents, and other chemicals. Gloves should not, however, be worn around revolving machinery because of the danger of a glove being caught and pulled into the machine.

Respiratory equipment must also be available for use in some situations. For example, masks should always be worn when working with asbestos–cement pipe because of the danger of inhaling asbestos fibers. Self-contained breathing apparatus should be available for emergency use wherever chlorine gas is being used.

Other personal safety equipment that should be used when a related danger exists includes safety goggles, face shields, steel-toed shoes, aprons, and ear protection.

Equipment Safety

Material Handling

One of the most common and most debilitating types of injury related to material handling is back injury. Lifting heavy objects can be done safely and easily if common sense and a few basic guidelines are followed. The recommended procedures that should be followed in lifting heavy objects are

1. Bend at the knees to grasp the weight, keeping the back straight.
2. Get a firm hold on the object.
3. Maintain good footing with feet about shoulder-width apart.
4. Keeping the back as straight and upright as possible, lift slowly by straightening the legs.
5. If the object is too heavy to lift alone, do not hesitate to ask for assistance.

Other general safety guidelines for workers who are handling material or doing manual labor are

- Do not lift or shove sharp, heavy, or bulky objects without the help of other workers or the use of tools.
- To change direction when carrying a heavy load, turn the whole body, including the feet, rather than just twisting the back.
- Never try to lift a load that is too heavy or too large to lift comfortably. Use a mechanical device to assist in lifting heavy objects.
- Even though pipes and fittings look tough, they should be handled carefully. They should be lifted or lowered from the truck to the ground—not dropped. In addition to potentially damaging the equipment, dropping it can be dangerous in several ways.

Courtesy of U.S. Pipe and Foundry Company.

Figure 19-1 Warning of the dangers of injury during pipe unloading

- When pipe is being unloaded from a truck, there is considerable danger of its rolling. All workers must be warned to stay clear of the load at all times. Figure 19-1 shows a sign warning of the dangers involved in unloading pipe.
- If several people are moving or placing a pipe, they must all work together. Only one person should give directions and signals.
- When a crane is handling pipe, only one person should direct the machine operator. No one should ever stand or walk under the suspended pipe or crane boom.
- If pipe is to be lowered by skids, it is important to make sure the skids are strong enough to hold the weight and are firmly secured. Snubbing ropes should be both strong enough to support the weight and large enough for workers to maintain a good grip.
- Individuals working with ropes should wear gloves to prevent rope burns.
- For lifting and moving large valves and fire hydrants, slings placed around the body should be carefully secured so as not to slip. Special lifting clamps for valves and hydrants should be used if possible.
- Equipment for transporting objects by hand, such as wheelbarrows and hand trucks, should be properly maintained and not overloaded.
- Workers using jackhammers must wear goggles, ear protection, and protective foot gear.
- Horseplay has been the cause of many serious accidents and should be absolutely prohibited on the job.

Trench Safety

Trenches can be made safe if the excavation is properly made and appropriate equipment is used. Proper trench shoring cannot be reduced to a standard formula. Each job is an individual problem and must be considered in relation to local conditions.

If an excavation is 5 ft (1.5 m) or more deep, cave-in protection is required under any soil conditions. Where soil is unstable, protection may be necessary in shallower trenches.

Confined-Space Safety

Dangers of confined spaces include injury, acute illness, disability, and death. The National Institute for Occupational Safety and Health estimates that, until recent years, an average of at least 174 confined-space deaths were occurring each year. Many of the incidents are extremely tragic because they involve multiple deaths. A common scenario is that a worker enters a confined space without proper safety preparations and equipment and is overcome, then co-workers attempt rescue and are also overcome. A great number of those who have died were water and wastewater system workers. Among the dangers that may cause injury or death in a confined space are oxygen-deficient or oxygen-enriched atmosphere, toxic gases, flammable gases, temperature extremes, flooding potential, slick or wet surfaces, falling objects, and electrical hazards.

The Occupational Safety and Health Administration (OSHA) established standards for confined-space entry (29 CFR Part 1910.146) in 1993. The number of yearly deaths is now decreasing, but is far from acceptable. A confined space is defined by OSHA as any space that

• has limited or restricted means of entry or exit
• is large enough for an employee to enter and perform work
• is not designated for continuous work occupancy

Examples of confined spaces in the water and wastewater industries include access holes for valves, meters, and air vents; sewer access holes; tanks; wet wells; digesters; and reservoirs.

Confined spaces are further defined by OSHA into two categories: permit-required and nonpermit-required. Permit-required (permit space) means a confined space that has one or more of the following characteristics:

• contains, or has a potential to contain, a hazardous atmosphere
• contains a material that has the potential for engulfing an entrant
• has an internal configuration such that an entrant could be trapped or asphyxiated by inwardly converging walls or by a floor that slopes downward and tapers to a smaller cross-section
• contains any other recognized serious safety or health hazard

Nonpermit confined space means a space that does not have any of the above hazards.

OSHA requires a written program for any permit-required, confined-space entry. This includes identifying locations and making preparations prior to entry. Before an employee enters a permit space, the internal atmosphere must be tested with a calibrated, direct-reading instrument for oxygen content, flammable gases and vapors, and potentially toxic air contaminants. In addition, the permit space must be periodically tested during work inside the space to ensure that acceptable conditions exist.

The employer is required to furnish the following equipment and to be sure that employees use them:

• testing and monitoring equipment
• ventilation equipment needed to obtain acceptable entry conditions
• communications equipment
• personal protective equipment
• lighting equipment needed to enable employees to see well enough to work safely
• barriers and shields as required
• ladders needed for safe entry and exit
• rescue and emergency equipment (Figure 19-2)

Figure 19-2
Confined space rescue and retrieval system

Courtesy of DBI/SALA.

The OSHA standards include many other requirements that must be observed. Additional information should be obtained from state and federal offices, and is summarized in publications listed at the end of this chapter.

Hand Tool Safety

Some of the basic rules for safe use of hand tools are as follows:

- Always use an appropriate tool for the job. A very large percentage of on-the-job injuries are caused by the use of an improper tool. A screwdriver is not the same as a crowbar, a wrench should not be used as a hammer, and so forth.
- Check the condition of tools frequently. Repair or replace them if they are damaged or defective.
- Avoid using tools on machinery that is moving. It is best to shut off the machine and lock it out before making adjustments.
- Check clearance at the workplace to make sure there is sufficient space to recover a tool if it should slip.
- Maintain good support underfoot to reduce the hazard of slipping, stumbling, or falling when working.

- Wearing rings while doing mechanical work should be discouraged.
- Carry sharp or pointed tools in covers and pointed away from the body. Do not carry sharp-edged tools in trouser pockets.
- Wear eye protection when using impact tools.
- After using tools, wipe them clean and put them away in a safe place. Keep the workplace orderly.
- Do not lay tools on tops of stepladders or other elevated places from which they could fall on someone below.
- Learn and use the correct way of using hand tools.
- Try not to hurry unduly under emergency conditions. When hurrying, one tends to forget good safety practices and take dangerous shortcuts.

Portable Power Tools

An electric power tool should be grounded unless it has an all-plastic case. A ground-fault interrupter circuit should always be used whenever a power tool is used outdoors or in a damp situation. Power cords should be inspected frequently and replaced if any breaks are noted. Power tools should not be lifted by the cords. A worker must make sure to have a firm footing before starting to use a power tool to avoid being thrown off balance when it starts.

Air tools can be dangerous if the hoses and connections are not properly maintained. Workers should not point air tools at anyone, and should not use compressed air to clean off their bodies or clothing.

Traffic Control

Barricades, traffic cones, warning signs, and flashing lights should be used to warn the public of construction work that is taking place. These devices should be placed far enough ahead of the work site so that the public has ample opportunity to stop or avoid the obstructions. If necessary, one or more flaggers should be used to slow and direct traffic. Everyone involved in work near roadways should wear bright reflective vests.

Approved traffic safety control devices and procedures for various classes of roadways are detailed in *Manual on Uniform Traffic Control Devices for Streets and Highways*, prepared by the US Department of Transportation, Federal Highway Administration. Most states have also prepared simplified booklets describing work area protection.

Water utility operators should be aware that they could be liable for damages if an accident occurs as a result of work on a street or highway that was not guarded in conformance with state-directed procedures. Figure 19-3 illustrates the guarding procedures required for construction work that will obstruct one lane of a low-traffic-volume, two-lane roadway.

Chemical Safety

Calcium hypochlorite in powder or tablet form is commonly used in the disinfection of new or rehabilitated distribution mains. Liquid bleach (sodium hypochlorite) is also used for this purpose. These chemicals are corrosive and proper care should be taken, such as eye goggles and gloves, when handling these chemicals. Chlorine gas may also be used as a disinfectant. This is highly toxic and special precautions (OSHA) must be followed for its safe use.

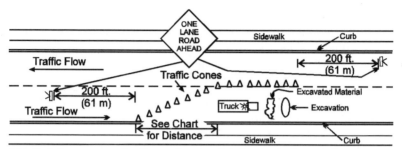

(If traffic is heavy or construction work causes interference in the open lane, one or more flaggers should be used.)

Speed Limit mph (km/h)	Lane Width 10 ft (3 m) Taper Length, ft	(m)	11 ft (3.5 m) Taper Length, ft	(m)	12 ft (3.7 m) Taper Length, ft	(m)	Number of Cones Required
20 (32)	70	(21)	75	(23)	80	(24)	5
25 (40)	105	(32)	115	(35)	125	(38)	6
30 (48)	150	(46)	165	(50)	180	(55)	7
35 (56)	205	(62)	225	(69)	245	(75)	8
40 (64)	270	(82)	295	(90)	320	(98)	9
45 (72)	450	(137)	495	(151)	540	(165)	13
50 (81)	500	(152)	550	(168)	600	(183)	13
55 (89)	550	(168)	605	(184)	660	(201)	13

Figure 19-3 Recommended barricade placement for working in a roadway

Vehicle Safety

Records indicate that most accidents in the water works industry involve vehicles. Workers should be particularly made aware of the potential dangers to themselves, fellow workers, and the public while they are operating large trucks and heavy construction equipment. Many utilities require all workers to periodically attend a safe-driving school.

Bibliography

AWWA Manual M3, *Safety Practices for Water Utilities.* 1990. Denver, Colo.: American Water Works Association.

Confined Space Entry. 1994. Alexandria, Va.: Water Environment Federation.

US Department of Transportation, Federal Highway Administration. 1998. *Manual on Uniform Traffic Control Devices for Streets and Highways.* Washington, D.C.: US Government Printing Office.

Chapter 20

Instrumentation and Control

Instruments allow a distribution system operator to monitor and control flow rates, pressures, and water levels. The main categories of instrumentation and control are

- *primary instruments*, which measure flow, pressure, level, and temperature
- *secondary instruments*, which respond to and display the information from the primary instruments
- *control systems*, which either manually or automatically operate equipment such as pumps and valves

Monitoring Sensors

The sensors that measure process variables are called *primary instrumentation* because they are basically necessary to obtain the information required to operate the monitoring system.

Flow Sensors

The various types of flow sensors (meters) used in a water distribution system are discussed in chapter 14. The types of meters primarily used for measuring flow in mains are differential pressure meters (such as venturi meters) and velocity meters (such as propeller meters). For monitoring flow at remote locations and for control purposes, meters must be provided with either a pulse or an electrical output that is proportional to the flow rate.

Pressure Sensors

Pressure sensors are commonly used to measure suction and discharge pressure on pumps and at points on the distribution system. The three common types of direct-reading pressure gauges that have been used for many years are illustrated in Figure 20-1. The bellows sensor uses a flexible copper can that expands and contracts with varying pressure. The helical sensor has a spiral-wound tubular element that coils and uncoils with changes in pressure. The Bourdon tube uses a semi-circular tube with a C shape that opens under increasing pressure.

Bellows Sensor

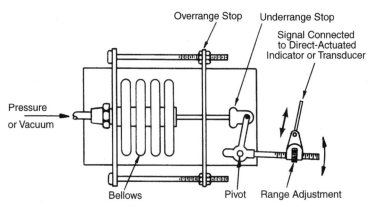

Helical Sensor

Bourdon Tube

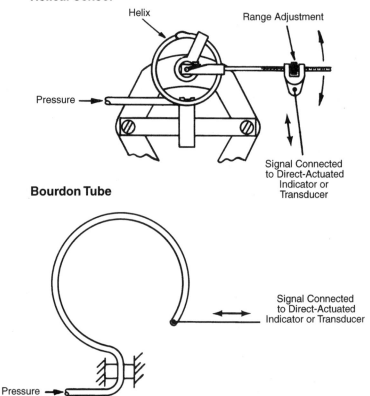

Figure 20-1 Types of pressure sensors

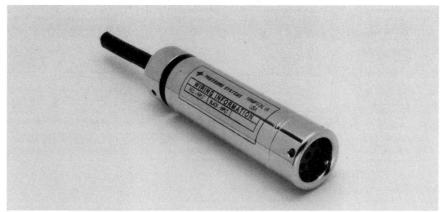

Courtesy of Pressure Systems, Inc. (KPSI Transducers).

Figure 20-2 Submersible pressure transducer

Most pressure sensing for operating electronic recorders and controls today is done with pressure transducers that produce an electrical current in proportion to pressure (Figure 20-2). Transducers are very accurate, require essentially no maintenance, and can be adjusted to register pressure over either a narrow or wide range.

Level Sensors

Several methods of measuring the depth of water in a tank or the elevation of a water surface are illustrated in Figure 20-3. One of the oldest types uses a float mechanism attached by a wire to a pulley on a shaft, which is rotated as the water level rises and falls.

The diaphragm element type of sensor operates on the principle that the confined air in the tube compresses in relation to the head of water above the diaphragm. Changes in pressure are detected by a transducer and electronically translated into water depth.

Bubbler tubes were once widely used for determining water depth, particularly in dirty water. A constant flow of air must be maintained in the tube, which is suspended in the water. Bubbler tubes work on the principle that the pressure required to discharge air from the tube is proportional to the head of water above the bottom of the tube. Although the bubbler assembly is essentially maintenance free, maintaining a continuous air supply presents some maintenance problems.

Ultrasonic units bounce radio signals off the water surface and translate the return times into distances. Knowing the elevation of the water surface one can then convert the figure into water depth.

Transducers are now widely used for measuring water depth. The pressure of the water over the unit can be translated directly into feet of head or pressure. In a similar fashion, a transducer can be installed at the base of a water tower to indicate the elevation of water in the tower.

Electronic probes may also be used for sensing water depth. An insulated metallic probe suspended in the water has an electronic circuit that detects a change in capacitance between the probe and water and electronically converts

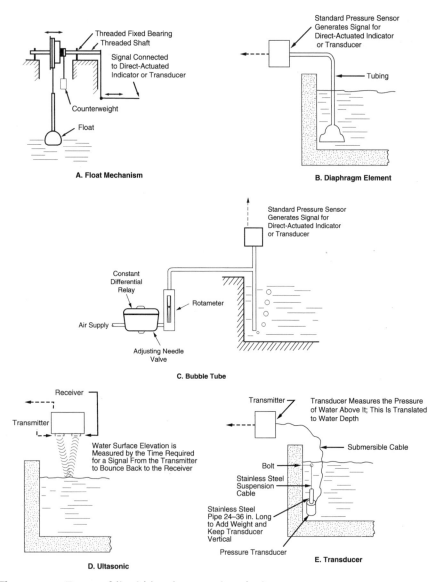

Figure 20-3 Types of liquid-level measuring devices

the information into depth. If a probe is installed in a nonmetallic tank, a second probe is required.

A variable-resistance level sensor consists of a wound resistor inside a semiflexible envelope. As the liquid level rises, the flexible outer portion of the sensor presses against the resistor and gradually shorts it out. The resistance is then converted to a liquid-level output signal.

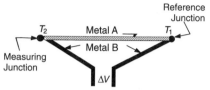

Voltage difference ΔV is signal sent to direct-acting indicator (voltmeter) or transducer.

A. Thermocouple

Change in electrical resistance $\Delta\Omega$ is the signal sent to direct-acting indicator (ohmmeter) or transducer.

B. Thermister

Figure 20-4 Types of temperature sensors

Temperature Sensors

Two types of temperature sensors that are commonly connected to instrumentation are thermocouples and thermistors. Thermocouples use two wires of different material, as illustrated in Figure 20-4. The wires are joined at two points. One is called the *sensing point* and the other the *reference junction*. Temperature changes between the two points causes a voltage to be generated, which can be read directly or amplified.

Thermistors are also called *resistance temperature devices* (RTDs). They use a semiconductive material, such as cobalt oxide, that is compressed into a desired shape from the powder form, and then heattreated to form crystals to which wires are attached. Temperature changes are reflected by a corresponding change in resistance as measured through the wires.

Electrical Sensors

It is frequently necessary to monitor the status of operating electrical equipment. The variables that may be measured are voltage (in volts), current (in amperes), resistance (in ohms), and power (in watts). The measurement of volts, amperes, and ohms can all be made with the same instrument, the D'Arsonval meter (Figure 20-5). Electric current passing through the meter's coil creates a

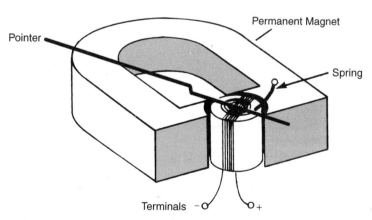

Figure 20-5 D'Arsonval meter

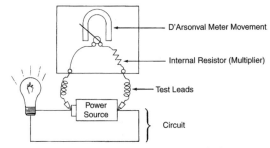

This setup measures voltage between the points where the test leads are connected.
Measuring Potential (Voltmeter Circuit)

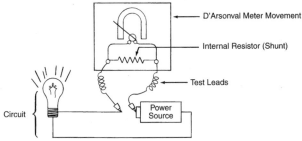

This setup measures current (amps) passing through the circuit.
Measuring Current (Ammeter Circuit)

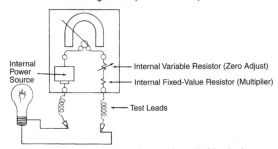

This setup measures the resistance (ohms, Ω) of the circuit.
Measuring Resistance (Ohmmeter Circuit)

Figure 20-6 Circuits used to measure volts, amps, and ohms by D'Arsonval meter movement

magnetic field, which reacts with the field of the permanent magnet and causes the indicator needle to move. The parameter measured by the meter depends on how it is connected in the circuit, as shown in Figure 20-6. The D'Arsonval meter is now rapidly being replaced by digital equipment that indicates the electrical value directly.

To measure power, an instrument must combine the measurements of volts and amperes (watts = volts × amps, assuming the power factor is 1). The electrical energy used is measured and totalized by a wattmeter that reads in kilowatt-hours (kW·h). One thousand watts (1 kW) drawn by a circuit for 1 hour results in an

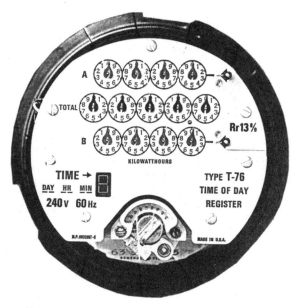

Figure 20-7 Totalizing wattmeter

energy consumption of 1 kW·h. Meters that register kilowatt-hour usage are essentially totalizing wattmeters (Figure 20-7).

A rotating disk can be seen through the glass front on older kilowatt-hour meters, and the rotations can be timed with a stopwatch to determine power consumption. Newer meters have other types of dial and digital readouts. A local power utility representative can be consulted on how to read power consumption on your meter.

Equipment Status Monitors

Some of the more common equipment status monitors are vibration sensors, position and speed sensors, and torque sensors. Vibration sensors are one of the most commonly used types in the water industry and are often mounted on pumps and motors that are located in unsupervised locations. The sensors are usually wired into the power circuit to disconnect power to the motor and activate an alarm if the vibration in the equipment exceeds a specified value.

Process Analyzers

Because of increasingly stringent water quality requirements, many water systems are installing on-line monitoring equipment to continuously analyze water quality. Typical equipment of this type includes turbidity, pH, and chlorine residual monitors; particle counters; and streaming current meters. These monitors provide automatic analyses of water quality parameters, and will activate alarms if values go above or below preset limits. They may also feed into a computer control system that will automatically make corrective adjustment of the operating system.

Secondary Instrumentation

Secondary instruments display information provided by sensors. The display may be mounted adjacent to the sensor, in a nearby control room, or in a distant control center.

Signal Transmission

Many older plants have instrumentation that transmits signals and control equipment using pneumatic (compressed air) run through small diameter tubing. The standard operating range of this type of system is 3 to 15 psig (20 to 100 kPa gauge).

Because of improvements in electronic circuitry, most new equipment operates with electrical transmission using either current or voltage. The most common is 4–20 mA direct current (DC). It is also possible to convert a pneumatic signal to an electrical signal (P/I converted), or an electrical to a pneumatic signal (I/P converted).

Receivers and Indicators

Receivers and indicators convert signals from sensors for use by the water system operator or to be fed into the control system. Alternative methods include the following:

- direct-reading value of the parameter (for example, gpm, volts, or pressure)
- recording of the information (as on a strip chart)
- total accumulated value since the unit was last reset (for example, 5,000 gal)
- some combination of the above

There are two types of instrument display—analog and digital. An example of an analog display is a dial indicator (Figure 20-8). The values range smoothly from the minimum to the maximum, and it is easy to see the relative position of the reading to the entire range. An analog display makes it easy to estimate readings that fall between the primary divisions on the dial.

A digital display shows decimal numbers. The numbers may be a mechanical readout or an electronic display like a digital watch (Figure 20-9). Digital indicators are generally more accurate than analog displays because they are not subject to the errors associated with mechanical systems. They are also easier to read correctly. A disadvantage is that there is no way of estimating the exact value when it is between the divisions provided on the display.

Telemetry

When the distance between a sensor and the indicator is relatively short, the information can be transmitted between them by using variations in current or voltage. But if there is an appreciable distance between them, telemetry must be used because the signal must be a type that will not vary in spite of variations in the wiring or radio signal.

Early telemetry equipment used audio tones or electrical pulses. Most new systems are digital and use a binary code. The sensor signal feeds into a transmitter that generates a series of on–off pulses that represent the exact numerical value of the measured parameter. For example, off–on–off–on represents the number 5. The receiver then translates the code to number or letter readings.

The transmitting device in a digital system is called a *remote terminal unit* (RTU) and the receiver is called the *control terminal unit* (CTU).

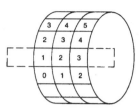

Figure 20-8 Analog indicator display

Figure 20-9 Examples of digital readouts

Courtesy of Orion Research, Inc.

Multiplexing

Several methods are available for sending signals from more than one sensor over the same transmission line.

Tone-frequency multiplexing sends several signals over one wire or radio signal by having tone-frequency generators in the transmitter and sending each parameter at a different frequency. Filters in the receiver then sort out the signals and send them to the proper indicator. As many as 21 frequencies can be sent over a single voice-grade telephone line.

Scanning equipment transmits the value of each of several parameters one at a time, in a set sequence. The receiver decodes the signal and displays each one in turn. Scanning can be used with all types of signals and all types of transmission. Scanning and tone-frequency multiplexing can be combined to allow even more signals over a single line. For example, a four-signal scanner combined with a 21-channel, tone-frequency multiplexer would yield 84 signal channels.

Polling is another method of sending several different signals over a single line. In this system, each instrument has a unique address (identifying number). A system controller, usually located at the central control center, sends out a message requesting a specific piece of equipment to transmit its data.

The controller can poll the instruments as often as necessary, which may be every few minutes to every hour or so. In more sophisticated units, the controller regularly polls each piece of equipment to determine whether there is any new information. If the status report indicates there is new information, the instrument is instructed to send its data. Some systems also provide for key instruments to interrupt other transmissions to send urgent new data.

Duplexing also allows an operator to send control signals back to the site of a transmitting sensor. The three ways this can be done using a single transmission line are

- *Full duplex* allows signals to pass in both directions at the same time.
- *Half-duplex* allows signals to pass in both directions, but only in one direction at a time.
- *Simplex* allows signals to pass in only one direction.

Transmission Channels

There are basically four types of transmission channels that are regularly used by water utilities for transmitting telemetry signals. These channels include a privately owned cable, such as a wire between two buildings on the same property; a leased telephone line; a radio channel; and a microwave system. A system using space satellites is also available, but is presently quite expensive, and new equipment is now available that can send signals over a cellular phone.

A leased telephone line is usually the least expensive transmission channel and is generally quite reliable and free of interference. Most modern telemetry transmitters are designed to operate over voice-grade lines. Radio channels may be in the VHF (very high frequency) or UHF (ultra-high frequency) bands. Both radio and microwave systems generally require line-of-sight paths, with no obstructions such as buildings.

Control Systems

The control of equipment can be accomplished in a variety of ways, from completely manual to completely automatic.

Direct Manual Control

Under complete manual control, each piece of equipment is adjusted by the water system operator by directly turning it on and off, for example, turning the handwheel on a valve. Manual control has the advantage of low initial cost and little complicated equipment to maintain. It may require more work for the operator, however, and proper operation of the equipment depends completely on the operator's expertise and judgment. If the equipment to be operated is at different locations, the operator must go to each location to perform the operation.

Remote Manual Control

Remote manual control still requires the operator to initiate each adjustment, but it is not necessary to go to the equipment location. Instead, the operator has a remote station, such as a switch or push button, which turns the equipment on and off. Examples of actuators for remote operation are solenoid valves, electric relays, and electric motor actuators. Proper operation of the equipment is still dependent on the judgment of the plant operator.

Semiautomatic Control

Semiautomatic control combines manual control by the plant operator with automatic control of specific pieces of equipment. For example, a circuit breaker will disconnect automatically in response to an overload, but must then be reset manually.

Automatic Control

Automatic control systems turn equipment on and off or adjust their operation in response to signals from sensors and analytical instruments. The plant operator does not have to exercise any control. A simple example is the thermostat on a heating system. There are two general modes of operation of automatic control—on–off differential and proportional control.

On–off differential control turns a piece of equipment either full on or off in response to a signal. In the example in Figure 20-10, the same signal that activates the service pump turns on the chlorinator. If there is any need to adjust the chlorine feed rate, it must be done manually by the plant operator.

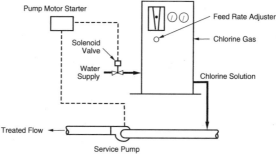

Figure 20-10 Start-stop control of chlorine feed

Proportional control can adjust the operation of a piece of equipment in response to a signal in several different ways.

Feedforward proportional control measures a variable and adjusts the equipment proportionally. An example is the adjustment of chlorinator feed rate from a flowmeter signal (Figure 20-11). The faster the water flows through the meter, the more chlorine is fed. As long as the chlorine demand of the water remains constant, this method of operation is satisfactory.

Feedback proportional control measures the output of the process and reacts backward to adjust the operation of the piece of equipment. In the illustration in Figure 20-12, the chlorine residual analyzer is set by the operator to maintain a specific chlorine residual. It then adjusts the feed rate of the chlorinator to maintain the residual in spite of variations in both chlorine demand and changes in the water flow rate. This is also called *closed-loop control* because it is continuously self-correcting. The principal problem with this control system is that, if there are wide variations in water flow rate, the system will spend a lot of time seeking the correct value. If the flow rate increases, the analyzer will detect a low residual and will increase the feed rate. But it will probably overfeed for a short time, then underfeed again, and so on until it finds the correct feed rate.

The ultimate automatic control for this situation is a combination of both feedforward and feedback control, as illustrated in Figure 20-13. The chlorinator is set up to primarily adjust in response to changes in flow rate, but the analyzer then monitors the residual and makes minor adjustments in the feed rate as necessary to maintain the selected residual in the finished water.

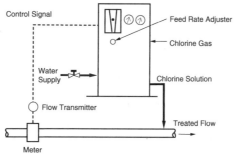

Figure 20-11 Proportional pacing of chlorine feed

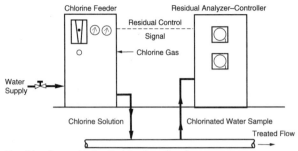

Figure 20-12 Residual control of chlorine feeder

Supervisory Control and Data Acquisition

Supervisory control and data acquisition (SCADA) is rapidly becoming the principal method of control in the water industry. A SCADA system consists of four basic components. The first two components have already been discussed—sensors (RTUs) to monitor the variables and telemetering to send the information to a central location. The third component is a central control location that has equipment for monitoring the operation and sending back commands. The fourth component is equipment for reviewing the operation, giving commands to the remote equipment, and recording information for historical purposes. This generally consists of a video screen, a keyboard, and computer data storage equipment.

When a water system has everything controlled from a single computer, it is called *centralized computer control*. Early SCADA systems were of this type, having one big computer to control everything on the water system. Two problems with this type of operation are the great dependency on the computer and on the telemetry links to the remote locations. For example, if a remote pumping station is completely controlled from a central computer and there is loss of the telephone telemetry line, the station would shut down and be unusable. The only way to operate it is to have someone operate it manually from the station.

As smaller, more powerful, and less expensive computers have become available, SCADA systems called *distributed computer control* have been developed. It is now possible to have local computer control of subsystems and individual pieces of

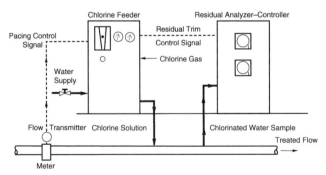

Figure 20-13 Combined flow and residual control of a chlorine feeder

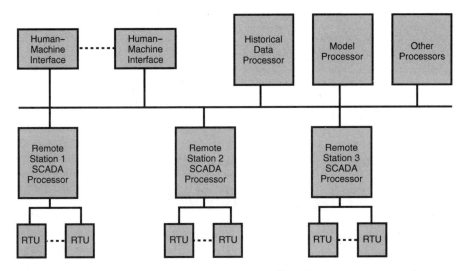

Figure 20-14 Distributed SCADA system controlling three remote pumping stations

equipment. The trend is now extending to the development of "smart equipment," which adjusts itself and monitors its own operation. Figure 20-14 illustrates a distributed system with three remote stations that are individually computer operated, and a central computer system that monitors all operations, records data, and provides a means of communicating with the remote stations to adjust their operations.

State regulatory agencies typically have mixed views about operating water system equipment completely by computer control. On the plus side, the computer eliminates the possibility of human error—the computer cannot fall asleep on the job. On the other hand, breakdown of a computer system or an error in the software could result in loss of pressure or contamination of the system. State agencies will always want to see that an automated system is furnished with all possible monitoring and reporting capabilities, and programmed to fail safe in the event of an emergency.

Bibliography

Automation Management Strategies for Water Treatment Facilities. 1996. Denver, Colo.: American Water Works Association.

AWWA Manual M2, Automation and Instrumentation. 1994. Denver, Colo.: American Water Works Association.

Skrentner, R.G. 1988. *Instrumentation Handbook for Water and Wastewater Treatment Plants.* Chelsea, Mich.: Lewis Publishers.

Chapter 21

Distribution System Maps and Records

The several different types of maps and records described in this chapter have been developed over the years and are the standards for well-run water systems. Many water systems are now changing to computerized records, but the same information is required, it is just stored and available in a different format.

Distribution System Maps

Various types of maps are necessary to provide information on mains, hydrants, and services. Because most of the distribution system equipment is underground, taking time to keep careful records during construction and repair saves a lot of time in the long run by knowing where everything is and being able to quickly find it. Records are also necessary for maintaining a valuation on the distribution system and essential for engineers to perform an analysis to determine how the water system must be improved as it grows.

Comprehensive Maps

A map that provides an overall picture of the entire system is usually called a *comprehensive map*, or *wall map*, because a large copy of it is usually hung on a blank wall in the distribution center office for ready reference by everyone. The information that should appear on the map includes

- street names
- distribution water mains with the sizes noted
- transmission mains shown in a code different than distribution mains
- fire hydrants and valves with their designated numbers
- reservoirs, tanks, and booster stations
- water source connections and interconnection with other water systems
- pressure zone limits
- notation of the street-numbering grid

Part of a typical comprehensive map is shown in Figure 21-1. The map should be as large as possible and should not be cluttered with unnecessary

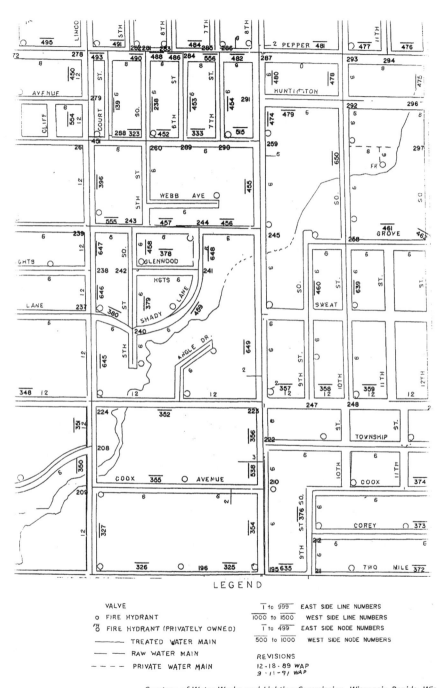

LEGEND

VALVE		1 to 999	EAST SIDE LINE NUMBERS
o	FIRE HYDRANT	1000 to 1500	WEST SIDE LINE NUMBERS
FH/o	FIRE HYDRANT (PRIVATELY OWNED)	1 to 499	EAST SIDE NODE NUMBERS
———	TREATED WATER MAIN	500 to 1000	WEST SIDE NODE NUMBERS
—— ——	RAW WATER MAIN	REVISIONS	
— — — —	PRIVATE WATER MAIN	12-18-89 WAP	
		9-11-91 WAP	

Courtesy of Water Works and Lighting Commission, Wisconsin Rapids, Wis.

Figure 21-1 Part of a comprehensive map

information that would be distracting. A good map scale for a small water system is 500 ft to 1 in. (6 m to 1 mm). Larger systems often use 1,000 ft to 1 in. (12 m to 1 mm).

Ordinary commercial maps are sometimes available to use as basic layouts, but they should be carefully checked for accuracy before they are used. After any corrections are made, they can be enlarged by a professional reproduction firm, but care must be taken that the scale is not seriously distorted in the process. Copies of the comprehensive map are often provided to the municipal engineering department and the fire department.

Sectional Maps

A sectional map (also commonly called a *plat*) is a series of maps covering sections of the water system, usually stored in a plat book. The maps are usually at a scale of either 50 or 100 ft to 1 in. (0.6 or 1.2 m to 1 mm) for small and medium-sized communities, and 200 ft to 1 in. (2.4 m to 1 mm) for larger systems. In addition to the information on the comprehensive map, the following details are usually included:

• type of main material (i.e., cast iron [CI], ductile iron [DI], polyvinyl chloride [PVC], or asbestos–cement [A–C])
• main installation date
• main distance from property line if other than standard
• block numbers

If the scale of the map allows, details such as house numbers and curb boxes may be shown. However, if all this information would cause undue clutter on the map, it is best provided on other maps or records.

Sectional maps should not overlap each other. Each should have a definite cut-off line on each side so that one map butts to the next one (Figure 21-2). The maps should be indexed, and for quick reference, the number of the adjoining map in each direction should be indicated. A common method of numbering maps is shown in Figure 21-3. Water systems that may experience growth in any direction sometimes use a variation of this numbering, starting at a central location with four quadrants so that the map number would also have a designation such as SE or NW on it.

Sectional maps can often be developed from tax assessment maps, insurance maps, subdivision maps, or city engineering maps, but they should be carefully checked for accuracy before being used. The historical method of preparing sectional maps was to have the original copies drawn in ink on tracing cloth, and many older systems are still using this method. The reasoning behind this method was that copies could be made for everyday use to reduce wear on the originals.

The originals should be kept in a safe place, such as a fireproof vault. Changes to the originals should preferably be made as soon as possible. New prints should be made and distributed whenever a significant number of changes have been made. One method of ensuring that the almost priceless information on sectional maps is never lost is to have microfilm copies made and stored at a separate, secure location.

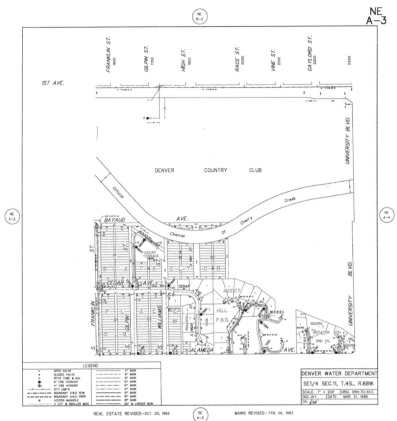

Figure 21-2 Sectional map

Courtesy of Denver Water.

1E	1D	1C	1B	1A
2E	2D	2C	2B	2A
3E	3D	3C	3B	3A

Figure 21-3 Small, comprehensive map divided into sections

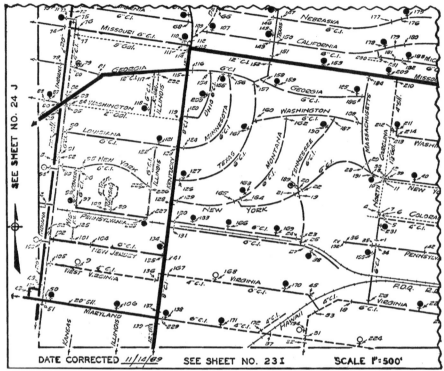

Figure 21-4 Part of a valve plat

Valve and Hydrant Maps

Many water systems also prepare valve and hydrant maps, either combined, or as two separate maps. These maps are of sufficient detail to locate every valve and hydrant, and are primarily for use by field crews during maintenance or emergencies. Notes should also be included for special information, such as valves and hydrants that operate in reverse from most of the system.

Many systems use individual plat sheets of convenient size, such as illustrated in Figure 21-4. Another alternative is the plat-and-list method, in which a relatively small map identifies the valves and hydrants by number. This is used in conjunction with a list that provides basic information, such as the type, make, size, street location, and location measurements.

Another variation is to use the basic location maps with detailed street intersection cards that are usually kept in a looseleaf book (Figure 21-5). One advantage of this system is that the location map rarely needs to be corrected because it shows only an overview of part of the system. The intersection plats have plenty of room for all required field information, and are usually updated immediately in the field as changes are made. With this system, each intersection must be given an identifying number that is shown on the basic location map.

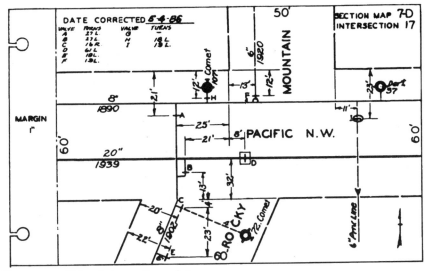

Figure 21-5 Valve intersection plat

Plan and Profile Drawings

Plan and profile drawings are usually provided by an engineer for all new construction. They show the *proposed* location of the new main and appurtenances and indicate how they connect with the existing system, and how it is anticipated they will avoid all obstructions, such as sewers, gas mains, cables, trees, and telephone poles. The engineers often use abbreviations on these drawings that are not explained. Some of these are

- POT—point on tangent
- POC—point on curve
- BC or PC—beginning of a curve
- EC or PT—end of a curve
- PI—point of intersection
- EL—elevation

Distances are usually provided in terms of stationing, starting with 0+00 at the beginning connection. For example, 2 + 42 on the map will indicate 242 ft from the starting point.

Installations are rarely constructed exactly as anticipated on the drawings. Some unanticipated obstructions are usually encountered that require deviation from the plan, and these changes must be quickly recorded on a copy of the plan so they are not forgotten. Good practice is then to prepare a set of "as-built" drawings at the completion of the job to keep as a permanent record.

Information from the construction drawings should be transferred to the other water system drawings, and the plans should be identified so they may be easily found if needed in the future. The plans should be filed in a safe, dry, clean location.

Item	Job Sketches	Sectional Plats	Valve Record Intersection Sheets	Comprehensive Map and Valve Plats
3-in. (80-mm) and smaller mains	··········	··········	··········	··········
4-in. (100-mm) mains	— — —	— — —	— — —	— — —
6-in. (150-mm) mains	——	——	——	——
8-in. (200-mm) mains	——	——		
Larger mains	Size Noted	Size Noted	12 in. (300 mm) 24 in. (600 mm) 36 in. (900 mm)	12 in. (300 mm) 24 in. (600 mm) 36 in. (900 mm)
Valve				
Valve, closed				
Valve, partly closed				
Valve in vault				
Tapping valve and sleeve				
Check valve (flow ——➤)				
Regulator	®	®	®	®
Recording gauge	G	G	G	G
Hydrant (2½-in. (65-mm) hose nozzles)	① ②			
Hydrant with hose and steamer nozzles	① ②			
Crossover (option 1)				
Crossover (option 2)				
Tee and cross	BSB BSBB			
Plug, cap, and dead end	Plug Cap			
Reducer	BS BS	12 in. 8 in. (300 mm) (200 mm)		
Bends, horizontal	Deg. Noted	Deg. Noted	Deg. Noted	
Bends, vertical	Up Down	No Symbol	No Symbol	No Symbol
Sleeve				
Joint, bell and spigot	Bell Spigot			
Joint, dresser type				
Joint, flanged				
Joint, screwed				

① Open circle: hydrant on 4-in. (100-mm) branch
② Closed circle: hydrant on 6-in. (150-mm) branch
B = bell
S = spigot

Table 21-1 Typical map symbols

Map Symbols

Every water utility should adopt a set of map symbols that are used on all maps and records. They must be simple, clear, and preferably the same as symbols used by other water systems. Commonly used symbols are shown in Table 21-1.

Equipment Records

Card records are often kept for details that cannot be included on maps for each valve, hydrant, water service, and water meter. Computer programs are also available for maintaining these records.

Valve Records

A valve record card usually has information on the make, size, type, and location of the value on one side, and maintenance information on the other (Figure 21-6). Valves may be assigned numbers, which are referenced on the distribution maps, and are then filed numerically. It is wise to keep as much location information as possible on the cards so that the valve can be located quickly in an emergency. For example, although distances to trees are handy reference points in winter when there is snow on the ground, there should also be other measurements to more permanent markers, such as lot stakes, because the trees may sometime be cut down.

Hydrant Records

Like valve records, hydrant records should include information on both the hydrant and auxiliary valve on one side, and maintenance and repair

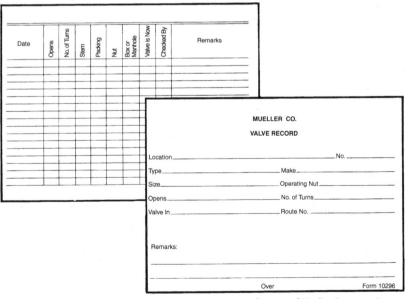

Courtesy of Mueller Company, Decatur, Ill.

Figure 21-6 Valve record card (front and back)

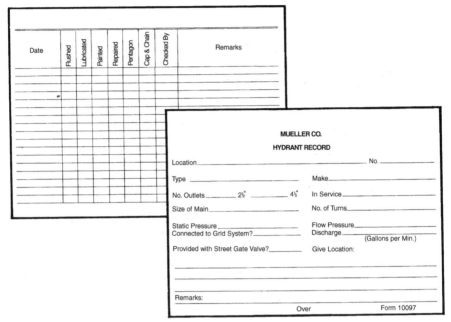

Date	Flushed	Lubricated	Painted	Repaired	Pentagon	Cap & Chain	Checked By	Remarks

MUELLER CO.

HYDRANT RECORD

Location_____ No. _____

Type _____ Make_____

No. Outlets_____ 2½" _____ 4½" In Service_____

Size of Main_____ No. of Turns_____

Static Pressure_____ Flow Pressure_____
Connected to Grid System?_____ Discharge_____
　　　　　　　　　　　　　　　　　　　　(Gallons per Min.)
Provided with Street Gate Valve?_____ Give Location:

Remarks:

Over　　　　　　　　　　　Form 10097

Courtesy of Mueller Company, Decatur, Ill.

Figure 21-7 Hydrant record card (front and back)

information on the other (Figure 21-7). Although it is a job that almost everyone would like to put off, carefully kept hydrant maintenance records are particularly important. If a hydrant should ever fail to operate properly when there is a fire, and there is serious property loss from the fire, there is a good chance that the property owner will sue the water utility for damages. The best defense the utility can have is records showing that there is a continuous, planned hydrant maintenance program.

Service Records

Many utilities also maintain a card file with details of each water service. Information on the front includes installation date, name of the installing plumber or contractor, and details of all materials. The back of the card is then used to draw a rough sketch of the installation with dimensions, burial depth, point of entering the building, meter location, and anything else that may be of interest in future years. Details of the installation of plastic service lines should be particularly thorough because they are difficult to locate once they are covered. The best time to prepare the service card is during the plumbing inspection, before the contractor is allowed to backfill the trench.

Meter Records

Meter records are also often maintained on cards. Information on the face of the card identifies the meter make, size, model, and purchase date. The bottom of the card has space to record test data and installation location.

Technical Information

Every water distribution system should develop a workable file system for technical information. An example would be to establish a file section for fire hydrants. Within that section there should be file folders with literature on equipment from each manufacturer, and additional files for purchases, warranties, correspondence, and factory and local representative phone numbers.

New catalogs should be dated when they are received, and as they are filed, old ones should be discarded unless they have some special historical value. Most files gradually grow to unreasonable thickness because nobody takes the time to throw out old material.

Computerized Water Distribution Records

As computers become less expensive and more powerful, their use increases for maintaining water distribution records. It is sometimes difficult for older people to adapt to computer operations, but as younger persons familiar with computers take over, they will find use of computer records to be relatively simple.

Types of Computerized Records

Water utilities that ventured early into computerization spent considerable sums to have special software programs prepared. But now, increasing numbers of standard programs are available from AWWA and other sources at relatively nominal cost. In addition, the programs are becoming increasingly user-friendly, the user is guided through the operations, and just about anyone with nominal computer experience can use them.

Almost all large water utilities are changing or have already changed to use of computer records. One big advantage is saving record space. But even more important, computer records can be manipulated. For example, with computerized fire hydrants records, one can immediately determine how many fire hydrants are of a particular type or age, or when they were last serviced. The full history of the hydrant can be quickly accessed by simply entering a code number.

There are other water distribution functions, in addition to the maps and records discussed previously in this chapter, that are being computerized. Some examples are main failure analysis, maintenance management, tracking of work orders, laboratory information management, leakage control, emergency response, and many possible applications in source of supply and treatment operations.

System Integration

At the present time, many of the applications discussed are freestanding; however, the ultimate systems will have them all integrated so information can be considered in the relationship of two or more different programs. As an example, maintenance management could automatically generate work orders for hydrant maintenance by drawing information from the hydrant record file showing when each hydrant was last tested.

Another example is that the human resources department could establish codes identifying special skills of each employee. Work orders could then automatically direct specific employees to each job based on their skills. Many other possible applications will probably be used in future years.

Transferring Records to Computer Format

System operators wishing to change from hard copy to computerized records are advised to obtain professional assistance to start. In a field where technology improves very quickly, advice on the best type and size of computer is valuable. Even if off-the-shelf software is used, the operation will probably go more quickly and smoothly with professional training for everyone who will be using the new system. Transferring records from card files is rather straightforward, so almost anyone can do it. Many high school and college students are very adept in computer operations, so one possibility is to hire a student part-time or during the summer to do the data entry.

Transferring maps to the computer may be more complicated. In general, the original map data can be scanned into the computer, but the conversion may require some manipulation to put them in acceptable form. This process also requires some specialized equipment. Many water utilities prefer to have a professional engineering or computer firm do the initial transfer work.

Adding and changing information on the computerized maps is also somewhat more complicated because it may require knowledge of a computer-assisted design (CAD) program. Either someone within the organization can be trained to do this entry, or arrangements can to be made to contract with an experienced outside person to periodically update the maps.

Bibliography

Customer Work Order Software. 1993. Demonstration disk. Denver, Colo.: American Water Works Association.

Main Failure Analysis Software. 1993. Demonstration disk. Denver, Colo.: American Water Works Association.

Meter Inventory Sotware. 1988. Demonstration disk. Denver, Colo.: American Water Works Association.

Service Line Management Software. 1993. Demonstration disk. Denver, Colo.: American Water Works Association.

Valve Management Software. 1993. Demonstration disk. Denver, Colo.: American Water Works Association.

Water Transmission and Distribution. 1996. Demonstration disk. Denver, Colo.: American Water Works Association.

Chapter 22

Public Relations

It is important for a water utility to maintain public confidence. Satisfied customers will pay their bills without protest, are less likely to complain if they are temporarily inconvenienced during system maintenance and construction, and more likely to be supportive of rate increases and bond issues.

Workers Who Have Contact With the Public

Distribution system personnel generally have the closest contact with the public, and the impression they make can go a long way in maintaining a good public image for the water utility.

Meter Readers

Meter readers are in the unenviable position of being naturally associated with the water bill. If the customer feels the bill is too high for any reason, the meter reader is the most available target for complaint. In addition, the meter reader must deal with bad weather, unfriendly dogs, and sometimes, unfriendly people.

Through all of this, the meter reader must remain informative and polite. Following are some guidelines for behavior of meter readers:

- Meter readers must maintain a neat appearance. Customers are understandably reluctant to admit to their homes people who are dirty, unshaven, or are wearing grubby clothes. Most utilities now provide uniforms, which not only ensure neat appearance, but also make workers easily identifiable with the water utility.
- Customers are increasingly reluctant to let strangers into their homes. Meter readers should display name tags and carry credentials that can be produced if a customer asks for verification of employment.
- Meter readers do not have to answer all questions asked by customers. They should not be expected to know all the correct answers on all subjects, but they must listen as politely as possible. It is a good idea for the utility to have informative brochures available on current subjects that the meter readers can hand to the customers. A number of brochures of this type are available from the AWWA bookstore.

- If a leak on the water service is noticed, it should be reported to the customer immediately. If the customer is not home, a note should be left in the door or mailed reporting the problem.
- Meter readers should try to stay pleasant and polite and display enthusiasm for their work.
- Customers should be addressed properly, such as *Miss*, *Sir*, *Mrs.*, etc.

Maintenance Workers

Although maintenance workers may not have as much direct contact with the public as do meter readers, they are highly visible. Their appearance and conduct can go a long way in forming a good public impression of the water utility. Some guidelines for behavior of maintenance workers are as follows:

- Although there are times when it is difficult, they should stay as well groomed as possible.
- Local residents often ask maintenance workers what they are doing. If the work being done is obvious, there is a strong temptation to give a stupid answer such as "digging for gold." A few people may find this funny, but most will take offense. The best policy is to give a short, straight answer. If residents want more than short answers, it is generally best to refer them to a supervisor.
- Customers should be notified in advance of temporary shutoffs if at all possible. Even when shutting down for a serious main break, one or more workers should be dispatched as soon as possible to warn residents and suggest that they fill some containers with water for drinking and washing.
- If the shutdown is planned in advance, letters can be printed on utility letterhead and distributed to each building, or a doorknob card such as the one illustrated in Figure 22-1 can be hung on a door to each building.
- Residents should also be warned that the water may be cloudy for a short time after it is turned back on. They should be advised to not wash clothes until the water has cleared.
- Work sites should be maintained as neatly as possible, and should be restored as close to their original conditions as possible when the work is completed.
- Residents generally do not like having workers lounging on their lawns while eating lunch or taking a coffee break. It is better to move to a more secluded location.
- Vehicles and other equipment should be kept clean.
- Vehicles should be parked out of the way of local residents if possible.
- Workers should not nap in a truck in a visible location during their break. The public is sure to get the wrong impression.
- If it is known in advance that repair work will block a road, local residents should be warned in advance with either a letter or posted sign, with alternate traffic routes suggested.

Vehicle Operators

Almost all water distribution system employees drive vehicles at least occasionally. Employees should be frequently reminded that their actions while driving can

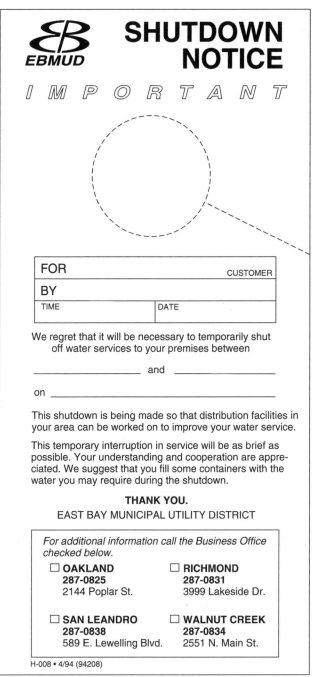

Source: Developed by East Bay Municipal Utility District (EBMUD), Oakland, Calif.

Figure 22-1 Example of a customer service card

be very important in determining the public's opinion of the utility. Following are some important points for drivers:

- Careless driving is dangerous and causes accidents.
- Careless driving makes people angry; hence, they develop a poor opinion of the water utility as a whole.
- Conversely, courteous driving forms a good impression.
- Utility personnel must exercise good judgment on where they park vehicles. Parking a vehicle in front of a tavern is not a good idea, even though workers may actually be working at a house nearby. If vehicles are frequently seen in front of coffee or doughnut shops, everyone immediately draws the conclusion that this is where the workers are spending most of their time.

Some municipalities or water utilities have developed programs in cooperation with local police in which all vehicle drivers periodically attend a four-hour safe driving course. Workers usually feel that they already know everything and dislike attending, but experience has proven that the program is definitely worth the time invested.

Dealing With the Media

On occasion, distribution system employees may be approached by reporters from the local media asking about the work they are doing. Although one must be courteous, the general rule in talking to reporters is, *Don't unless you absolutely have to!* There are many opportunities for being misquoted, and it is quite embarrassing to see the wrong information in print.

The best policy is to give a very brief explanation and offer no more information than is requested. Beyond that, the workers should say they are not qualified to go into more detail. Large municipalities and water utilities maintain a public relations department whose job is to deal with the media, so reporters should be referred there for additional details. If such a department does not exist, the reporter should be referred to the utility manager, city manager, or mayor.

Bibliography

Serviceworks: A Customer Service Workbook for Water Utilities. 1993. Denver, Colo.: American Water Works Association.

So the People May Know: A Guide to Water Utility Public Information Practices. 1993. Denver, Colo.: American Water Works Association.

Symons, J.M. 1994. *Plain Talk About Drinking Water: Questions and Answers About the Water You Drink.* 2nd ed. Denver, Colo.: American Water Works Association.

Appendix A

Conversion of US Customary Units

Linear Measurement

fathoms	x 6	=	feet (ft)
feet (ft)	x 12	=	inches (in.)
inches (in.)	x 0.0833	=	feet (ft)
miles (mi)	x 5,280	=	feet (ft)
yards (yd)	x 3	=	feet (ft)
yards (yd)	x 36	=	inches (in.)

Circular Measurement

degrees (angle)	x 60	=	minutes (angle)
degrees (angle)	x 0.01745	=	radians

Area Measurement

acres	x 43,560	=	square feet (ft^2)
square feet (ft^2)	x 144	=	square inches (in.^{2})
square inches (in.^{2})	x 0.00695	=	square feet (ft^2)
square miles (mi^2)	x 640	=	acres
square miles (mi^2)	x 27,880,000	=	square feet (ft^2)
square miles (mi^2)	x 3,098,000	=	square yards (yd^2)
square yards (yd^2)	x 9	=	square feet (ft^2)

Volume Measurement

acre-feet (acre-ft)	x 43,560	=	cubic feet (ft^3)
acre-feet (acre-ft)	x 325,851	=	gallons (gal)
barrels water (bbl)	x 42	=	gallons (gal)
cubic feet (ft^3)	x 1,728	=	cubic inches (in.^{3})
cubic feet (ft^3)	x 7.48052	=	gallons (gal)
cubic feet (ft^3)	x 29.92	=	quarts
cubic feet (ft^3)	x 0.000023	=	acre feet (acre-ft)
cubic inches (in.^{3})	x 0.00433	=	gallons (gal)
cubic inches (in.^{3})	x 0.00058	=	cubic feet (ft^3)
gallons (gal)	x 0.1337	=	cubic feet
gallons (gal)	x 231	=	cubic inches (in.^{3})
gallons (gal)	x 0.0238	=	barrels (bbl)
gallons (gal)	x 4	=	quarts (qt.)
gallons, US	x 0.83267	=	gallons, Imperial
gallons (gal)	x 0.00000308	=	acre-feet (acre-ft)
gallons (gal)	x 0.0238	=	barrels (42 gal) (bbl)
gallons, Imperial	x 1.20095	=	gallons, US
pints (pt)	x 2	=	quarts (qt.)
quarts (qt)	x 4	=	gallons (gal)
quarts (qt)	x 57.75	=	cubic inches (in.^{3})

Pressure Measurement

atmospheres	X	29.92	=	inches of mercury
atmospheres	X	33.90	=	feet of water
atmospheres	X	14.70	=	pounds per square inch (lb/in.^{2})
feet of water	X	0.8826	=	inches of mercury
feet of water	X	0.02950	=	atmospheres
feet of water	X	0.4335	=	pounds per square inch (lb/in.^{2})
feet of water	X	62.43	=	pounds per square foot (lb/ft^2)
feet of water	X	0.8876	=	inches of mercury
inches of mercury	X	1.133	=	feet of water
inches of mercury	X	0.03342	=	atmospheres
inches of mercury	X	0.4912	=	pounds per square inch (lb/in.^{2})
inches of water	X	0.002458	=	atmospheres
inches of water	X	0.07355	=	inches of mercury
inches of water	X	0.03613	=	pounds per square inch (lb/in.^{2})
pounds/square in. (lb/in.^{2})	X	0.01602	=	feet of water
pounds/square foot (lb/ft^2)	X	6,954	=	pounds per square inch (lb/in.^{2})
pounds/square in. (lb/in.^{2})	X	2.307	=	feet of water
pounds/square inch (lb/in.^{2})	X	2.036	=	inches of mercury
pounds/square inch (lb/in.^{2})	X	27,70	=	inches of water
feet suction lift of water	X	0.882	=	inches of mercury

Weight Measurement

cubic feet of ice	X	57.2	=	pounds (lb)
cubic feet of water (50°F)	X	62.4	=	pounds of water
cubic inches of water	X	0.036	=	pounds of water
gallons water (50°F)	X	8.3453	=	pounds of water
milligrams/litre (mg/L)	X	0.0584	=	grains per gallon (US) (gpg)
milligrams/litre (mg/L)	X	0.07016	=	grains per gallon (Imp)
milligrams/litre (mg/L)	X	8.345	=	pounds per million gallons (lb/mil gal)
ounces (oz)	X	437.5	=	grains
parts per million			=	milligrams per litre (for normal water applications)
grains per gallon (gpg)	X	17.118	=	parts per million (ppm)
grains per gallon (gpg)	X	142.86	=	pounds per million gallons (lb/mil gal)
percent solution	X	10,000	=	milligrams per litre (mg/L)
pounds (lb)	X	16	=	ounces
pounds (lb)	X	7,000	=	grains
pounds (lb)	X	0.0004114	=	tons (short)
pounds/cubic inch (lb/in.^{3})	X	1,728	=	pounds per cubic foot (lb/ft^3)
pounds of water	X	0.0166032	=	cubic feet (ft^3)
pounds of water	X	2,768	=	cubic inches (in.^{3})
pounds of water	X	0.1198	=	gallons (gal)
tons (short)	X	2,000	=	pounds (lb)
tons (short)	X	0.89287	=	tons (long)
tons (long)	X	2,240	=	pounds (lb)
cubic feet air (@60°F and 29.92 in. mercury)	X	0.0763	=	pounds

Flow Measurement

barrels per hour (bbl/h)	x	0.70	=	gallons per minute (gpm)
acre-feet/minute	x	325.851	=	gallons per minute (gpm)
acre-feet/minute	x	726	=	cubic feet per second (ft³/s)
cubic feet/minute (ft³/min)	x	0.1247	=	gallons per second (gal/s)
cubic feet/minute (ft³/min)	x	62.43	=	pounds of water per minute
cubic feet/second (ft³/s)	x	448.831	=	gallons per minute (gpm)
cubic feet/second (ft³/s)	x	0.646317	=	million gallons per day (mgd)
cubic feet/second (ft³/s)	x	1.984	=	acre-feet per day (acre-ft/d)
gallons/minute (gpm)	x	1,440	=	gallons per day (gpd)
gallons/minute (gpm)	x	0.00144	=	million gallons per day (mgd)
gallons/minute (gpm)	x	0.00223	=	cubic feet per second (ft³/s)
gallons/minute (gpm)	x	0.1337	=	cubic feet per minute (ft³/min)
gallons/minute (gpm)	x	8.0208	=	cubic feet per hour (ft³/h)
gallons/minute (gpm	x	0.00442	=	acre-feet per day (acre-ft/d)
gallons/minute (gpm)	x	1.43	=	barrels (42 gal) per day (bbl/d)
gallons water/minute	x	6.0086	=	tons of water per 24 hours
million gallons/day (mgd)	x	1.54723	=	cubic feet per second (ft³/s)
million gallons/day (mgd)	x	92.82	=	cubic feet per minute (ft³/min)
million gallons/day (mgd)	x	694.4	=	gallons per minute (gpm)
million gallons/day (mgd)	x	3.07	=	acre-feet per day (acre-ft/d)
pounds of water/minute	x	26.700	=	cubic feet per second (ft³/s)
miner's inch			=	flow through an orifice of 1 in.² under a head of 4 to 6 in.
miner's inches (9 gpm)	x	8.98	=	gallons per minute (gpm)
miner's inches (9 gpm)	x	1.2	=	cubic feet per minute (ft³/min)
miner's inches (11.25 gpm)	x	11.22	=	gallons per minute (gpm)
miner's inches (11.25 gpm)	x	1.5	=	cubic feet per minute (ft³/min)

Work Measurement

British thermal units: *Formerly defined as the quantity of heat required to raise the temperature of 1 lb of water by 1°F; now defined as 1,055.06 joules.*

British thermal units (Btu)	x	777.5	=	foot-pounds (ft-lb)
British thermal units (Btu)	x	39,270	=	horsepower-hours (HP-h)
British thermal units (Btu)	x	29,280	=	kilowatt-hours (kW-h)
foot-pounds (ft-lb)	x	1,286	=	British thermal units (Btu)
foot-pounds (ft-lb)	x	50,500,000	=	horsepower-hours (HP-h)
foot-pounds (ft-lb)	x	37,660,000	=	kilowatt-hours (kW-h)
horsepower-hours (HP-h)	x	2,547	=	British thermal units (Btu)
horsepower-hours (HP-h)	x	0.7457	=	kilowatt-hours (kW-h)
kilowatt-hours (kW-h)	x	3,415	=	British thermal units (Btu)
kilowatt-hours (kW-h)	x	1.241	=	horsepower-hours (HP-h)

Power Measurement

boiler horsepower	x	33,480	=	British thermal units per hour (Btu/h)
boiler horsepower	x	9.8	=	kilowatts (kW)
British thermal units/second (Btu/s)	x	1.0551	=	kilowatts (kW)
British thermal units/minute (Btu/min)	x	12.96	=	foot-pounds per second (ft-lb/s)
British thermal units/minute (Btu/min)	x	0.02356	=	horsepower (HP)
British thermal units/minute (Btu/min)	x	0.01757	=	kilowatts (kW)
British thermal units/hour (Btu/h)	x	0.293	=	watts (W)
British thermal units/hour (Btu/h)	x	12.96	=	foot-pounds per minute (ft-lb/min)
British thermal units/hour (Btu/h)	x	0.00039	=	horsepower (HP)
foot-pounds per second (ft-lb/s)	x	771.7	=	British thermal units per minute (Btu/min)
foot-pounds per second (ft-lb/s)	x	1,818	=	horsepower (HP)
foot-pounds per second (ft-lb/s)	x	1,356	=	kilowatts (kW)
foot-pounds per minute (ft-lb/min)	x	303,000	=	horsepower (HP)
foot-pounds per minute (ft-lb/min)	x	226,000	=	kilowatts (kW)
horsepower (HP)	x	42.44	=	British thermal units per minute (Btu/min)
horsepower (HP)	x	33,000	=	foot-pounds per minute (ft-lb/min)
horsepower (HP)	x	550	=	foot-pounds per second (ft-lb/s)
horsepower (HP)	x	1,980,000	=	foot-pounds per hour (ft-lb/h)
horsepower (HP)	x	0.7457	=	kilowatts (kW)
horsepower (HP)	x	745.7	=	watts (W)
kilowatts (kW)	x	0.9478	=	British thermal units per second (Btu/s)
kilowatts (kW)	x	56.92	=	British thermal units per minute (Btu/min)
kilowatts (kW)	x	3,413	=	British thermal units per hour (Btu/h)
kilowatts (kW)	x	44,250	=	foot-pounds per minute (ft-lb/min)
kilowatts (kW)	x	737.6	=	foot-pounds per second (ft-lb/s)
kilowatts (kW)	x	1.341	=	horsepower (HP)
tons of refrig. (US)	x	288,000	=	British thermal units per 24 hours
watts (W)	x	0.05692	=	British thermal units per minute (Btu/min)
watts (W)	x	0.7376	=	foot-pounds (force) per second (ft-lb/s)
watts (W)	x	44.26	=	foot-pounds per minute (ft-lb/min)
watts (W)	x	1,341	=	horsepower (HP)

Velocity Measurement

feet/minute (ft/min)	x	0.01667	=	feet per second (ft/s)
feet/minute (ft/min)	x	0.01136	=	miles per hour (mph)
feet/second (ft/s)	x	0.6818	=	miles per hour (mph)
miles/hour (mph)	x	88	=	feet per minute (ft/min)
miles/hour (mph)	x	1.467	=	feet per second (ft/s)

Miscellaneous

grade: 1 percent (or 0.01)		=	1 foot per 100 feet

Appendix B

Metric Conversions

Linear Measurement

inch (in.)	x	25.4	= millimetres (mm)
inch (in.)	x	2.54	= centimetres (cm)
foot (ft)	x	304.8	= millimetres (mm)
foot (ft)	x	30.48	= centimetres (cm)
foot (ft)	x	0.3048	= metres (m)
yard (yd)	x	0.9144	= metres (m)
mile (mi)	x	1,609.3	= metres (m)
mile (mi)	x	1.6093	= kilometres (km)
millimetre (mm)	x	0.03937	= inches (in.)
centimetre (cm)	x	0.3937	= inches (in.)
metre (m)	x	39.3701	= inches (in.)
metre (m)	x	3.2808	= feet (ft)
metre (m)	x	1.0936	= yards (yd)
kilometre (km)	x	0.6214	= miles (mi)

Area Measurement

square metre (m^2)	x	10,000	= square centimetres (cm^2)
hectare (ha)	x	10,000	= square metres (m^2)
square inch (in.^{2})	x	6.4516	= square centimetres (cm^2)
square foot (ft^2)	x	0.092903	= square metres (m^2)
square yard (yd^2)	x	0.8361	= square metres (m^2)
acre	x	0.004047	= square kilometres (km^2)
acre	x	0.4047	= hectares (ha)
square mile (mi^2)	x	2.59	= square kilometres (km^2)
square centimetre (cm^2)	x	0.16	= square inches (in.^{2})
square metres (m^2)	x	10.7639	= square feet (ft^2)
square metres (m^2)	x	1.1960	= square yards (yd^2)
hectare (ha)	x	2.471	= acres
square kilometre (km^2)	x	247.1054	= acres
square kilometre (km^2)	x	0.3861	= square miles (mi^2)

Volume Measurement

cubic inch (in.^{3})	x	16.3871	= cubic centimetres (cm^3)
cubic foot (ft^3)	x	28,317	= cubic centimetres cm^3)
cubic foot (ft^3)	x	0.028317	= cubic metres (m^3)
cubic foot (ft^3)	x	28.317	= litres (L)
cubic yard (yd^3)	x	0.7646	= cubic metres (m^3)
acre foot (acre-ft)	x	123.34	= cubic metres (m^3)
ounce (US fluid) (oz)	x	0.029573	= litres (L)
quart (liquid) (qt)	x	946.9	= millilitres (mL)
quart (liquid) (qt)	x	0.9463	= liters (L)

gallon (gal)	x	3.7854	= liters (L)
gallon (gal)	x	0.0037854	= cubic metres (m^3)
peck (pk.)	x	0.881	= decalitres (dL)
bushel (bu.)	x	0.3524	= hectolitres (hL)
cubic centimetres (cm^3)	x	0.061	= cubic inches ($in.^3$)
cubic metre (m^3)	x	35.3183	= cubic feet (ft^3)
cubic metre (m^3)	x	1.3079	= cubic yards (yd^3)
cubic metre (m^3)	x	264.2	= gallons (gal)
cubic metre (m^3)	x	0.000811	= acre-feet (acre-ft)
litre (L)	x	1.0567	= quart (liquid) (qt)
litre (L)	x	0.264	= gallons (gal)
litre (L)	x	0.0353	= cubic feet (ft^3)
decalitre (dL)	x	2.6417	= gallons (gal)
decalitre (dL)	x	1.135	= pecks (pk)
hectolitre (hL)	x	3.531	= cubic feet (ft^3)
hectolitre (hL)	x	2.84	= bushels (bu.)
hectolitre (hL)	x	0.131	= cubic yards (yd^3)
hectolitre (hL)	x	26.42	= gallons (gal)

(Note: US gallons are listed above.)

Pressure Measurement

pound/square inch (psi)	x	6.8948	= kilopascals (kPa)
pound/square inch (psi)	x	0.00689	= pascals (Pa)
pound/square inch (psi)	x	0.070307	= kilograms/square centimetre (kg/cm^2)
pound/square foot (lb/ft^2)	x	47.8803	= pascals (Pa)
pound/square foot (lb/ft^2)	x	0.000488	= kilograms/square centimetre (kg/cm^2)
pound/square foot (lb/ft^2)	x	4.8824	= kilograms/square metre (kg/m^2)
inches of mercury	x	3,376.8	= pascals (Pa)
inches of water	x	248.84	= pascals (Pa)
bar	x	100,000	= newtons per square metre
pascals (Pa)	x	1	= newtons per square metre
pascal (Pa)	x	0.000145	= pounds/square inch (psi)
kilopascals (kPa)	x	0.145	= pounds/square inch (psi)
pascal (Pa)	x	0.000296	= inches of mercury (at 60°F)
kilogram/square centimetre (k/cm^2)	x	14.22	= pounds/square inch (psi)
kilogram/square centimetre (k/cm^2)	x	28.959	= inches of mercury (at 60°F)
kilogram/square meter (k/m^2)	x	0.2048	= pounds per square foot (lb/ft^2)
centimetres of mercury	x	0.4461	= feet of water

Weight Measurement

ounce (oz)	x	28.3495	= grams (g)
pound (lb)	x	0.045359	= grams (g)
pound (lb)	x	0.4536	= kilograms (kg)
ton (short)	x	0.9072	= megagrams (metric ton)
pounds/cubic foot (lb/ft^3)	x	16.02	= grams per litre (g/L)
pounds/million gallons (lb/mil gal)	x	0.1198	= grams per cubic metre (g/m^3)
gram (g)	x	15.4324	= grains

gram (g)	x	0.0353	=	ounces (oz)
gram (g)	x	0.0022	=	pounds (lb)
kilograms (kg)	x	2.2046	=	pounds (lb)
kilograms (kg)	x	0.0011	=	tons (short)
megagram (metric ton)	x	1.1023	=	tons (short)
grams/litre (g/L)	x	0.0624	=	pounds per cubic foot (lb/ft^3)
grams/cubic metre (g/m3)	x	8.3454	=	pounds/million gallons (lb/mil gal)

Flow Rates

gallons/second (gps)	x	3.785	=	litres per second (L/s)
gallons/minute (gpm)	x	0.00006308	=	cubic metres per second (m^3/s)
gallons/minute (gpm)	x	0.06308	=	litres per second (L/s)
gallons/hour (gph)	x	0.003785	=	cubic metres per hour (m^3/h)
gallons/day (gpd)	x	0.000003785	=	million litres per day (ML/d)
gallons/day (gpd)	x	0.003785	=	cubic metres per day (m^3/d)
cubic feet/second (ft^3/s)	x	0.028317	=	cubic metres per second (m^3/s)
cubic feet/second (ft^3/s)	x	1,699	=	litres per minute (L/min)
cubic feet/minute (ft^3/min)	x	472	=	cubic centimetres /second (cm^3/s)
cubic feet/minute (ft^3/min)	x	0.472	=	litres per second (L/sec)
cubic feet/minute (ft^3/min)	x	1.6990	=	cubic metres per hour (m^3/h)
million gallons/day (mgd)	x	43.8126	=	litres per second (L/s)
million gallons/day (mgd)	x	0.003785	=	cubic metres per day (m^3/d)
million gallons/day (mgd)	x	0.043813	=	cubic metres per second (m^3/s)
gallons/square foot (gal/ft^2)	x	40.74	=	litres per square metre (L/m^2)
gallons/acre/day (gal/acre/d)	x	0.0094	=	cubic metres/hectare/day (m^3/ha/d)
gallons/square foot/day (gal/ft^2/d)	x	0.0407	=	cubic metres/square meter/day (m^3/m^2/d)
gallons/square foot/day (gal/ft^2/d)	x	0.0283	=	litres/square metre/day (L/m^2/d)
gallons/square foot/minute (gal/ft^2/min)	x	2.444	=	cubic metres/square metre/hour (m^3/m^2/h) = m/h
gallons/square foot/minute (gal/ft^2/min)	x	0.679	=	litres/square metre/second (L/m^2/s)
gallons/square foot/minute (gal/ft^2/min)	x	40.7458	=	litres/square metre/minute (L/m^2/min)
gallons/capita/day (gpcd)	x	3.785	=	litres/day/capita (L/d per capita)
litres/second (L/s)	x	22,824.5	=	gallons per day (gal/d)
litres/second (L/s)	x	0.0228	=	million gallons per day (mgd)
litres/second (L/s)	x	15.8508	=	gallons per minute (gpm)
litres/second (L/s)	x	2.119	=	cubic feet per minute (ft^3/min)
litres/minute (L/min)	x	0.0005886	=	cubic feet per second (ft^3/s)
cubic centimeters/second	x	0.0021	=	cubic feet per minute (ft^3/min)
cubic metres/second (m^3/s)	x	35.3147	=	cubic feet per second (ft^3/s)
cubic metres/second (m^3/s)	x	22.8245	=	million gallons per day (mgd)
cubic metres/second (m^3/s)	x	15,850.3	=	gallons per minute (gpm)
cubic metres/hour (m^3/s)	x	0.5886	=	cubic feet per minute (ft^3/min)
cubic metres/hour (m^3/s)	x	4.403	=	gallons per minute (gpm)
cubic metres/day (m^3/d)	x	264.1720	=	gallons per day (gpd)
cubic metres/day (m^3/d)	x	0.00026417	=	million gallons per day (mgd)
cubic metres/hectare/day	x	106.9064	=	gallons per acre per day (gal/acre/d)

cubic metres/sq metre/day	x	24.5424	= gallons/square foot/day (gal/ft²/d)
litres/square metre/minute	x	0.0245	= gallons/square foot/minute (gal/ft²/min
litres/square metre/minute	x	35.3420	= gallons/square foot/day (gal/ft²/d)

Work, Heat, and Energy

British thermal units (Btu)	x	1.0551	= kilojoules (kJ)
British thermal units (Btu)	x	0.2520	= kilogram-calories (kg-cal)
foot-pound (force) (ft-lb)	x	1.3558	= joules (J)
horsepower-hour (hp-h)	x	2.6845	= megajoules (MJ)
watt-second (W-s)	x	1.000	= joules (J)
watt-hour (W-h)	x	3.600	= kilojoules (kJ)
kilowatt-hour (kW-h)	x	3,600	= kilojoules (kJ)
kilowatt-hour (kW-h)	x	3,600,000	= joules (J)
British thermal units per pound (Btu/lb)	x	0.5555	= kilogram-calories per kilogram (kg-cal/kg)
British thermal units per cubic foot (Btu/ft³)	x	8.8987	= kilogram-calories/cubic metre (kg-cal/m³)
kilojoule (kJ)	x	0.9478	= British thermal units (Btu)
kilojoule (kJ)	x	0.00027778	= kilowatt-hours (kW-h)
kilojoule (kJ)	x	0.2778	= watt-hours (W-h)
joule (J)	x	0.7376	= foot-pounds (ft-lb)
joule (J)	x	1.0000	= watt-seconds (W-s)
joule (J)	x	0.2399	= calories
megajoule (MJ)	x	0.3725	= horsepower-hour (hp-h)
kilogram-calories (kg-cal)	x	3.9685	= British thermal units (Btu)
kilogram-calories per kilogram (kg-cal/kg)	x	1.8000	= British thermal units per pound (Btu/lb)
kilogram-calories per litre (kg-cal/L)	x	112.37	= British thermal units per cubic foot (Btu/ft³)
kilogram-calories/cubic metre (kg-cal/m³)	x	0.1124	= British thermal units per cubic foot (Btu/ft³)

Velocity, Acceleration, and Force

feet per minute (ft/min)	x	18.2880	= metres per hour (m/h)
feet per hour (ft/h)	x	0.3048	= metres per hour (m/h)
miles per hour (mi/h)	x	44.7	= centimetres per second (cm/s)
miles per hour (mi/h)	x	26.82	= metres per minute (m/min)
miles per hour (mi/h)	x	1.609	= kilometres per hour (km/h)
feet /second/second (ft/s²)	x	0.3048	= metres/second/second (m/s²)
inches/second/second (in./s²)	x	0.0254	= metres/second/second (m/s²)
pound force (lbf)	x	4.44482	= newtons (N)
centimetres/second (cm/s)	x	0.0224	= miles per hour (mph)
metres/second (m/s)	x	3.2808	= feet per second (ft/s)
metres/minute (m/min)	x	0.0373	= miles per hour (mph)
metres per hour (m/h)	x	0.0547	= feet per minute (ft/min)
metres per hour (m/h)	x	3.2808	= feet per hour (ft/h)
kilometres/second (km/s)	x	2.2369	= miles per hour (mph)
kilometres/hour (km/h)	x	0.0103	= miles per hour (mph)
metres/second/second (m/s²)	x	3.2808	= feet/ second/second (ft/s²)
metres/second/second (m/s²)	x	39.3701	= inches/ second/second (in./s²)
newtons (N)	x	0.2248	= pounds force (lbf)

Appendix C

Celsius/Fahrenheit Comparison Graph

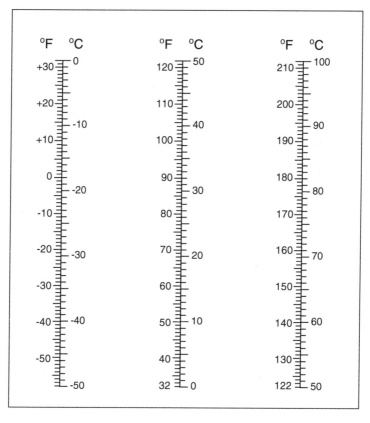

0.555 (°F − 32)	=	degrees Celsius (°C)
(1.8 x °C) + 32	=	degrees Fahrenheit (°F)
°C + 273.15	=	degrees Kelvin (°K)
boiling point	=	212°F
	=	100°C
	=	373°K
freezing point	=	32°F
	=	0°C
	=	273°K

Appendix D

Sources of Additional Information

Concrete Pipe:
American Concrete Pipe Association
222 W. Las Colinas Blvd., Suite 641
Irving, TX 75039

American Concrete Pressure Pipe Association
11800 Sunrise Valley Drive, Suite 309
Reston, VA 22091

Ductile-Iron Pipe:
Ductile Iron Pipe Research Association
245 Riverchase Parkway East, Suite O
Birmingham, AL 35244

Plastic Pipe:
Plastic Pipe Institute
1801 K Street, NW, Suite 600
Washington, DC 20006

UniBell PVC Pipe Association
2655 Villa Creek Drive, Suite 155
Dallas, TX 75234

Corrugated Polyethylene Pipe Association
4235 Monroe Street, Suite 124
Toledo, OH 43606

Steel Pipe:
Steel Tube Institute of North America
8500 Station Street, Suite 270
Mentor, OH 44060

Valves:
Valve Manufacturers Association of America
1050 17th Street, NW, Suite 280
Washington, DC 20036

International Society for Backflow Prevention and Cross-Connection Control
P.O. Box 335
Eastlake, CO 80614

Pipe Installation:

National Utility Contractors Association
4301 N. Fairfax Drive, Suite 360
Arlington, VA 22203

North American Society for Trenchless Technology
435 N. Michigan Ave., Suite 1717
Chicago, IL 60611

Trench Shoring & Shielding Association
25 N. Broadway
Tarrytown, NY 10591

Steel Tanks:

Steel Plate Fabricators Association
11315 Reed Hartman Drive, # 104
Cincinnati, OH 45341

Metering:

Automatic Meter Reading Association
60 Revere Drive, Suite 500
Northbrook, IL 60062

Appendix E

AWWA Standards

A100–97	Water Wells
B100–96	Filtering Material
B101–94	Precoat Filter Media
B200–98	Sodium Chloride
B201–91	Soda Ash
B202–93	Quicklime and Hydrated Lime
B300–99	Hypochlorites
B301–99	Liquid Chlorine
B302–95	Ammonium Sulfate
B303–95	Sodium Chlorite
B402–95	Ferrous Sulfate
B403–98	Aluminum Sulfate—Liquid, Ground, or Lump
B404–98	Liquid Sodium Silicate
B405–94	Sodium Aluminate
B406–97	Ferric Sulfate
B407–98	Liquid Ferric Chloride
B408–98	Liquid Polyaluminum Chloride
B451–98	Poly (Diallyldimethylammonium Chloride)
B452–98	EPI-DMA Polyamines
B453–96	Polyacrylamide
B501–98	Sodium Hydroxide (Caustic Soda)
B502–94	Sodium Polyphosphate, Glassy (Sodium Hexametaphosphate)
B503–94	Sodium Tripolyphosphate
B504–94	Monosodium Phosphate, Anhydrous
B505–95	Disodium Phosphate, Anhydrous
B510–95	Carbon Dioxide
B511–96	Potassium Hydroxide
B512–97	Sulfur Dioxide
B550–96	Calcium Chloride
B600–96	Powdered Activated Carbon
B601–93	Sodium Metabisulfite
B602–91(R97)	Copper Sulfate
B603–98	Potassium Permanganate
B604–96	Granular Activated Carbon
B605–99	Reactivation of Granular Activated Carbon
B701–99	Sodium Fluoride
B702–99	Sodium Fluorosilicate
B703–94	Fluorosilicic Acid
C104/A21.4–95	Cement-Mortar Lining for Ductile-Iron Pipe and Fittings for Water
C105/A21.5–99	Polyethylene Encasement of Ductile-Iron Pipe Systems

C110/A21.10–98	Ductile-Iron and Gray-Iron Fittings, 3 In. Through 48 In. (75 mm Through 1200 mm), for Water and Other Liquids
C111/A21.11–95	Rubber-Gasket Joints for Ductile-Iron Pressure Pipe and Fittings
C115/A21.15–99	Flanged Ductile-Iron Pipe with Ductile-Iron or Gray-Iron Threaded Flanges
C116/A21.16–98	Protective Fusion-Bonded Epoxy Coatings for the Interior and Exterior Surfaces of Ductile-Iron and Gray-Iron Fittings for Water Supply Service
C150/A21.50–96	Thickness Design of Ductile-Iron Pipe
C151/A21.51–96	Ductile-Iron Pipe, Centrifugally Cast, for Water
C153/A21.53–94	Ductile-Iron Compact Fittings, 3 In. Through 24 In. (76 mm Through 610 mm) and 54 In. Through 64 In. (1,400 mm Through 1,600 mm), for Water Service
C200–97	Steel Water Pipe—6 In. (150 mm) and Larger
C203–97	Coal-Tar Protective Coatings and Linings for Steel Water Pipelines—Enamel and Tape—Hot Applied
C205–95	Cement-Mortar Protective Lining and Coating for Steel Water Pipe—4 In. (100 mm) and Larger—Shop Applied
C206–97	Field Welding of Steel Water Pipe
C207–94	Steel Pipe Flanges for Waterworks Service—Sizes 4 In. Through 144 In. (100 mm Through 3,600 mm)
C208–96	Dimensions for Fabricated Steel Water Pipe Fittings
C209–95	Cold-Applied Tape Coatings for the Exterior of Special Sections, Connections, and Fittings for Steel Water Pipelines
C210–97	Liquid-Epoxy Coating Systems for the Interior and Exterior of Steel Water Pipelines
C213–96	Fusion-Bonded Epoxy Coating for the Interior and Exterior of Steel Water Pipelines
C214–95	Tape Coating Systems for the Exterior of Steel Water Pipelines
C215–99	Extruded Polyolefin Coatings for the Exterior of Steel Water Pipelines
C216–94	Heat-Shrinkable Cross-Linked Polyolefin Coatings for the Exterior of Special Sections, Connections, and Fittings for Steel Water Pipelines
C217–99	Cold-Applied Petrolatum Tape and Petroleum Wax Tape Coatings for the Exterior of Special Sections, Connections, and Fittings for Buried or Submerged Steel Water Pipelines
C218–99	Coating the Exterior of Aboveground Steel Water Pipelines and Fittings
C219–97	Bolted, Sleeve-Type Couplings for Plain-End Pipe
C220–98	Stainless-Steel Pipe, 4 In. (100 mm) and Larger
C221–97	Fabricated Steel Mechanical Slip-Type Expansion Joints
C222–99	Polyurethane Coatings for the Interior and Exterior of Steel Water Pipe and Fittings
C300–97	Reinforced Concrete Pressure Pipe, Steel-Cylinder Type, for Water and Other Liquids

C301–92	Prestressed Concrete Pressure Pipe, Steel-Cylinder Type, for Water and Other Liquids
C302–95	Reinforced Concrete Pressure Pipe, Noncylinder Type
C303–95	Concrete Pressure Pipe, Bar-Wrapped, Steel-Cylinder Type
C304–99	Design of Prestressed Concrete Cylinder Pipe
C400–93(R98)	Asbestos-Cement Pressure Pipe, 4 In. Through 16 In. (100 mm Through 400 mm), for Water Distribution Systems
C401–93(R98)	Selection of Asbestos-Cement Pressure Pipe, 4 In. Through 16 In. (100 mm Through 400 mm), for Water Distribution Systems
C402–95	Asbestos-Cement Transmission Pipe, 18 In. Through 42 In. (450 mm Through 1,050 mm), for Water Supply Service
C403–95	Selection of Asbestos-Cement Transmission Pipe, Sizes 18 In. Through 42 In. (450 mm Through 1050 mm), for Water Supply Service
C500–93	Metal-Seated Gate Valves for Water Supply Service
C501–92	Cast-Iron Sluice Gates
C502–94	Dry-Barrel Fire Hydrants
C503–97	Wet-Barrel Fire Hydrants
C504–94	Rubber-Seated Butterfly Valves
C507–99	Ball Valves, 6 In. Through 48 In. (150 mm Through 1200 mm)
C508–93	Swing-Check Valves for Waterworks Service, 2 In. (50 mm) Through 24 In. (600 mm) NPS
C509–94	Resilient-Seated Gate Valves for Water Supply Service
C510–97	Double Check Valve Backflow-Prevention Assembly
C511–97	Reduced-Pressure Principle Backflow-Prevention Assembly
C512–99	Air Release, Air/Vacuum, and Combination Air Valves for Waterworks Service
C513–97	Open Channel, Fabricated-Metal Slide Gates
C515–99	Reduced Wall, Resilient-Seated Gate Valves for Water Supply
C540–93	Power-Actuating Devices for Valves and Sluice Gates
C550–90	Protective Epoxy Interior Coatings for Valves and Hydrants
C600–99	Installation of Ductile-Iron Water Mains and Their Appurtenances
C602–95	Cement-Mortar Lining of Water Pipelines in Place—4 In. (100 mm) and Larger
C603–96	Installation of Asbestos-Cement Pressure Pipe
C605–94	Underground Installation of Polyvinyl Chloride (PVC) Pressure Pipe and Fittings for Water
C606–97	Grooved and Shouldered Joints
C651–99	Disinfecting Water Mains
C652–92	Disinfection of Water-Storage Facilities
C653–97	Disinfection of Water Treatment Plants
C654–97	Disinfection of Wells
C700–95	Cold-Water Meters—Displacement Type, Bronze Main Case
C701–88	Cold-Water Meters—Turbine Type, for Customer Service
C702–92	Cold-Water Meters—Compound Type

C703–96	Cold-Water Meters—Fire-Service Type
C704–92	Propeller-Type Meters for Waterworks Applications
C706–96	Direct-Reading, Remote-Registration Systems for Cold-Water Meters
C707–82 (R92)	Encoder-Type Remote-Registration Systems for Cold-Water Meters
C708–96	Cold-Water Meters—Multijet Type
C710–95	Cold-Water Meters—Displacement Type, Plastic Main Case
C800–89	Underground Service Line Valves and Fittings
C900–97	Polyvinyl Chloride (PVC) Pressure Pipe, and Fabricated Fittings, 4 In. Through 12 In. (100 mm Through 300 mm), for Water Distribution
C901–96	Polyethylene (PE) Pressure Pipe and Tubing, $^1/_2$ In. (13 mm) Through 3 In. (76 mm), for Water Service
C905–97	Polyvinyl Chloride (PVC) Pressure Pipe and Fabricated Fittings, 14 In. Through 48 In. (350 mm Through 1200 mm), for Water Transmission
C906–99	Polyethylene (PE) Pressure Pipe and Fittings, 4 In. Through 63 In., for Water Distribution
C907–91	Polyvinyl Chloride (PVC) Pressure Fittings for Water—4 In. Through 8 In. (100 mm Through 200 mm)
C908–97	PVC Self-Tapping Saddle Tees for Use on PVC Pipe
C909–98	Molecularly Oriented Polyvinyl Chloride (PVC) Pressure Pipe, 4 in. Through 12in. (100 mm Through 300 mm), for Water Distribution
C950–95	Fiberglass Pressure Pipe
D100–96	Welded Steel Tanks for Water Storage
D102–97	Coating Steel Water-Storage Tanks
D103–97	Factory-Coated Bolted Steel Tanks for Water Storage
D104–97	Automatically Controlled, Impressed-Current Cathodic Protection for the Interior of Steel Water Tanks
D110–95	Wire- and Strand-Wound Circular, Prestressed Concrete Water Tanks
D115–95	Circular Prestressed Concrete Water Tanks with Circumferential Tendons
D120–84 (R89)	Thermosetting Fiberglass-Reinforced Plastic Tanks
D130–96	Flexible-Membrane-Lining and Floating-Cover Materials for Potable Water Storage
E101–88	Vertical Turbine Pumps—Line Shaft and Submersible Types
F101–96	Contact-Molded, Fiberglass-Reinforced Plastic Wash Water Troughs and Launders
F102–96	Matched-Die-Molded, Fiberglass-Reinforced Plastic Weir Plates, Scum Baffles, and Mounting Brackets

Index

Note: f. indicates figure; t. indicates table.